D1162410

A QUESTION OF PLACE

The Development of Geographic Thought

BY

ERIC FISCHER

ROBERT D. CAMPBELL

ELDON S. MILLER

Department of Geography
THE GEORGE WASHINGTON UNIVERSITY
WASHINGTON, D. C.

BEATTY

Arlington, Virginia

1969

First Edition - 1967
Second Edition - 1969

Library of Congress Catalog Card Number 63-22112

Published by
R. W. BEATTY, LTD.
P. O. Box 26
Arlington, Virginia 22210

Printed in the United States of America

ACKNOWLEDGEMENTS

The authors wish to express their thanks to the following persons, publishing firms, and professional societies for their generous permission to translate and reprint copyrighted materials: Random House, Inc.; Routledge & Kegan Paul, Ltd.; Alfred A. Knopf, Inc.; Geographisches Institute der Johann Wolfgang Goethe Universität, Rhein-Mainische Forschugen; B. G. Teubner Verlagsgesellschaft; Petermanns Geographische Mitteilungen; Prof. Dr. C. Troll; Prof. Dr. Hans Bobek; Prof. Dr. J. Schmithüsen; Ferd Dümmlers Verlag; Prof. Dr. h. c. Hermann Lautensach; Prof. Walter Christaller; Dr. C. W. Baskin; Librairie Armand Colin; George G. Harrap & Co. Ltd.; Rand McNally & Co.; René Julliard éditeur; Royal Geographical Society; Dr. Griffith Taylor; Instituto di Geographia della Università di Napoli; Signora Margherita Mori Almagia'; Dr. Geza Teleki; Dr. Olav Granö; American Geographical Society; The Macmillan Company; American Council of Learned Societies; National Geographic Society; Association of American Geographers; and Dr. Carl O. Sauer.

PREFACE

The idea for this compilation was born in a graduate seminar — The Development of Geographic Thought — at the George Washington University. Even the riches of the Library of Congress could not satisfy our students, who soon learned that very little of the geographical literature of Europe had been translated into English. And so this effort was made.

Quite apart from the matter of selections, about which more is said in the Introduction, the compilation of this set of geographical writings became largely a series of mechanical problems. It is apparently quite difficult to transfer excerpts of writings correctly to the typed pages of a manuscript — particularly when this is done by a number of different typists. It becomes even more difficult when a translation is made, and to compile these writings it was necessary that the senior author translate over half of them — from German, French, Italian, and Latin.

In the process of final editing it became obvious that most of the footnotes in the original publication were of little value to potential American readers, because they referred to generally unavailable sources in a foreign language. Moreover, because the bulk of the articles here have been "excerpted," the footnotes were often confusing. Since they added nothing, and since they are still attached to the original sources if anyone is interested in following up statements or ideas attributed to others, they were omitted from this volume.

For helping with the compiling and editing problems several people deserve special mention. Ann Schoenberg supervised the editing and typing of the first draft. Geza Teleki both selected and translated excerpts from his father's works — a labor of love! Adam Bilecky helped straighten out some difficult spots in Russian articles; and Eldon Miller undertook a final editing and correction, in addition to seeking permission to use most of the writings. Finally, the time he spent seemed to merit something more than mention in the Preface.

We are grateful to the George Washington University for a small grant which paid for the early editorial work. And we are particularly appreciative of the unusually helpful and cooperative attitude of librarians in the various government libraries we used.

CONTENTS

INTRODUCTION

Man has always been intrigued by the fact that no two areas on the earth's surface are exactly alike. The differences between familiar and unfamiliar places have never ceased to interest and entertain him. So geography — the science of place — has not only a very long history, but it has also as strong a romantic appeal to the layman as it has an intellectual appeal to the scholar. It may as well be admitted at the outset that there are two kinds of geographers — those who simply go, or dream about going, to unfamiliar places, and those who make place the object of scholarly investigation. The former — the real or armchair travelers, mountain climbers, and explorers — vastly outnumber the latter. And yet it is with the latter that this book deals, because it is they who recognize that many of the crucial issues of life are fundamentally "questions of place." Their preoccupation, quite properly, has been with the nature of the whole gamut of place questions — in other words with the nature of the geographic science.

For such a small society of scholars, the academic geographers of the world have produced a remarkable literature of geographic philosophy and methodology. In the United States he is a rare geographer who does not have on his bookshelves Hartshorne's THE NATURE OF GEOGRAPHY and PERSPECTIVE ON THE NATURE OF GEOGRAPHY and James' and Jones' AMERICAN GEOGRAPHY: INVENTORY AND PROSPECT. Since the publication in 1933 of the Dickinson and Howarth book, THE MAKING OF GEOGRAPHY, at least eight volumes printed in English have dealt with the nature and development of geography.

It hardly seems possible to add anything to this almost embarrassing wealth of geographic ideas, and yet something is definitely missing. The thorough student invariably wants to sample the flavor of the original statement, but an attempt to do this to any important extent will just as invariably be frustrating. In the unlikely event that his library holds all of the books and all of the sets of periodicals, American and foreign, widely known and obscure, that he may want, he will still find that few of the foreign works have been translated. Where is the young graduate student — or for that matter, the professional geographer — who can read French, German, Italian, Greek, Latin, Polish, Finnish, Swedish, Arabic, Hungarian, and Russian?

So this book differs from the others in that here the scholars who have been a part of the development of the science speak for themselves. From Herodotus to Hartshorne, their ideas are stated in their own (translated) words, a symposium of geographic concepts from the golden era of Greek culture to the present era of scientific revolution.

As one might expect, most of the scholars represented here were, or are, prominent. But a great many other prominent scholars are not included—largely because they never bothered to put down their thoughts about the nature of geography. In any case, the point is that the major task that faced the compilers of this book was to make judgments and to select. Having done this by consensus — the only true democratic process — they realize how unlikely it is that anyone who reads this book will agree entirely with their selections.

The process of selection posed one particularly difficult question: how current should the selections be? At one point the decision was made to exclude the writings of any geographer still alive, but this proved to be an erratic criterion, to say the least. It was finally decided to conclude with writings that were contemporary but clearly in the traditional vein.

The traditional geography is a science of place — real, descriptive, verbal. It answers useful questions. It adds needed perspective and dimension to man's knowledge of the world. But it is not the *only* geography. The new geography is a science of earth spaces — theoretical, analytical, symbolic in language. The range of its questions is not known, but the need for its perspectives and dimensions is unquestionable. It does not replace traditional geography; it supplements it. One day it will be possible to compile a companion volume to this, marking the philosophical borders and identifying the methodological purposes of space-oriented geography. That will be a new chapter in the long history of the development of geography. Meanwhile, the omission of such giants as von Thünen and Lösch, such stimulating contemporary writers as Isard and Bunge, is explained.

The writings are in two parts — Early Geography and Modern Geography. The term "early" was used to describe the whole variety of geographic thought and writing that preceded twentieth century geography. Writings of Greek, Roman, Arab, and renaissance geographers are sampled. There are excerpts from the writings of Kant, Herder and de Saussure — men who were not geographers but who greatly influenced the development of a geographic philosophy. And finally the great masters, von Humboldt and Ritter, are represented. With them is Malte Brun, not because he deserves the title "father of geography," but to show that France, starting with de Saussure, has had an uninterrupted tradition.

The organization of "modern" geography is largely by national groups, chiefly German, French, British, Russian, and American, with a sampling from other European countries. Each group is arranged somewhat chronologically in terms of the publication date of the excerpts selected. The arrangement is not entirely chronological, because in some cases an author is represented by more than one selection.

Also, the German "dissenters" are put by themselves, and this requires some explanation. There have been dissenters in most countries. In a sense, Vallaux did not represent the general trend in France. American "dissenters" have been numerous, and some people will argue with the omission of Schaefer's article in the American "school." But it was felt that the German dissenters represented serious philosophical departures from the general trend of development of the geographic science which are perhaps not generally recognized by the American student.

Both pre- and post-Soviet geographers have been selected from among the Russians, and the reason for this is obvious. Not so obvious, perhaps, is the choice of "other Europeans." But the very familiarity of the names is significant.

Finally, although they require no translation and are generally available, writings of American geographers have been selected for the final chapter. This choice was the most difficult and will unquestionably prove to be the least satisfactory.

A final word needs to be said about the implications of the organization outlined sketchily above. In some cases a geographer is represented by a statement which is not really "culminating," in the sense that it is not the most recent of his writings. For example, Sauer's "Morphology of Landscape" preceded a number of methodological papers, and in this sense the inclusion of a statement made in 1925 may not seem fair. But, since the fundamental idea here is really "development," and since development is almost necessarily sequential, the basic pattern of organization is essentially chronological. Primarily, this book is a collection of ideas about geography in the order in which they developed. An indexing system has been appended to help the reader who is looking for a particular concept or a particular geographer.

Part I
EARLY GEOGRAPHY
INTRODUCTION

Geography, though one of the oldest sciences, was quite slow in developing a distinct philosophy. There was probably no time when man did not need to know something about the country in which he lived and about neighboring areas and their inhabitants, but whenever men started to look at their environment as a rational, organized entity, their attention was focused more upon the universe in its astronomic aspects than upon the details of the earth itself. Gradually it was recognized that knowledge of our immediate environment, and of the world as a whole, could be approached with the same mental tools. This development took place in Greece, where all specialized sciences began to develop their individuality, branching off from philosophy, a general contemplation of the problems of the world. But even the specialists still embraced more than one science, as these sciences are presently defined. There are scarcely any Greek writers who cannot be claimed by more than one discipline. Of the three geographers whose works are represented here, Herodotus was an historian as well as a geographer, Strabo was an historian and philosopher, and Ptolemy was an astronomer and mathematician. If Strabo is regarded by many as only a geographer, it is probably due to the fact that his historical writings have been lost and only his geographical works remain.

The Romans, successors to the Greeks on the world stage, added to the amount of factual geographical knowledge by their conquests of hitherto unknown areas but did not make significant contributions to geographical thought. Their military road maps are perhaps their most important contribution to science. During the Roman period, such Greeks as Strabo continued to produce the only geographical work of renown.

In the last centuries of the Roman empire, and increasingly during the Middle Ages, the written reports of travelers who were interested in geography took on new importance. Most traveling was undertaken for such nongeographical purposes as pilgrimages or commercial ventures, the most famous being that of Marco Polo, which started as an adventurous merchants' expedition, yet yielded valuable additions to the knowledge of Asia. As important as such reports are for their descriptions of unkown places, they are almost devoid of conscious geographic thinking.

The Arabs were the first to travel for the specific purpose of increasing geographic knowledge. Here the Greek tradition was the stimulus for original geographical thinking. Selections have been made from three Arab geographers: the first, Al Idrisi, a man devoted to undertaking a comprehensive survey of the knowledge that had been accumulated; the second, Ibn Battuta, a traveler motivated by the desire to see foreign countries; and the third, Ibn Khaldun, a man of philosophical cast who viewed geographical conditions as the basis of human life.

In Europe, the gradual augmentation of geographical knowledge after the Crusades was aided by translations from Greek and Arab authors. This trend was especially noticeable in the period of the great discoveries, but despite this stimulus no great development of geography as a science occurred. Indeed, there was a good deal of descriptive writing about foreign countries, a tremendous development of cartography in the Low Countries, and a flourishing of mathematical geography in Italy, Catalonia, and Portugal. But geographic thought remained rather sterile. The two selected writers, Clüver and Varens, are somewhat exceptional and may not be very impressive, except when viewed against the background of their own period. Their influence upon their contemporaries was limited, but they both made contributions to the development of geography during a time when philosophical additions to the literature were minimized.

During the 18th century geography began to receive recognition which had previously been withheld. For the first time, geography was taught at the university level, and philosophers and romanticists began to see the splendors of nature as something other than obstacles to the activities of man. However, geography was still only a fundamental part of other disciplines and had not yet attained an independent status. Kant, a philosopher, Herder, a theologian of great importance in the romantic movement in Europe literature, and de Saussure, a geologist, the men who have been chosen to represent the thinking of the last pre-modern phase, instigated an increased interest in geography and paved the way for the Fathers of Modern Geography.

The period of Early Geography is concluded with the deaths of von Humboldt and Ritter in 1859. Unquestionably the geography of the first half of the 19th century was dominated by these two men. There is a large and growing volume of literature about their influence, their common ideas, and about the fact that von Humboldt's predisposition for physical geography and general conclusions were in opposition to Ritter's preoccupation with regional and historical geography. The fact that so much attention has been paid to their ideas, both in their agreement and their probably exaggerated diversity, is indicative of the importance of these two masters.

Though Brun cannot be compared in importance with von Humboldt or Ritter, he was the first to perfect the regional monograph and helped to make this form of geographical expression a characteristic of French Geography. He is therefore included with his German contemporaries as one of the Fathers of Modern Geography.

CHAPTER I

GREEK AND ROMAN GEOGRAPHERS

In ancient Greece, science began as undifferentiated thinking about man, his life, and the universe. Gradually knowledge of the world increased, and men began to specialize. However, to the very end of antiquity the philosopher — polyhistor — rhetor remained the one who tried to embrace and teach all facets of knowledge. The scientist, the student of some special science, remained in the second line. Of the individual sciences, geography was among the first to be recognized as a separate field of knowledge. However, geography long maintained a close connection with other fields of knowledge, especially history, and for a much longer time with astronomy. The widening horizon of the Greeks through normal trading, traveling, and finally conquests is probably the most important cause of the early development of a separate science of geography.

HERODOTUS (c. 484-c. 425 B. C.)

Herodotus of Halicarnassus is often called the father of history, as well as the father of geography, which is indicative of the common origin of scientific history and geography, the desire of man to explain, on a rational basis, the conditions of his existence. It is not surprising that historical roots and environmental conditions originally were treated together. However, in Herodotus' *History*, a definite preoccupation with history is evident, while his geography, based on travel and exploration, set the precedent for the treatment of geography as an auxiliary to history, which, with few exceptions, was its position into the nineteenth century. But he is truly the father of geography, the first to advance beyond the stage of gathering curiosities or unconnected data from foreign countries, as it is found before him in Egyptian and cuneiform documents, and, most advanced, in the Bible. The following excerpts are taken from his History, which was originally written over a period of about thirty years and was completed only a short time before his death.

The Persian Wars[1]

What they said of their country, seemed to me very reasonable. For anyone who sees Egypt, without having heard a word about it before, must perceive, if he has only common powers of observation, that the Egypt to which the Greeks go in their ships is an acquired country, the gift of the river. The same is true of the land above the lake,[2] to the distance of three days' voyage, concerning which the Egyptians say nothing, but which is exactly the same kind of country.

The following is the general character of the region. In the first place, on approaching it by sea, when you are still a day's sail from the land, if you let down a sounding-line you will bring up mud, and find yourself in eleven fathoms' water, which shows that the soil washed down by the stream extends to that distance . . .

From the coast inland as far as Heliopolis the breadth of Egypt is considerable, the country is flat, without springs, and full of swamps. The length of the route from the sea up to Heliopolis is almost exactly the same as that of the road which runs from the altar of the twelve gods at Athens to the temple of Olympian Jove at Pisa . . .[3]

As one proceeds beyond Heliopolis up the country, Egypt becomes narrow, the Arabian range of hills, which has a direction from north to south, shutting it in upon the one side, and the Lybian range upon the other. The former ridge runs on without a break and stretches away to the sea called the Erythraean;[4] it contains the quarries whence the stone was

[1] Translated by George Rawlinson in *Modern Library Series No. 255* with an introduction by Francis R. B. Godolphin, Random House, New York, 1942. (p. 118-128)

[2] Lake Moeris.

[3] Today usually referred to as Olympia in the Peloponnes.

[4] The Red Sea.

cut for the pyramids of Memphis: and this is the point where it ceases its first direction, and bends away in the manner above indicated. In its greatest length from east to west, it is, as I have been informed, a distance of two months' journey; towards the extreme east its skirts produce frankincense. Such are the chief features of this range. On the Lybian side, the other ridge whereon the pyramids stand, is rocky and covered with sand; its direction is the same as that of the Arabian ridge in the first part of its course. Above Heliopolis, then, there is no great breadth of territory for such a country as Egypt, but during four days' sail Egypt is narrow; the valley between the two ranges is a level plain, and seemed to me to be, at the narrowest point, not more than two hundred furlongs [5] across from the Arabian to the Lybian hills. Above this point Egypt again widens . . .

The greater portion of the country above described seemed to me, as the priests declared, a tract gained by the inhabitants. For the whole region above Memphis, lying between the two ranges of hills that have been spoken of, appeared evidently to have formed at one time a gulf of the sea. It resembles (to compare small things with great) the parts about Ilium and Teuthrania, Ephesus, and the plain of the Meander.[6] In all these regions the land has been formed by rivers, whereof the greatest is not to compare for size with any one of the five mouths of the Nile . . .

In Arabia,[7] not far from Egypt, there is a long and narrow gulf running inland from the sea, called the Erythraean, of which I will set down here the dimension. Starting from its innermost recess, and using a rowboat, you take forty days to reach the open main, while you may cross the gulf at its widest part in the space of half a day. In this sea there is an ebb and flow of the tide every day. My opinion is that Egypt was formerly very much such a gulf as this — one gulf penetrated from the sea that washes Egypt on the north, and

---

[5] A furlong is ⅛ of a mile.

[6] All three are small alluvial deltas in western Asia Minor, the home of Herodotus.

[7] The Greeks regarded the country between the Nile valley and the Red Sea as part of Arabia. It is still called the Arabian Desert.

extended itself toward Ethiopia; another entered from the southern ocean, and stretched toward Syria; the two gulfs ran into the land so as almost to meet each other, and left between them only a very narrow tract of country. Now if the Nile chooses to divert its waters from their present bed into this Arabian gulf, what is there to hinder it from being filled up by the stream within, at the utmost, twenty thousand years? For my part, I think it would be filled in half that time. How then should not a gulf, even of much greater size, have been filled up in the ages that passed before I was born, by a river that is at once so large and so given to working changes?

Thus I give credit to those from whom I received this account of Egypt, and am myself, moreover strongly of the same opinion, since I remarked that the country projects into the sea further than the neighboring shores, and I observed that there were shells upon the hills, and that salt exuded from the soil to such an extent as even to injure the pyramids; and I noticed also that there is but a single hill in all of Egypt where sand is found, namely, the hill above Memphis; and further, I found the country to bear no resemblance either to its borderland Arabia, or to Lybia — nay, nor even to Syria, which forms the seaboard of Arabia; but whereas the soil of Lybia is, we know, sandy and of a reddish hue, and that of Arabia and Syria inclines to stone and clay, Egypt has a soil that is black and crumbly, being alluvial and formed of the deposits brought down by the river from Ethiopia.

One fact which I learned of the priests, is to me a strong evidence of the origin of the country. They said that when Moeris was king, the Nile overflowed all Egypt below Memphis, as soon as it rose as little as eight cubits. Now Moeris had not been dead 900 years at the time when I heard this of the priests; yet at the present day, unless the river rise sixteen, or, at the very least, fifteen cubits, it does not overflow the lands . . .[8] If, as I said before, the country below Memphis,

---

[8] Modern researchers have estimated that Lower Egypt accumulated alluvial soil of 1.2 inchs depth every century before modern regulations changed the rate.

which is the land that is always rising, continues to increase at the rate at which it has risen in the times gone by, how will it be possible for the inhabitants of that region to avoid hunger, when they will certainly have no rain, and the river will not be able to overflow their cornlands? At present, it must be confessed, they obtain the fruits of the field with less trouble than any other people in the world, the rest of the Egyptians included, since they have no need to break up the ground with the plough, nor to use the hoe, nor to do any of the work which the rest of mankind find necessary if they are to get a crop; but the husbandman waits till the river has of its own accord spread itself over the fields and withdrawn again to its bed, and then sows its plot of ground, and after sowing turns his swine into it — the swine tread in the corn — after which he has only to await the harvest. The swine also serve him to thrash the grain, which is then carried to the garner . . .

Concerning the nature of the river, I was not able to gain any information either from the priests or from others. I was particularly anxious to learn from them why the Nile, at the commencement of the summer solstice, begins to rise, and continues to increase for a hundred days — and why, as soon as that number is past, it forthwith retires and contracts its stream, continuing low during the whole of the winter until the summer solstice comes round again. On none of these points could I obtain any explanation from the inhabitants, though I made every inquiry, wishing to know what was commonly reported. They could neither tell me what special virtue the Nile has which makes it so opposite in its nature to all other streams, nor why, unlike every other river, it gives forth no breezes from its surface.

Some of the Greeks, however, wishing to get a reputation for cleverness, have offered explanations for the phenomena of the river, for which they have accounted in three different ways. Two of these I do not think it worthwhile to speak of, further than simply to mention what they are. One pretends that the Etesian winds cause the rise of the river by preventing the Nile-water from running off into the sea. But in the first place it has often happened, when the Etesian winds did not blow, that the Nile has risen according to its usual wont; and further, if the Etesian winds produced the effect, the other rivers which flow in a direction opposite to those winds ought to present the same phenomena as the Nile, and the more so as they are all smaller streams, and have a weaker current. But these rivers, of which there are many both in Syria and Libya,[9] are entirely unlike the Nile in this respect.

The second opinion is even more unscientific than the one just mentioned, and also, if I may so say, more marvelous. It is that the Nile acts so strangely, because it flows from the ocean, and that the ocean flows all around the earth.

The third explanation, which is very much more plausible than either of the others, is positively the furthest from the truth; for there is really nothing in what it says, any more than in the other theories. It is, that inundation of the Nile is caused by the melting of snows. Now, as the Nile flows out of Libya, through Ethiopia into Egypt, how is it possible that it can be formed by melted snow, running, as it does, from the hottest regions of the earth into cooler countries: Many are the proofs whereby any one capable of reasoning on the subject may be convinced that it is most unlikely this should be the case. The first and strongest argument is furnished by the winds, which always blow hot from these regions. The second is that rain and frost are unkown there. Now, whenever snow falls, it must of necessity rain within five days; so that, if there were snow, there must be rain also in those parts. Thirdly, it is certain that the natives of this country are black from the heat, that the kites and the swallows remain there the whole year, and that the cranes, when they fly from the rigours of a Scythian winter, flock thither to pass the cold season. If then, in the country whence the Nile has its source, or in that through which it flows, there fell ever so little snow, it is absolutely impossible that any of these circumstances could take place . . .

Perhaps, after censuring all of the opinions that have been put forward on this obscure subject, one ought to propose

[9] Greeks and Egyptians called Africa, except the part east of the Nile, by the name Libya.

some theory of one's own. I will therefore proceed to explain what I think to be the reason of the Nile's swelling in the summer time. During the winter the sun is driven out of its usual course by the storms, and removes to the upper parts of Libya. This is the whole secret in the fewest possible words; for it stands to reason that the country to which the Sun-god approaches the nearest, and which he passes most directly over, will be scantest of water, and that there the streams which feed the rivers will shrink the most . . .

Let us leave these things, however, to their natural course, to continue as they are and have been from the beginning. With regard to the sources of the Nile, I have found no one among all those with whom I have conversed, whether Egyptians, Libyans, or Greeks, who professed to have any knowledge. . . . All that I succeeded in learning further of the more distant portions of the Nile, by ascending myself as far as Elephantine, and making inquiries concerning the parts beyond, was the following: . . .

The course of the Nile is known not only throughout Egypt, but to the extent of four months' journey either by land or by water above the Egyptian boundary. . . . There the direction of the river is from west to east. Beyond, no one has any certain knowledge of its course, since the country is uninhabited by reason of the excessive heat.

I did hear, indeed, what I will now relate, from certain natives of Cyrene. . . . Above the coast line and the country inhabited by the maritime tribes, Libya is full of wild beasts; while beyond the wild beast region there is a tract which is wholly sand, very scant of water, and utterly and entirely a desert. . . . After journeying for many days over a wide extent of sand, (some young Nasamonians) came at last to a plain where they observed trees growing; . . . (here) some dwarfish men, under the middle height, seized them and carried them off . . . to a town, where all the men were of the height of their conductors, and black complexioned. A great river flowed by the town, running from west to east, and containing crocodiles. . . . Etearchus conjectured it to be the Nile; and reason favors that view.[10]

STRABO (c. 64 B.C.-c. 22 A.D.)

Strabo is often considered the main representative of ancient geography, not only because of the merits of his work, but because, by the fortunate accident of preservation, most of his geographical work is available today.[11] His work was an important step forward because it was the first and, for a long time, the only regional geography. It integrated the observations of his extensive traveling with the advances in mathematical geography of men like Eratosthenes and Hipparchus and with the large amounts of material collected by observant travelers. He believed that the universe was geocentric and, in that respect, disavowed the work of Aristarchus and Hipparchus, proponents of a heliocentric system.

Unlike Herodotus, who wrote geography in the form of physical descriptions but did not discuss the nature or purpose of geography, Strabo devoted a large portion of the first two books of his *Geography* to discussions of the definition, scope, and utility of geography and its relation to other sciences. The pages which follow were taken from the first volume of the eight volume translation of his *Geography*.

The Geography of Strabo[12]

The science of Geography, which I now propose to investigate, is, I think, quite as much as any other science, a concern

[10] It is commonly believed that the Nasamonians reached the Niger, and that their captors were Pygmies. We know that the Pygmies were forced out of the steppe into the uninviting forest habitat of today at a relatively recent date by advancing Bantu tribes. Some anthropologists assume that this retreat was connected with loss of cultural inventory.

[11] Actually, his contemporaries do not appear to have had great respect for his history and philosophy, of which only those parts contained in his *Geography* have been preserved. He considered himself a philosopher of the Stoic School.

[12] English translation by Horace Leonard Jones, 8 vols., Harvard University Press, Cambridge, Mass., 1949, Vol. I. (Date of the original is probably 7 B.C.)

of the philosopher; and the correctness of my view is clear for many reasons. In the first place, those who in earliest times ventured to treat the subject were, in their way, philosophers — Homer, Anaximander of Miletus, and Anaximander's fellow-citizen Hecataeus — just as Eratosthenes has already said; . . . In the second place, wide learning, which alone makes it possible to undertake a work on geography, is possessed solely by the man who has investigated things both human and divine — knowledge of which, they say, constitutes philosophy. And so, too, the utility of geography — and its utility is manifold, not only as regards the activities of statesmen and commanders but also as regards knowledge both of the heavens and of things on land and sea, animals, plants, fruits, and everything else to be seen in various regions — the utility of geography, I say, presupposes in the geographer the same philosopher, the man who busies himself with the investigation of the art of life, that is, of happiness.

Assuredly, . . . there is need of encyclopaedic learning for the study of geography, as many men have already stated; and Hipparchus, too, in his treatise *Against Eratosthenes*, correctly shows that it is impossible for any man, whether layman or scholar, to attain to the requisite knowledge of geography without the determination of the heavenly bodies and of the eclipses which have been observed; for instance, it is impossible to determine whether Alexandria in Egypt is north or south of Babylon, or how much north or south of Babylon, it is, without investigation through the means of the "climata."[13] In like manner, we cannot accurately fix points that lie at varying distances from us, whether to the east or the west, except by a comparison of the eclipses of the sun and the moon. (That is, by a comparison of the observations of the same eclipse, made from the different points of observation.)

Well, then, to this encyclopaedic knowledge let us add terrestial history — that is, the history of animals and plants and

[13] Climata, meaning literally the inclinations, was used by Hipparchus for zones of latitude; by Strabo, however, for the parallels of latitude themselves.

everything useful or harmful that is produced by land or sea. In fact all such studies are important as preliminary helps toward complete understanding. And to this knowledge of the nature of the land, and of the species of animals and plants, we must add a knowledge of all that pertains to the sea; for in a sense we are amphibious, and belong no more to the land than to the sea. That the benefit is great to anyone who has become possessed of information of this character, is evident both from ancient traditions and from reason. At any rate, the poets declare that the wisest heroes were those who visited many places and roamed over the world; for the poets regard it as a great achievement to have "seen the cities and known the minds of many men." [14]

It is . . . plain that geography as a whole has a direct bearing upon the activities of commanders; for it describes continents and seas — not only the seas inside the limits of the whole inhabited world, but also those outside these limits. And the description which geography gives is of importance to these men who are concerned as to whether this or that is so or otherwise, and whether known or unknown. For thus they can manage their various affairs in a more satisfactory manner, if they know how large a country is, how it lies, and what are its peculiarities either of sky or soil.

The utility of geography in matters of small concern, also, is quite evident; for instance, in hunting. A hunter will be more successful in the chase if he knows the character and extent of the forest; and again, only one who knows a region can advantageously pitch camp there, or set an ambush, or direct a march. The utility of geography is more conspicuous, however, in great undertakings, in proportion as the prizes of knowledge and the disasters that result from ignorance are greater. Thus Agamemnon and his fleet ravaged Mysia in the belief that it was Troy-land, and came back home in disgrace.

The person who attempts to write an account of the countries of the earth must take many of the physical and mathematical principles as hypotheses and elaborate his whole treatise with reference to their intent and authority. For, as

---

[14] Homer, *Odyssey*, 1:3.

I have already said, no architect or engineer would be competent even to fix the site of a house or a city properly if he had no conception beforehand of "climata" and of the celestial phenomena, and of geometrical figures and magnitudes and heat and cold and other such things — much less a person who would fix positions for the whole of the inhabited world.

Now as for the matters which he regards as fundamental principles of his science, the geographer must rely upon the geometricians who have measured the earth as a whole; and in their turn the geometricians must rely upon the astronomers; and again the astronomers upon the physicists. Physics is a kind of *Arete* (supreme excellence); and by *Aretai* they mean those sciences that postulate nothing but depend upon themselves, and contain within themselves their own principles a well as the proofs thereof. Now what we are taught by the physicists is as follows: The universe and the heavens are sphere-shaped. The tendency of the bodies that have weight is towards the centre. And, having taken its position about this centre in the form of a sphere, the earth remains homocentric with the heavens, as does also the axis through it, which axis extends also through the centre of the heavens. The heavens revolve round both the earth and its axis from east to west; and along with the heavens revolve the fixed stars, with the same rapidity as the vault of the heavens. Now the fixed stars move along parallel circles, and the best known parallel circles are the equator, the two tropics, and the arctic circles; whereas the planets and the sun and the moon move along certain oblique circles whose positions lie in the zodiac. Now the astronomers first accept these principles, either in whole or in part, and then work out the subsequent problems, namely, the movements of the heavenly bodies, their revolutions, their eclipses, their sizes, their respective distances, and a host of other things. And, in the same way, the geometricians, in measuring the earth as a whole, adhere to the doctrines of the physicists and the astronomers, and, in their turn, the geographers adhere to those of the geometricians.

The man who would most closely approximate the truth by constructed figures must needs make for the earth a globe like that of Crates, and lay off on it the quadrilateral(the inhabited world, which he also compares to a *chlamys,* a cloak), and within the quadrilateral put down the map of the inhabited world. But since there is need of a large globe, so that the section in question (being a small fraction of the globe) may be large enough to receive distinctly the appropriate parts of the inhabited world and to present the proper appearance to observers, it is better for him to construct a globe of adequate size, if he can do so; and let it be no less than ten feet in diameter. But if he cannot construct a globe of adequate size or not much smaller, he should sketch his map on a plane surface of at least seven feet.[15] For it will make only a slight difference if we draw straight lines to represent the circles, that is, the parallels and meridians, by means of which we clearly indicate the "climata," the winds and the other differences, and also the positions of the parts of the earth with reference both to each other and to the heavenly bodies— drawing parallel lines for the parallels and perpendicular lines for the circles perpendicular to the parallels, for our imagination can easily transfer to the globular and spherical surface the figure or magnitude seen by the eye on a plane surface. And the same applies also, we say, to the oblique circles and their corresponding straight lines. Although the several meridians drawn through the pole all converge on the sphere toward one point, yet on our plane-surface chart it will not be a matter of importance merely to make the straight meridian lines converge slightly; for there is no necessity for this in many cases, nor are the converging lines, when the lines of the sphere are transferred to the plane chart and drawn as straight lines, as easily understood as are the curved lines on the sphere.

And so in what I have to say hereafter I shall assume that our drawing has been made on a plane chart. Now I shall tell what part of the land and sea I have myself visited and concerning what part I have trusted to accounts given by others by word of mouth or in writing. I have traveled westward

[15] Apparently his choice of seven feet was to ease the computations of scale for he wrote elsewhere that the length of the inhabited world was 70,000 stadia, a little over 8,000 miles.

from Armenia as far as the regions of Tyrrhenia[16] opposite Sardinia, and southward from the Euxine Sea[17] as far as the frontiers of Ethiopia.[18] And you could not find another person among the writers on geography who has traveled over much more of the distances just mentioned than I; indeed, those who have traveled more than I in the western regions have not covered as much ground in the east, and those who have traveled more in the eastern countries are behind me in the western; and the same holds true in regard to the regions towards the south and north. However, the greater part of our material both they and I receive by hearsay and then form our ideas of shape and size and also other characteristics, qualitative and quantitative, precisely as the mind forms its ideas from sense impressions. . . . While the senses perceive only the parts, the mind forms a concept of the whole from what the senses have perceived. And men who are eager to learn . . . trust as organs of sense those who have seen or wandered over any region, no matter, some in this and some in that part of the earth, and they form in one diagram their mental image of the whole inhabited world. . . . And he who claims that only those have knowledge who have actually seen abolishes the criterion of the sense of hearing, though this sense is much more important than sight for the purposes of science.

Now my first and most important concern, both for the purposes of science and for the needs of the state, is this —to try to give, in the simplest possible way, the shape and size of that part of the earth which falls within our map, indicating at the same time what the nature of that part is and what portion it is of the whole earth; for this is the task proper of the geographer. . . . And since different places exhibit different good and bad attributes, as also the advantages and inconveniences that result therefrom, some due to nature and other resulting from human design, the geographer should mention those that are due to nature; for they

[16] Tuscany.
[17] Black Sea.
[18] Sudan.

are permanent, whereas the adventitious attributes undergo changes. And also of the latter attributes he should indicate such as can persist for a long time, or else such as can not persist for long and yet somehow possess a certain distinction and fame, which, by enduring to later times, make a work of man, even when it no longer exists, a kind of natural attribute of a place; hence it is clear that these latter attributes must also be mentioned.

CLAUDIUS PTOLEMAIUS[19] (PTOLEMY) (90-168 A.D.)

Ptolemy was one of the most influential astronomers, mathematicians, and geographers of ancient times. His work contains no traces of physical descriptions of the world or of any region but is largely mathematical geography, devoted to the reformation of the map of the world. He coined the terms "longitude" and "latitude" and reduced the exaggerations of the longitudinal measurements (in proportion to latitudinal measurements) of his predecessors. His astronomy, the famous *Almagest,* and astrology remained influential in the Arab countries and in Byzanz throughout the Middle Ages, but his geography was less well known. In the fifteenth century, Ptolemy's writings were revived in Europe and his geography especially became quite influential. For the next three centuries, most geographical writing consisted of expansion and minor correction of the work of Ptolemy, which dealt largely with attempts to map the known world. His views on geography quoted here are taken from the *Geography of Claudius Ptolemy.*

Geography of Claudius Ptolemy[20]

Geography is a representation in picture of the whole known world together with the phenomena which are contained therein.

---

[19] The name Ptolemaius indicates apparently his home town Ptolemais, a Macedo-Greek colony in Egypt, not a family-relationship to the Ptolemy dynasty.

[20] Translated into English and edited by Edward Luther Stevenson, N. Y., The New York Public Library, 1932, p. 26-39.

It differs from Chorography in that Chorography, selecting certain places from the whole, treats more fully the particulars of each by themselves — even dealing with the smallest conceivable localities, such as harbors, farms, villages, river courses, and such like.

It is the prerogative of geography to show the known habitable earth as a unit in itself, how it is situated and what is its nature; and it deals with those features likely to be mentioned in a general description of the earth, such as the larger towns and the great cities, the mountain ranges and the principal rivers. Besides these it treats only of features worthy of special note on account of their beauty.

The end of Chorography is to deal separately with a part of the whole, as if one were to paint only the eye or the ear by itself. The task of Geography is to survey the whole in its just proportions, as one would the entire head. For as in an entire painting we must first put in the larger features, and afterwards those detailed features which portraits and pictures may require, giving them proportion in relation to one another so that their correct measure apart can be seen by examining them, to note whether they form the whole or a part of the picture. Accordingly it is not unworthy of Chorography, or out of its province, to describe the smallest details of places, while Geography deals only with regions and their general features.

The habitable parts of the earth should be noted rather than the parts which are merely of equal size, especially the provinces of regions and their divisions, the differences between these being rather the more important. Chorography is most concerned with what kind of places those are which it describes, not how large they are in content. Its concern is to paint a true likeness, and not merely to give exact position and size. Geography looks at the position rather than the quality, noting the relation of distances everywhere, and emulating the art of painting only in some of its major descriptions. Chorography needs an artist and no one presents it rightly unless he is an artist. Geography does not call for the same requirements, as any one, by means of lines and plain notations can fix positions and draw general outlines.

Moreover Chorography does not have need of mathematics, which is an important part of Geography. In Geography one must contemplate the extent of the entire earth, as well as its shape, and its position under the heavens, in order that one may rightly state what are the peculiarities and proportions of the past with which one is dealing, and under what parallel of the celestial sphere it is located, for so one will be able to discuss the length of its days and nights, the stars which are fixed overhead, the stars which move above the horizon, and the stars which never rise above the horizon at all; in short all things having regard to our earthly habitation.

. . . We propose to describe our habitable earth, and in order that the description may correspond as far as possible with the earth itself, we consider it fitting at the outset to put forth that which is the first essential, namely, a reference to the history of travel, and to the great store of knowledge obtained from the reports of those who have diligently explored certain regions; whatever concerns either the measurement of the earth geometrically or the observation of the phenomena of fixed localities; whatever relates to the measurement of the earth that can be tested by pure distance calculations to determine how far apart places are situated; and whatever relations to fixed positions can be tested by meteorological[21] instruments for recording shadows. This last is a certain method, and in no respect doubtful. The other method is less perfect and needs other support, since first of all it is necessary to know in determining the distance between two places, in what direction each place lies from the other; to know how far this place is distant from that, we must also know under what part of the sky each is located, that is, whether each extends towards the north, or, so to speak, toward the rising of the sun (the east), or in some other particular direction.

Travelers who have journeyed over the regions of the earth one by one, had they made use of observations of a similar kind, would have been able to give us a wholly correct description of our habitable earth. But when no one except Hip-

[21] The Greek word meteorology means the science of things above the ground; it acquired the present restricted meaning only in modern times.

parchus [22] has given us the elevation of the north pole, and even he, of only a few places out of the great number known to geographers, and since he has marked only a small number of the sites that are on the same meridian; and when others coming after him have noted the position of the places opposite each other, not giving us those of equal distance from the equator, but only those lying on the same meridian, taking this from successful voyages made to the north and south; and calculating most of their distances, especially those which extended to east or west, from a certain general tradition, not because of any lack of skill or because of indolence, on the part of the writers, but because in their time, the use of exact mathematics had not yet been established . . .

Since, however, all regions can not be known fully on account of their great size, or because they are not always of the same shape or because not yet satisfactorily explored, and a greater length of time makes our knowledge of them more certain, we think we should say something to the readers of our geography on the subject of varying traditions at various times, viz., of some portions of our continents, on account of their great size, we have as yet no knowledge; with regard to other parts we do not know what is their real nature, because of the negligence of those who have explored them in failing to give us carefully prepared reports; other parts of the earth are different today from what they were, either on account of revolution or from transformation in which processes they are known to have partially passed into ruin.

We consider it necessary therefore for us to pay more atten-

---

[22] Hipparchus (active period 146-127 B.C.), primarily an astronomer, was the first to recognize the importance of exact location by geographical coordinates. He also established the system of zones, delimited by latitude. He called these zones by a Green name, "climata." His great authority, however, also caused the survival of two basic errors. Upon his authority geographers, such as Strabo and Ptolemy, rejected in favor of Posidonius (135-50 B.C.) the nearly correct estimates of Eratosthenes (276-194 B.C.) of the meridian and the heliocentric system of Aristarchus (about 280 B.C.), which was revived only by Copernicus (1473-1543) independently. The underestimate of the size of the globe and mistakes derived from it, led Columbus to believe that he could reach India by crossing a relatively narrow ocean.

tion to the newer records of our time, weighing, however, in our description these new records and those of former times and deciding what is credible, and what is incredible.

Marinus the Tyrian,[23] the latest of the geographers of our time, seems to us to have thrown himself with the utmost zeal into this matter.

He is known to have found out many things that were not known before. He has searched most diligently the works of almost all the historians who preceded him. He has not only corrected their errors, but the reader can clearly see that he has undertaken to correct those parts of the work which he himself had done badly in the earlier editions of his geographical maps.

We therefore are undertaking a double labor, first in keeping the intention that Marinus had throughout his whole work, besides that which we have obtained through corrections; and second in adding these things, with as much accuracy as possible, which to him were not known, partly on account of history then unwritten, and partly on account of a later series of more accurate maps.

In addition we have given special attention to a better method in fixing the boundaries of each particular country; we have given their particular position both in longitude and in latitude. After that we have recorded noteworthy information concerning the inhabitants of the various countries, and their relations one to another. We have noted the chief cities, rivers, gulfs, and mountains, and all other things which in the map itself might show distances where they are worth knowing, that is to say how many degrees. . . . We are able therefore to know at once the exact position of any particular place; and positions of the various countries, how they are situated in regard to one another, (and) how situated as regards the whole inhabited world.

[23] Marinus of Tyre (70-130 A.D.). None of his books or maps have been preserved, but from what we know indirectly, he must have been one of the prominent geographers of his time.

CHAPTER 2

ARAB GEOGRAPHERS

Like ancient Greek geography, Arabic geography also profited from far-flung conquests, the possibility of traveling through large areas, and the resulting intensified commercial connections. The Arabs could also build on a Greek heritage; and, as in other fields of science, ancient geographical thought (Ptolemy's *Almagest,* for example) was transmitted to modern times mainly in Arabic form. However, though the Arabs contributed much to our factual knowledge, they were less influential in contributing to geographical concepts.

ABOU-ABDALLAH-MOHAMMED AL IDRISI (1099-1166)

Al Idrisi is probably the best known of the medieval Arab geographers. He owes this reputation not only to his actual achievements, which placed him first among Arab travelers and geographers of the Middle Ages, but also to the fact that he did most of his work in a Christian country, at the court of King Roger II, the Norman ruler of Sicily in the middle of the 12th century. Under the protection of several unusually tolerant rulers of the Norman and Staufen dynasties the kingdom of Sicily became a fertile meeting ground for Arab, Byzantine and nascent western civilization. Al Idrisi's "Geography" is a commentary on his main geographical work, the supervision of the construction of a celestial planisphere and a round world map engraved in silver. Much of his work has been lost, but that part which has been preserved contains the most elaborate description of the world of medieval times. Unlike most Arab geographies, his work contains discussions of Christian, as well as Arab, countries.

Geography of Al Idrisi[1]

PREFACE OF THE AUTHOR

Thanks be rendered unto the Lord, the greatest, powerful being, bodiless, endowed with kindness, a benevolent spirit and forbearing sovereign judge who can do everything, who possesses infinite knowledge, who has bestowed upon all his creatures perfect forms, the knowledge of whom is engraved in every heart and rests in every mind because of the visible and incontestable proofs[2] . . .

Among all the beings which have been created by this divine will, the eye cannot see neither the mind imagine a more accomplished man than the illustrious Roger, King of Sicily, Italy, Lombardy and Calabria, and Roman prince. This great king, upon whom heaven has heaped glory and power, protector of the religion of Christ, is the most famous and best among all monarchs . . .[3]

After the expanse of his possessions had been enlarged just as the respect which one paid to his subjects had grown, and when he submitted under his power the domains conquered from other Christian princes, Roger of Sicily occupied himself with the statistics of his wide domain because of the interest which he had in exalted and curious knowledge. He wanted not only to know very definitely the location of the borders of his domain, the routes by land and by sea which traverse them, the climatic zones in which they are located, the seas which bathe their coasts, and the canals and rivers which irrigate them, but also he wanted knowledge of countries other than those which depended on his rule, in all seven climatic zones. Therefore he relied on the authority of writers who have studied geography and who have tried to determine

---

[1] Translated from the French of P. Amédée Joubert from the Arab original, published as the 5th volume of *Receuil de Voyages et de Memoirs*, Sociétè de Géographie, Paris, Imprimerie Royale, 1836. p. xv-xxxi, 1-14, 81, 422.

[2] There follows another full page of similar enumeration of the qualities of the Lord.

[3] There follows exactly two more full pages of panegyric praise for Roger.

the extent, the subdivisions, and the dependencies of each climatic zone; for this purpose he consulted the following books: . . .[4]

However, instead of finding in these writings clear, precise, and detailed facts, there were nothing but obscure passages and reasons for doubt; thus he let especially well informed persons come into his presence and put questions before them and discussed those questions with them; but he did not get more clarification. When he realized the situation, he decided to search throughout all his lands for educated travelers; he ordered them to come into his presence and interrogated them through interpreters, either in groups or separately. Every time they agreed on a point and their reports were unanimous regarding some fact, this item was admitted and regarded as certain. If they held divergent views, their opinions were rejected and put aside.

He occupied himself for fifteen years without relaxing, examining all geographical problems, in order to find solutions, verify the facts, and finally to acquire the complete knowledge which he desired.

Then he wanted to know in definite terms the longitude and the latitude of places and the distance between those points on which the mentioned persons had agreed. For this purpose he had a drawing board prepared, on which he had located, one by one, with the help of an iron compass, the places which had been indicated in the reference books and those places on which the authorities had come to an agreement . . . Finally, he ordered a planisphere (a round table) to be engraved in pure silver of an immense size and weighing 450 Roman pounds, each pound having 112 drachmes. He had skilled artisans engrave the configuration of the regions, countries, coastal areas, and seas with their straits and currents of the seven climatic zones, indicating which countries were deserts and which cultivated, their respective distances along the most frequented routes in miles or other known measures,[5] and the

---

[4] Al Idrisi gives here a list of twelve authors; Ptolemy, Eresias of Antioch, and ten Arbs, of whom only Masudi is well known in the West.

[5] Such as journey of a day by horse or by camel, etc.

designation of the ports; and he admonished his artisans to follow scrupulously the draft engraved on the drawing board without deviating in any way from the configurations which they found indicated on it.

To promote better understanding of this map he ordered the writing of a book containing the complete description of cities and territories, the nature of cultures and housing conditions, and the extent of seas, mountains, rivers, plains, and lowlands. This book was also to contain the types of grain, fruit, and plants in general, which every country produced, the properties of these plants, the arts and occupations in which its population excelled, its commerce of exports and imports, curious objects which were observed or which were found among the famous people of the seven zones, the condition of the population, their customs, their religion, their costumes, and their languages.

I gave to this book the title of *Recreation for People Who Desire to Know Thoroughly the Different Countries of the World.*

PRELIMINARY REMARKS

We begin with the discussion of the figure of the earth, the description of which was presented by Ptolemy . . .

The conclusion that results from the opinions of philosophers, famous scholars, and observers skilled in the knowledge of the celestial bodies, is that the earth is round like a sphere and that the waters cling to it and are kept on it through a natural equilibrium which does not experience any variation.

The land as well as the water is, therefore, immersed in space, like the yellow in the middle of an egg, which is in a central position. Air surrounds it on all sides; it pulls it towards the empty space or pushes it back from there; only God knows what is the truth concerning this point. The Earth is stable in the center of space, and all created things are stable on the surface of the Earth. . . .

The inhabitable part of the earth was divided by the scholars into seven climatic zones, each of which extends from west to east. This division is not established to follow lines existing in nature, but rather according to ideal lines invented by the astronomers. In each climatic zone exist a great number of cities, fortresses, towns, and peoples which have no resemblance to each other. There are also found high mountains, vast plains, springs, water courses, quiet lakes, minerals, plants, and animals of different kinds.

The seven climatic zones are traversed by seven seas of which we shall speak later, if God will permit it. These seven seas are also called gulfs. Six of them are contiguous; only one is separate and has no connection with the other . . .

In the country of the blacks one does not see any fruits, either dried or fresh, except dates which come from Sedjelmassa and the country of the Zab and are brought by the inhabitants of the desert of Wardjelan. The river Nile flows in this country from east to west. Reeds, ebony trees, cedars, willows, and divers kinds of tamarisks grow at the banks of the river in thick forests, where the wild animals live and where they retire for protection from the excessive heat. One meets here lions, giraffes, gazelles, hyenas, elephants, hares, and weasels . . . .

The arms which these peoples use are bows and arrows. . . . All of what we are about to tell about their habits and customs, about their manner of eating, of quenching thirst, of dressing, and of beautifying themselves, refers to the majority of the countries of the blacks, countries which are very dry and hot. Referring to agriculture, the sedentary among them plant onions, pumpkins and watermelons, which attain an enormous size. They have no cereals except sorghum, from which they extract a drink. Their main food consists of fish or camel meat, dried in the sun . . .

SICILY

From Milazzo to Messina is an easy journey.[7] The city of

[7] Milazzo is about twenty miles west of Messina.

The following two descriptions have been selected to give an idea of the character of Al Idrisi's work by giving an example of a place he knew well and another sufficiently remote to be known only by the stories of travelers.

Messina lies toward the easternmost point of Sicily and is backed by mountains. Its seaboard offers a beautiful view; its territory comprises orchards and gardens which produce fruits abundantly and is furrowed by water courses which turn several mills. It is one of the most remarkable cities, very well built and very much visited by people, who are continually coming and leaving. Ships are constructed here, and other ships from all the maritime parts of Christendom come to moor here. This is the place where one can find both the largest ships, and travelers and merchants from all parts of the Christian and Islamic worlds. Its bazaars are well stocked, and it is possible to conclude here the most advantageous deals because of the great influx of sellers and buyers. The mountains produce iron which is exported to the neighboring countries by ship. The harbor is one of the best in the world, as shown by the fact that the very largest ships can anchor so close to shore that a person on land can easily take into his hands any object out of the hands of somebody on board the vessel.

Near Messina one sees the narrows which separate Sicily from Calabria; the passage through them is difficult, especially when the wind blows against the current, or when the rising tide meets the waters of the descending current. In such a case a vessel which finds itself caught between the two opposing forces can be saved only with the permission of God. The greatest width of this sound is ten miles and the smallest three miles.

SEVENTH CLIMATIC ZONE

FIRST SECTION

IRELAND AND SCOTLAND

This whole section comprises a part of the Dark Ocean and several deserted and uninhabited islands. The largest of these islands is Berlanda (Ireland), the extreme southern end of which is a three and a half day voyage from Brittany.

From the extreme northern point to the deserted island of Scosia (Scotland) is a two day journey.

However, the author of the *Book of Marvels*[8] reports that three towns existed on the latter island at one time, that the island had been inhabited, that ships came there in order to buy amber and colored stones, and that some of the people wanted to conquer the others and rule over them. He says there followed civil wars, hostilities, and ravages, and in their wake a part of the inhabitants emigrated to the continent, leaving their towns deserted and ruined.

ABU ABDALLAH MUHAMMAD IBN 'ABDALLAH IBN MUHAMMAD AL-LAWATI AL-TANJI IBN BATTUTA (1304-1368)

Ibn Battuta has been called "The Traveler of Islam," for he saw more of the world than any other Arab traveler of the Middle Ages. It has been estimated that he traveled about 75,000 miles, considerably more than Marco Polo or any other traveler prior to the development of steam power. He seems to have been driven by an insatiable desire to see any country or place open to him and to meet famous theologians and scholars. Although his point of view was never that of a geographer, and he had little use for or knowledge of maps, he augmented the geographical knowledge of his contemporaries to a considerable extent by being the first to describe for the West many of the countries through which he had traveled. The passages included here are from the *Rihlat ibn Battuta* (the translation has been titled *Travels in Asia and Africa 1325-1354*), which was completed in 1355, and are representative of a large part of Arab "geographical" literature.

Travels in Asia and Africa 1325-1354[9]

Among those who presented themselves at the illustrious gates of our lord the Caliph and Commander of the Faithful Abú Inán Faris was the learned and most veracious traveler

[8] By the renowned Arab geographer and historian Abu'l Hasan Ali ibn Husain ibn ul Masudi, who lived in the first half of the 10th century.

[9] Translated and selected by H. A. R. Gibb, Routledge and Kegan Paul Ltd., London, 3rd impression 1953.

Abú Abdalláh Muhammed of Tangier, known as Ibn Battuta . . . who having journeyed round the world and visited its cities observantly and attentively, having investigated the diversities of nations and experienced the customs of Arabs and non-Arabs, laid down the staff of travel in this noble metropolis.[10] A gracious command prescribed that he should dictate an account of the cities which he had seen on his journeys, of the interesting events which he had retained in his memory, and of the rulers of countries, learned men and pious saints whom he had met . . .[11]

The Egyptian Nile surpasses all rivers of the earth in sweetness of taste, length of course, and utility. No other river in the world can show such a continuous series of towns and villages along its banks, or a basin so intensely cultivated. Its course is from south to north contrary to all other (great) rivers. One extraordinary thing about it is that it begins to rise in the extreme hot weather, at the time when rivers generally diminish and dry up, and begins to subside just when rivers begin to increase and overflow.[12] The river Indus resembles it in this feature. The Nile is one of the five great rivers of the world, which are the Nile, Euphrates, Tigris, Syr Darya, and Amu Darya; five other rivers resemble these, the Indus, which is called Panj Ab, the river of India which is called Gang — it is to it that the Hindus go on pilgrimage, and when they burn their dead they throw the ashes into it, and they say that it comes from Paradise — the river Jún (Jumna or perhaps Brahmaputra) in India, the river Itil (Volga) in the Qipchag steppes . . . and the river Sarú (Hwang-Ho) in the land of Cathay (China). . . .[13]

---

[10] Fez, Morocco.

[11] From the introduction of Ibn Juzayy, who wrote down and edited the oral narrative of Ibn Battúta.

[12] This passage should be compared to Herodotus' passage on the Nile. While Herodotus proceeds to inquire and speculate about the causes of their behaviour, Ibn Battúta is satisfied with the observation of the actual behaviour.

[13] Ibn Battúta had crossed all these big rivers on his travels, but could not free himself from the ancient scheme of only five big rivers. Even by adding five more, he could not accommodate the Yang-tse-kiang and the Niger, both of which he had seen himself.

I had heard of the city of Bulghar [14] and desired to visit it, in order to see for myself what they tell of the extreme shortness of the night there and also the shortness of the day in the opposite season . . . We reached it in the month of Ramadan, and when we had breakfasted after the sunset prayer we had just sufficient time for the night prayers before dawn . . .[15] I had intended to visit the Land of Darkness. . . . The only way of reaching it is to travel on sledges drawn by dogs.

ABD AR RAHMAN IBN MUHAMMAD IBN KHALDUN (1332-1406)

Ibn Khaldun was the most famous Arab historian and philosopher of the Middle Ages. However, for his world-embracing mind, history comprised everything which explained the present state of individual nations and of mankind in general. He believed that the life and activities of mankind were rigorously conditioned by geographical factors, and he devoted a large portion of his writings to discussions of those factors. His geographical writings break with the traditional travel descriptions which characterized Arab geography of the Middle Ages. He reflected a knowledge of the work of Ptolemy and Al Idrisi and continued the ancient speculations on the proportion of land areas to sea areas. But Ptolemy's mapping system had been accepted as standard and had undergone few changes, so that Ibn Khaldun, nearly twelve hundred years later, still lacked accurate maps of the places about which he wrote.

Ibn Khaldun's life was that of a trained lawyer and politician in the service of many princes, from Morocco and Spain to Egypt, and at times he even commanded troops. In his later years, when recognized as a great scholar, he was a high judge in Egypt, frequently removed and reinstated for political reasons. In the enforced intervals of retirement he devoted his capacities to writing, drawing widely upon his worldly experiences for his judgment of men and countries. The ex-

---

[14] The ancient capital of one branch of the Bulgarians on the Volga near the mouth of the Kama and the great bend of the river.

[15] That is somewhat exaggerated, as Bulghar was located at approximately 55°N.

cerpts from his writings included here are taken from the French version of his work, *Les Prolegomènes d' Abd ar Rahman ibn Muhammad Ibn Khaldun,* published in 1863.

Prolegomena [16]

Man is distinguished from all other living beings by qualities which are peculiar to him, including first, sciences and arts; . . . second, the need for an authority which can reprimand his mistakes; . . . third, industry and work which furnish the different tools for his livelihood; . . . fourth, sociability; . . . fifth and sixth, the two forms of his life in society, nomadic and sedentary. The former is to be found on the plains and mountains among the nomads who migrate through the pastures located in the deserts and near the limits of the sandfilled regions. The second is found in the cities, towns, villages and hamlets, where men live for safety's sake, protected by walls. Under all these circumstances life in society suffers essential modification in the interactions of man and society. Therefore, it is necessary that this first volume, and the material with which it deals, should be divided into six sections:

First, about society in general, varieties of the human race, and the countries which humans inhabit;

Second, about the civilization of the nomads, about tribes, and semisavage peoples;

Third, about government by dynasties . . .

Fourth, about the character of civilization as a result of sedentary life, and the role which cities and provinces play in it;

Fifth, about occupations . . .

Sixth, about sciences . . .

I put the nomadic way of life before the sedentary, because it preceded all the forms which the latter could assume . . .

---

[16] *Les Prolegomènes d' Abd ar Rahman ibn Muhammad Ibn Khaldun,* translated from the French version of M. de Slane, Paris, Imprimerie Imperial, 1863. Vol. 1, p. 84-100, 168-179.

Second Preliminary Essay

The second preliminary essay deals with the inhabited part of the Earth, the main seas, the great rivers and the forms of climate.

In the books of those philosophers who took the universe as the subject for their studies, one reads that the earth is spherical and is immersed in the Ocean, on which it seems to float like a raisin in water; that the water has retired from some coasts of the Earth because the Lord wanted to create animals which needed dry soil in order to live, and to put on it, as inhabitants, the human race, which should serve as his lieutenant in regard to the other animals. Accordingly, some thought, but wrongly so, that the water has been placed above the land. . . . The part of the earth which the water has left uncovered occupies half of the surface of the world. This portion, which is of a circular form, is surrounded by the liquid element, i.e., by a sea which is called *The Environmental*. . . . It is also called Ocean, which is a foreign word. The part of the earth which is left uncovered in order to serve for a dwelling place, comprises also deserted places, mostly in the south. The uninhabited portion is much larger than the populated portion.[17] The inhabited region extends farther north and has the form of a convex surface . . .

Supplement to the Second Preliminary Essay

Why does the northern quarter of the earth have a larger population than the southern quarter? The population agglomerates between the third and sixth climatic zones.[18] According to several philosophers, the extreme south is completely a desert because of the excessive heat and because, in this region, the sun departs only very little from the zenith.

We shall proceed to explain this doctrine by a convincing conclusion which, at the same time, will explain why the

---

[17] This concept, that the unknown parts of the earth are also uninhabited, is very ancient and was taken by the Arabs from Greek authors.

[18] Ibn Khaldun, like Ptolemy, distinguishes 7 climatic zones.

CHAPTER 3

RENAISSANCE AND POST-RENAISSANCE GEOGRAPHERS

The horizons of geography received their first great extension from the conquests of Alexander the Great, were broadened extensively by the Arabs, and widened by a third significant impulse from the discoveries and explorations of Portugal and Spain during the Renaissance. During this age of discovery, as in many subsequent periods of time, large amounts of travel literature and descriptions of exotic foreign countries were written, making factual additions to geographical knowledge. However, these geographical compendia remained unsystematic collections of unevaluated data for at least three centuries. During this period of time, such names as Blaeu and Mercator became world famous as significant progress was being made in the science of cartography. The two men chosen to represent the geographic thought of the Renaissance made significant contributions, although the period could boast of relatively few.

PHILIPP CLÜVER (CLUVERIUS) (1580-1623)

Cluverius was born in eastern Germany but spent much of his adult life in Holland when not travelling. His primary interest, typical of many Renaissance scholars, was ancient history and archaeology, and his main writings dealt with the ancient geography of Italy and Germany. His last book, *Introduction to General Geography,* which was one of the first attempts to broaden the field of geography, did not appear until after his death. The fusion of rationalistic concepts, transmitted through the Arabs from ancient Greece, with medieval concepts based on the Bible is visible in his writings.

The following excerpt is from his *Introduction to General Geography,* originally published in 1624.

Introduction to General Geography Modern as well as Ancient[1]

What is Geography, and what is the Globe? Geography is the description of the entire earth, as far as it is known. The word itself is Greek, namely from *gaia,* or *gaie,* which means earth, in composite words in the form of *geo,* and of *grapho,* I write. A composite word is geography, description of the earth.

Geography is distinguished from cosmography, like a part from the whole; from chorography, like the whole from a part. Cosmography, derived from *kosmos,* meaning world, and *grapho,* is the description of the World, of the entire universe, or of the world in its earthly as well as its atmospheric aspects. Chorography, a word derived from *choros* or *chora,* meaning region, and *grapho,* is the description of some particular locality, such as a field, landscape, town, or county. Such things as plowed fields, meadows, trees, streets, and houses also belong to this category. But geography describes only the qualities of the earth.[2]

In geography we do not conceive the *earth* as a separate fourth element, as the physicists do:[3] but the whole earth, together with the interrelated water (which is *infusis*), as the center of the whole universe, which, from its shape, is called an *orbe,* or *globe.* A globe is a solid body, round on all sides, within a single surface; as a centre it has what may be conceived as a point from which all lines to the surface are equal. A globe of any element is, therefore, a unique body; it has only one surface, and this is convex. Some geographers have divided this globe into circles and parts.

---

[1] Philippi Cluverii, *Introductionis in universam Geographiam, tam novam quam veterem,* Patavii (Padua), 1717. (Original—1624) p. 10-46. Translated from the Latin.

[2] This is one of the earliest, though not very clear, distinctions between general and regional geography.

[3] Reference to the four elements of ancient science: earth, water, fire, and air, which was still current in the 17th century.

Men are divided into three groups, distinguished by the kind of shadows they throw:

(1) *Amphiscii* or men with two shadows, who cast shadows to both sides at noon, that is, towards north or south in the different seasons. They are the peoples who live in the torrid zone, such as the Arabs, who were surprised, when they crossed the Tropic of Cancer into the northern temperate zone, that their shadows went to the north in summer, not towards the south as they had observed it in their homeland. When they have the sun in the zenith, they are called *Ascii*, meaning shadowless.

(2) *Heteroscii* or men with either shadow, live in the temperate zones where the noon shadow points to either of the poles, toward the Arctic pole for those who live in the northern, toward the Antarctic for those who live in the southern zone. They are also called *Antiscii*, because they live in opposite zones and have opposite shadows. These men are also either *Macroscii* or *Brachiscii*, because their noon shadows are now longer, now shorter; but this applies even more to the inhabitants of the torrid zone.

(3) *Periscii* or circum-shadowed men are those who live in the frigid zones, because they see their shadows rotate around them. This occurs since a major part of the zodiac is always above the horizon.

Summa Totius Orbis Divisio

Having discussed the seas and oceans, let us now discuss the dry land. The whole world is best divided into three parts, or three big islands, which the Ocean surrounds. The first is where we are living; the second, America; the third, Magalanica. The latter is also called Australis, or the Unknown,[4] because nothing is known to us but the coasts. Of these three islands, which you may also call continents, we shall first

[4] Up to the time of Cook it was believed that there ought to exist a southern continent. Some identified its northern coasts with Tierra del Fuego, from which the name Magalanica was derived. When it was realized that Tierra del Fuego was an island, the designation of Australis became common.

explain that one on which we are living and where our fatherland is located; it is for the most part the best known and longest studied. We have discussed previously the names of the surrounding oceans.

At all times it was best divided into three parts: Europe, Asia, and Africa; and it was believed that this threefold division goes back to Noah's three sons: Shem having inherited Asia; Cham, Africa; and Japheth, Europe. Whatever their original boundaries, through the foundation of empires, perhaps also by the whim of geographers, they were changed. Thus much of the land of Cham and Japheth fell to the descendants of Shem.[5]

Neither have later men, who lived in the Middle Ages, made the division the same way; some divided it only into two parts, namely, Asia and Europe; they recognized Africa under this name, but regarded it as subdivision; they even believed it split by a sound between the Calpe and Abyla mountains;[6] others recognized two parts divided by the Straits of Gibralter (fretum Gaditanum) and the Don river (Tanais); on this side Europe, on the other Asia; under that name they comprised also Africa.

Others again made a quadripartite division; Europe, Asia, Egypt, and Africa. Later there were those which established three parts: Europe, Asia, and Africa, and added Egypt to Asia. Much less convenient is the division between Asia and Africa by the Nile, as this way part of Egypt belongs to Asia, the other to Africa. The modern ones have made the Arab Gulf (Red Sea, sinus Arabicus) the boundary between Asia and Africa and consider Egypt a part of Africa. All these dicerent divisions are to be found in the ancient authors also.

[5] Apparently a reference to the conquests of the Arabs in North Africa, and of the Turks in Southeast Europe. The Turks, of course, have nothing to do with the peoples speaking Semitic languages. They are probably included here because of the Islamic religion which they share with the Arabs.

[6] That is, south of the Rif Mountains of the Atlas.

Object

The object of geography, or the subject of the science of the Earth, is primarily its surface and parts.

Relations

As far as they merit being taken into consideration, the relations seem to be of three different kinds, especially as far as they can be treated in special geography for the benefit of students and teachers, namely: celestial, terrestrial, and human relations. I call those relations celestial which depend on the apparent movement of the sun and the stars. They number eight: (1) co-latitude, distance of a place from the equator and from the pole; (2) obliqueness of the daily movement of the stars over the horizon of the respective place; (3) duration of the longest and shortest day; (4) climate and zones; (5) heat, cold, and weather throughout the year — for example, rain, snow, wind, and other atmospheric phenomena (although these things could be treated with the terrestrial relations, we have classed them nonetheless with the celestial ones, because they have close connection with the four seasons and the movement of the sun); (6) the rise of the stars, their time of visibility, and behavior above the horizon; (7) the stars which pass through the zenith of the respective place; and (8) amount and velocity of movement by which every place moves at any hour according to the Copernican hypothesis . . .

So much about the group of celestial relations. I call those relations terrestrial which we can investigate at the location of the respective region. There are ten of them: (1) limits and borders; (2) figure; (3) size; (4) mountains; (5) drainage features, such as rivers, springs, bays, etc.; (6) forests and deserts; (7) fertility or sterility, including kinds of products; (8) minerals and fossils; (9) animals; and (10) longitude, which also can be treated with the first terrestrial relation, namely the borders.

I designate as the third kind of relations, deserving observation in the individual regions, the human ones, which depend on men or the inhabitants of the individual regions. Of these, ten also can be proposed: (1) the build of the inhabitants, their looks, color, longevity, origin, and eating and drinking habits; (2) the livelihood and arts with which the inhabitants occupy themselves, commerce, and the wares which the region sends to others; (3) good and bad properties, erudition, talents, and schools, etc.; (4) customs concerning births, marriages, and funerals; (5) speech or language which the inhabitants use; (6) political order; (7) religion and establishment of the church; (8) cities and better known places; (9) memorable stories; and (10) famous men, works of art and inventions made by the inhabitants of the individual regions.

Those are the three kinds of relations with which special geography has to deal, although those which constitute the third group do not exactly belong to geography; but one must make some concession to custom and to practical utility for the student. In addition we have added many chapters to special geography about the use of geography. . . .

Principles

There are three principles which geography uses in order to prove its propositions: (1) the propositions of geometry, arithmetic, and trigonometry; (2) the precepts and theorems of astronomy, and it seems miraculous that we should owe so much to the celestial bodies in our quest of knowledge of the nature of the earth which we inhabit, since the former are so many myriads of miles distant from us; (3) experience. Indeed the greatest part of geography, especially special geography, is backed only by experience and the observations of people who described the individual regions.

Methods

One needs to know about methods, the way to prove the truth of the geographical dogmas, in order that most things in general geography, especially the celestial relations, may be confirmed by adequately performed derivations. In special geography, however, almost everything is explained without derivations (excepting celestial relations which can be proved) but by experience and observation; that means that the testimony of the senses confirms everything, and nothing can be proved any other way . . .

Most propositions are proven, or rather shown, by the use of an artificial earth globe and also of geographical maps. Some of the propositions which are shown this way could also be proven by legitimate proofs (which are omitted, nevertheless, because of the lack of comprehension by the readers). Others could not be proven by this method, but they are accepted as true because we suppose that all places on the globe and the maps are distributed as they are on the Earth itself. Nevertheless, in these things we shall follow descriptions furnished by geographical authors; the globe and maps will serve us for illustration and easier comprehension.

Origin of Geography[10]

Merits of Geography

The following things recommend the study of geography: first, it is dignified, because it is a study proper in the highest degree for man as the inhabitant of the earth, gifted with intelligence above all other living beings; second, it provides pleasure and recreation to contemplate the regions and properties of the Earth; third, it is useful and necessary, because neither theologians nor physicians nor lawyers nor historians nor writers can proceed without geographical knowledge if they want continual progress in their studies. That has been shown sufficiently by others and can be illustrated with many examples.

---

[10] Varenius mentions in this paragraph only the Roman road maps, the Pharaoh Necho and his despatch of the Phoenician seamen, the order of Darius to explore the river Indus, and the report that Alexander the Great had two topographers among the people in his camp.

CHAPTER 4

THE INSTIGATORS

Up to the 18th century a vast amount of factual knowledge had been accumulated. For centuries explorers and travelers had written reports of their journeys in foreign countries, thus adding to man's knowledge of the earth and expanding the horizons of his experience. In the 18th century, feudal decentralization began to yield to the rational, bureaucratic centralization of enlighted absolutism. The administrators of the emerging states of Europe began to collect statistics of their own countries and the countries with which they had commercial or political relations. The suggestions for a geographic approach to this material came from philosophers, like Kant and Montesquieu, and romantic admirers of nature, like Herder and Rousseau. Only very little of what they wrote would necessarily be considered geography, but they showed that nature could be something to be loved and studied, not to be avoided or, at best, taken as an inevitable evil. De Saussure is perhaps the man who best exemplifies all these traits in his writings.

IMMANUEL KANT (1724-1804)

Kant is well known as a philosopher, but less well known as one of the pioneers of modern geography. It is believed that he was the first university teacher to give classes in geography, his first one certainly before 1757. His somewhat younger contemporary, Johann Christoph Gatterer (1727-1799), better known as an historian, was the only other known 18th century geography teacher on the university level. The influence of both men was exerted more through their students than through their writings. Although his influence on his students is not as well known as Gatterer's influence on Ritter or de Saussure's on von Humboldt, Kant was probably the most important of the three because the influence of his thinking is seen in the thought and writings of the many prominent geographers of subsequent generations, even though his philosophy of geography was published only in limited editions of classroom notes which Kant himself did not recognize as authentic.

Kant considered a knowledge of physical geography, including man and his influence on the course of events on the earth, essential for an understanding of man's perceptions of the world. Therefore he taught geography as an introductory phase of his philosophy. The selection which follows is from a collection of his writings edited by Karl Vorländer.

Physical Geography[1]

The experience of nature and man together constitute the knowledge of the world. Anthropology teaches us how to know man; we owe knowledge of nature to *physical geography* or description of the earth. Indeed, *experiences*, in the strict sense of the word, do not exist, only perceptions which together constitute experience . . .[2]

Physical geography is, therefore, the first segment of knowledge of the world. It is part of a concept which can be called the *propaedeutic* (introduction) *to the knowledge of the world.* Instruction in this field still seems to be quite deficient. Nevertheless, it is just this knowledge which is extremely useful in all possible conditions of life. Therefore, it is necessary to become acquainted with geography as a branch of knowledge which can be expanded and improved by practical experience.

We anticipate future experience of the world by studying and by reviewing in such a way as to give us a preliminary idea. It is said that a man who has travelled much has seen the world. But there is more to knowing the world than merely having seen it. He who wants to profit from his travels must first draw up a plan; nor can he regard the world as but an object for his senses. . . .

---

[1] *Physische Geographie,* Königsberg, 1802. Translated from the 3rd edition (edited by Paul Gedan) of *Kant, Sämtliche Werke (Collected Writings)*, edited by Karl Vorländer, Felix Meiner, Leipzig, 1922. p. 8-15.

[2] Kant teaches that we never can touch reality, but know only our perception of reality. This is the doctrine of *transcendental* idealism.

Thus, even our present preparation is an *idea of the knowledge of the world.* We construct, therefore, an architectural idea — that is, an idea in which the various parts are derived from the whole.

The whole in this case is the world, the stage, on which we shall undergo all experiences. Contact with other people and travels broaden the scope of all our knowledge. . . . By travelling, knowledge of the external world is enhanced; that is, however, of little value if one has not gained some preliminary knowledge by studying.[3] If, therefore, it is said of someone that he knew the world, it is understood that he knew man and nature.

It may be we should heed only our own experiences; however, they are insufficient for a knowledge of everything. Man, in relation to time, lives but briefly and can, therefore, experience only little; and in relation to space, even if he travels, he is not able to see and observe many things. Therefore, we must use foreign experiences, which ought to be reliable. Thus written notes are preferable to mere oral reports.

We enlarge our knowledge by (second hand) information, as if we ourselves had lived through all past periods. We supplement our knowledge of the present world with information from foreign and remote countries, as if we ourselves lived there. However, it should be noted that every foreign experience is transmitted to us either as a *tale* or a *description.* The former is history, the other geography. The description of a specific place on the surface of the earth is called topography. Further, chorography is the description of a region and its properties; orography, the description of this or that mountain; and hydrography, the description of the waters.

Organization of knowledge according to concepts is the logical organization; organization according to time and space, the physical one. By the former we arrive at a system of nature . . ., by the latter, at a geographical description of nature.

---

[3] Kant never travelled beyond the vicinity of Königsberg, in East Prussia, where he spent all his adult life. He was born and grew up in a small town nearby.

If I say that all types of cattle belong to the class of quadruped animals, or even more specifically to that of the cloven-footed animals, that is a classification which I perform in my head, a logical division. The *systema naturae* is therefore a record-office of the whole, a place where I put all things, each one in its appropriate class, regardless of how scattered they may be over the earth.[4]

According to the physical division, things are considered primarily in respect to the localities which they occupy on the earth. A system assigns places in an order of classes. Geographical description of nature points out these places where those things actually can be found on earth . . .

We may call both geography and history descriptions, with the only difference being that one is a description in a temporal, the other in a spatial, order.

Therefore, history and geography widen our knowledge in respect to time and space. History deals with the happenings which occurred in time sequence; geography deals with phenomena which occur in space at the same time. According to its different objectives, it receives different designations. It is either physical, mathematical, political, moral, theological, literary, or mercantile geography.

The history of events which occurred at different periods and is true history is but continuous geography. Therefore, it is one of the gravest historical deficiencies not to state where something occurred or the properties of that place.

. . . The name geography designates the description of an object of nature, namely of the earth as a whole. Geography and history embrace the whole circle of our knowledge—geography that of space, history that of time.

Usually we assume the existence of an ancient and a modern geography, because geography existed at every time. But what existed first, geography or history? The latter is based upon the former, because happenings have to refer to something. History is in unending progress; but objects change and pro-

[4] Kant is a younger contemporary of the Swede Linnaeus and the Frenchman Buffon, who originated classification in botany and zoology respectively.

vide a different geography at different times. Geography is the basis; if we have ancient history, we must also have ancient geography.

We know best the geography of the present time. It serves, besides other obvious purposes, to elucidate ancient geography with the help of history. However, our ordinary school geography is very deficient, although nothing is more apt to educate one in common sense than geography. Because common sense relates only to matters of personal experience, it is unable to broaden its field to any considerable degree without the help of geography. News in the papers is of no interest to many people because they are unable to fit it into its proper place. They have no picture of the country, the sea, or the surface of the earth at all.

. . . Moral geography deals with the different customs and character of people. . . . If the first principle of a civilized society is a general law and an irresistible power to protect it against transgressions, and the law relates also to the properties of the place and its inhabitants, political geography belongs also to (geography) insofar as it is based totally upon physical geography. If the Russian rivers flowed south, it would be a great advantage for the whole empire; but unfortunately almost all of them flow into the Arctic Ocean. . . .[5]

If a country has a superabundance of a product which is completely lacking in another country, a uniform state may be maintained all over the earth through trade. In merchantilistic geography it is necessary to show why a country has an abundance of that product which another lacks.

JOHANN GOTTFRIED HERDER (1744-1803)

Herder is best known as one of the pioneers of classical German literature, the friend and source of inspiration of Goethe, a forerunner of the romantic movement in literature, and prophet of the concept of a world literature. He tried to make the best of all national literatures accessible to the Ger-

[5] At the time of this writing, the Russians had not reached the Black Sea and most of the Ukraine was not yet conquered. On the other hand, all of Siberia — but not Central Asia — was Russian.

man reading public by translating them himself and by encouraging others to translate them. By occupation a Lutheran theologian, but deeply influenced by the French Enlightenment, he combined a consuming desire to find causal connections with an ingrained conviction that the destiny of mankind is to be found in a purified Christianity. Though these concepts pervade in differing degrees both his numerous theological and philosophical writings, the excerpts from his *Ideen zu einer Philosophie der Geschichte der Menschheit (Contributions to a Philosophy of a History of Mankind)*, given below, are a good sample of his thought patterns. This book shows him, also, as a pioneer of the concept that history should be history of all nations, not only Christian nations. The latter idea dominated almost all historical writing up to his time and still persists in our schoolbooks today. All these many interests in the literature and history of foreign nations stimulated his interest in geography. Though Herder never considered any of his writings under this designation and never did any systematic geographical writing, he still must be regarded as an important forerunner of classical geography in Germany.

Outlines of a Philosophy of the History of Mankind[6]

In Asia the mountains stretch along the greatest breadth of the land, and their root is nearly in the middle: who would suppose, that in the opposite hemisphere they would stretch in a contrary direction, through the greatest length. Yet so it is. This alone renders the two divisions of the world totally different. The high land of Siberia, not only exposed to the cold north and north-east winds, but cut off from the warming south by the primitive mountains covered with eternal snow, must be as piercingly cold, even in many of its southern parts, particularly when the saline nature of its soil in several places is considered, as we know from description it is;[7] except where

[6] Translated from the German by T. O. Churchill, London, J. Johnson, 1800. Original German edition 1784. p. 23, 137, 154.

[7] Compare with Herodotus! Herder just notes the fact of salinity in soils; the Greek, more than 2000 years earlier, was looking for an explanation. However, this is a rare instance where Herder falls back into a medieval pattern of thought. In most other instances, as shown here, he was as eager to find answers as was Herodotus.

other rows of these mountains could shelter it from the sharper winds, and form more temperate vales. But what beautiful regions extend themselves immediately beneath these mountains, in the midst of Asia! These walls protect them from the benumbing winds of the north, and leave them only the cooling breeze. . . . In America again what difference! Northward the cold north and northwest winds blow a long way down the land, their course unbroken by a single mountain. They come from the wide regions of ice . . . with such sudden transitions from cold to heat, and from heat to cold, as in no other country. . . . What effects all these circumstances have on plants, animals, and men, the sequel will show.

On our hemisphere, where she intended to prepare the first abode of men and animal,[8] Nature went otherwise to work. She extended the mountains one after another in length and breadth, and spread them out into various branches, so that all the quarters of the Globe might be connected, and, notwithstanding the difference between regions and countries, the transition from one to another might be gentle. . . . Here, from the drier, milder, compounded region, the electric Sun could elicit finer aromatics, more lenient food, and a more perfect organization both in man, and in all other animals.

It would be highly gratifying, had we a map of mountains, or a mountain atlas, in which these pillars of the Earth were laid down, and depicted were every circumstance, that the history of man requires.[9] The direction and altitude of the mountains of many regions are pretty accurately determined; the elevation of the land above the level of the sea, the state of the ground on the surface, the flow of the rivers, the directions of the winds, the variation of the compass, and the degrees of heat and cold, have been observed in others; and some of these have already been noted on particular charts. If several of these remarks, now lying dispersed in books of travels and other publications, were carefully collected, and

---

[8] Herder was theologian, but also under the influence of 18th century Enlightenment.

[9] This suggestion of Herder's was taken up by Heinrich Berghaus, who produced the first physical atlas.

transferred to a map, what a beautiful and instructive *physical geography of the Earth* would the inquirer into the history and natural philosophy of man have before him at one view, the most precious supplement to the valuable works of Varenius, Luloff, and Bergmann.[10]

The form of the Kalmucs and Mongols is well known. With a middling stature they have at least remains of the flat visage, the thin beard, and the brown complexion of the northern climate; but they are distinguishable by the inner angle of the eye being acute, fleshy, and inclined obliquely to the nose . . . whence proceeds this form. Their bow-legs originate from their way of life. From their childhood they slide along upon their legs, or cling to the back of a horse; their lives are spent between sitting and riding. . . . If we consider, that extensive tracts of their country are strangers to rain, have little water, or at least none that is pure, and that thus from their infancy they scarcely know what it is to bathe: if we reflect on the salt lakes and marshes, and the saline nature of the soil where they dwell, the alkaline savour of which they relish in their food, and even in the deluges of tea, with which they daily enfeeble their digestive faculty; if to these we add the elevation of the country they inhabit, the thinner air, dry winds, alkaline effluvia, and long winters spent in the smoke of their huts is it not probable, that their figure originated from these causes some thousands of years ago?

No one is ignorant that America extends through all the zones . . . while at the same time its surface exhibits the loftiest and steepest mountains,[11] with the most level and extensive plains. . . . On the other hand, it results from the very situation of America, that this extensive region, so widely separated from the rest of the world, could not have been peopled from many different points. Notwithstanding the great variety of climates, and of nations which frequently endeavour to distinguish themselves from others by arts, that

---

[10] Note that Herder still regards geography only as auxiliary to other knowledge.

[11] It was believed that the Andes were higher than the Himalayas at that time.

do the greatest violence to nature, the figure of the people in general bears a stamp of uniformity, not to be found even in Negroland.

In the north of Asia, on this side of the mountains, most parts are much higher and colder. . . . This high, broken, steep land, the mountains and precipices of our ancient world, must have been for a considerable period the habitation of . . . half-savage hunters and nomads; and many parts of it will remain so probably forever. Necessity, and the circumstances of the country rendered men barbarous . . .

To the southward, where the surface of Asia gently declines, where the mountainous chains surround more temperate vales, and protect them from the cold north-eastern wind, immigrating colonies, led chiefly by the rivers, gradually drew toward the sea-coasts, assembled in towns, and formed nations; while a milder climate awakened in them more refined ideas, and gave rise to less rude regulations. At the same time, as Nature afforded man more leisure, and pleasurably stimulated more of his propensities, his heart expanded in passions and irregularities, the flowery weeds of which could not burst through the ice of the north. . . . Hence various laws and inhibitions to check them were required . . . and (they) were at length obliged to submit to restraint. But as despotism must accomplish what reason is yet unable to perform, . . . those pyramides and temples of the ancient world arose in the south of Asia.

HORACE BENEDICT DE SAUSSURE (1740-1799)

De Saussure occupied the chair of philosophy at the Academy of Geneva from an early age; however, he should be called a physicist with strong geological interests. As a physicist, he stressed minute observation and both constructed and improved instruments, such as the hygrometer. Interested in nature, especially mountains, he climbed most of the heights around Geneva before he was eighteen and became famous as the first man to climb Mount Blanc. His was the age of Rousseau, when it was discovered that mountains are beautiful as well as awesome. Later Saussure extended his mountain expeditions to all European mountains from Etna in Sicily to those in the British Isles. On all trips he amassed his observations on botany, hydrology, geology and climate, investigated the petrographic and chemical properties of the rocks, and wrote extremely readable descriptions of the landscape. He used, thereby, the true geographical approach, although his definition of geography differed slightly from the commonly accepted one of today. His fame was such that the young Alexander von Humboldt considered settling in Geneva to be close to him.

Travels in the Alps[12]

Everyone who has observed attentively the materials of which the Earth consists has been forced to recognize that this globe did suffer great revolutions which could occur only over a long series of centuries. Some even sought to find traces of these revolutions in the traditions of some ancient peoples. Ancient philosophers exercised their ingenuity in order to find the causes and the succession of these changes; but more intent to out-guess nature, than patient to study it, they relied on imperfect observations and on traditions which were disfigured by poetry and superstition. They forged cosmogonies, or hypotheses, about the origin of the world which were pleasing to the imagination rather than satisfying to the mind because they were a faithful interpretation of nature. . . .

The science which collects the facts which alone can serve as a basis for a theory of the Earth or geology is physical geography or the description of our Earth; of its natural divisions; of the nature, structure, and situation of its different parts; of the bodies which appear on the surface and those which it encloses in those depths into which our feeble means were able to penetrate.

The study of the mountains, primarily, can further this theory of the Globe. Plains are uniform; it is impossible in them to see a profile and the several layers except in some ex-

---

[12] *Voyages dans les Alps,* Neuchatel, Samuel Fauche, 1779 — Vol. I, pp. 1-14.

cavations which are made by water or man. That is quite insufficient, because such excavations are infrequent, little extended, and even the deepest are hardly two or three hundred *toises*[13] deep. On the contrary, the mountains are infinitely variegated in their material and forms; they openly present natural profiles of great extent which can be observed with great clarity; and they enable one to embrace with one glance the arrangement, the situation, the direction, the thickness and even the nature of the component strata and the transverse fissures.

However, the mountains offer such opportunities for observation in vain if those who observe do not understand how to consider these great objects as a unit and in their broadest context. The only object of most travellers who call themselves naturalists is collecting curiosities.[14] They go, or rather crawl, their eyes fixed on the ground, picking up small pieces here and there without noticing the overall picture. . . . It is not that I advocate neglecting the details; quite the opposite, I regard details as the only basis for solid knowledge. But, I wish that by observation of detail, one would not lose sight of the great masses and of the whole, and that the knowledge of the great objects and their relations always would remain the goal for which one studied the small parts.

In order to observe the wholes, it is not sufficient to follow the great routes which wind almost always on the bottom of the valleys and which traverse the mountain chains only through the deepest gorges. One must leave the accustomed routes and climb the elevated summits where the eye can embrace a multitude of objects at the same time. Such excursions are troublesome, I agree; one has to dispense with carriages, occasionally even with horses, undergo great fatigues, and expose oneself occasionally to fairly great dangers. . . . He arrives: his eyes, at the same time blinded and attracted from all sides, do not know where to look first; gradually they

---

[13] Approximately 1200 to 1800 feet.

[14] The 17th century saw the first collections of objects of nature, the predecessors of our museums of natural history. However, these collections were unsystematic, and among the valuable objects were mere curiosities, such as pieces of wood of strange form.

become accustomed to the great light; he chooses the objects which should occupy him primarily and determines the order in which to study them. But what words can express feelings and depict the ideas with which these great spectacles fill the soul of the philosopher.

The physicist, like the geologist, finds on the high mountains important subjects for admiration and study. These great chains, whose summits penetrate into the higher parts of the atmosphere, seem like a laboratory of Nature, the reservoir from which it draws the bad and good things which it spreads over our Earth — the rivers which irrigate it and the torrents which devastate it, the rains which fertilize it and the storms which desolate it. All physical phenomena present themselves with a greatness and majesty of which the inhabitants of the plains have no idea; the forces of wind and aerial electricity occur with surprising strength; clouds develop under the very eye of the observer; and frequently he sees beneath his feet the birth of storms which devastate the plains, while the rays of the sun are glittering around him and the sky is clear and pure above his head.

. . . I made all these travels, with the hammer of the miner in my hand, for no other purpose than to study natural science. I climbed all accessible summits which promised me any interesting observation; and I carried away samples from mines and mountains, especially those which offered something theoretically important, so that I could look at and study them again according to my desire. I also made it a strict rule always to take notes on the spot and to rewrite them in an orderly fashion within twenty-four hours, whenever this was possible.

I took a precaution which I think was very useful. Before each trip, I prepared a systematic and detailed agenda of the researches to which that trip was devoted. . . . Despite all my precautions to overlook nothing, when I was in the quiet of my room mentally I again repeated all the subjects which I observed on my trips. Very often doubts arose in my mind which I felt could not be put to rest without new observations and new travels. . . . I offer my observations with the greatest qualification, in the conviction that the naturalists, who will see the objects which I describe later on, will discover many things which escape my observations.

For instance, I treated with fair detail the lithological part, because I believe that the knowledge of the soils and rocks is an indispensable element of the theory of the Earth. One needs to know the nature of a thing and the elements of which it is composed before one can formulate hypotheses of its origin and how it developed. It would be impossible to ascertain for sure the nature of these elements and of their combinations without chemical analysis. . . . It is, therefore, necessary to enter the artificial laboratories in order to learn the working of Nature. . . . I have confined myself to describing the rounded pebbles of our vicinity. I found this convenient because the different kinds of rocks which are to be found among the rounded pebbles are exactly the same kinds which I most frequently found occasion to mention on my travels in the Alps.

CHAPTER 5

FATHERS OF MODERN GEOGRAPHY

The suggestions of the 18th century bore fruit early in the 19th century. Ritter and von Humboldt in Germany and Brun in France are regarded as the first modern geographers of stature. Von Humboldt was the polyhistor, having had command of most of the knowledge of his time in the natural sciences. Soon the accumulation of detail was to make this type of scholar impossible. Ritter, on the other hand, expressed the close connection of geography and history in his work. Brun, though of less influence upon future developments, exemplifies the fact that the new geographical approach was not due just to isolated cases of genius, but was in the general direction of scientific progress.

ALEXANDER VON HUMBOLDT (1769-1859)

Humboldt was one of the rare scholars who could and did embrace most of the knowledge of his time and was able to contribute original work to such diverse sciences as physiology and mining, meteorology and anthropology. He is rightly considered to be one of the founders of modern, scientific geography, as it is distinguished from the compendium-like, disconnected collections of geographic facts and statistics which were characteristic of preceding periods. Despite such writers as Herodotus, Strabo, Ptolemy, Ibn Khaldun, and Kant, no continuous tradition of geography had developed by the end of the 18th century. Nor did the numerous travels, explorations, and discoveries from the 15th century on have such an effect.

Though for many years he held the record for the highest altitude climbed by man, after he ascended almost to the summit of Chimborazo, von Humboldt was the first great scholar-traveler who was not as intent on entering new lands as he was on gaining an understanding of the impact upon one another of all natural factors of an area, including surface, geology, climate, plants, animals and man. His painstaking diligence in collecting and recording detailed observations never caused him to lose sight of the whole. His travel work on New Spain (Mexico) was one of the first accomplished geographical presentations of a whole country. On the other hand, in his *Cosmos,* written from the time he was sixty-five years old until his death in his ninetieth year, he took a transcending view of the entire universe. Because he never taught at an academic institution, he had no disciples in the proper sense. Nevertheless, his influence was far-reaching. The breadth of interests contained in his writing makes it difficult, if not impossible, to select continuous statements which express his ideas on geography alone. Several brief excerpts must be pieced together to achieve such a statement.

Letter to Freisleben, June 1799[1]

I am sailing on the Spanish frigate *Pizzaro.* We will land in the Canary Islands, and on the coast of Caracas in South America. . . . I shall collect plants and fossils, and make astronomic observations with the best of instruments. Yet this is not the main purpose of my journey. I shall endeavor to discover how nature's forces act upon one another and in what manner the geographic environment exerts its influence on animals and plants. In short, I must find out about the harmony in nature.

Cosmos: An Attempted Physical Description of the Earth[2]

The most important aim of all physical science is this: to recognize unity in diversity, to comprehend all the single aspects as revealed by the discoveries of the last epochs, to judge single phenomena separately without surrendering to their bulk, and to grasp nature's essence under the cover of

[1] Published and translated by Helmut de Terra, *Humboldt,* A. Knopf, Inc., N. Y., 1955. Pp. 86-87.

[2] *Kosmos. Entwurf einer physichen Erdbeschreibung,* Alexander von Humboldt. 5 vol's., Stuttgart, 1845-1862. Translation from the 1st vol. of the Kosmos. P. 370.

outer appearances. In so doing, our endeavor passes the narrow confines of the sensual world so that we may hope to master with the binding force of ideas the crude substance of empirical knowledge. . . .[3] The purpose of this introductory chapter is to indicate the manner in which natural science can be endowed with a higher purpose through which all phenomena and energies are revealed as one entity, pulsating with inner life. Nature is not dead matter. She is, as Schelling[4] expressed it, the sacred and primary force. . . .

The philosophy of *Cosmos* comprises four propositions:

1. The definition and limitation of a physical description of the world as a special and separate discipline.

2. The objective content, which is the actual and empirical aspect of nature's entity in the scientific form of a portrait of nature.

3. The action of nature on the imagination and emotion as an incentive to nature studies — through media like travel descriptions, poetry, landscape painting, and the display of contrasting groups of exotic plants.

4. The history of natural philosophy, the gradual emergence of concepts pertaining to the cosmos as an organic unit.

Aspects of Nature[5]

The goals for which I strove were to depict nature in its prime traits, to find proof of the interworking of (natural) forces, and to achieve a sense of enjoyment which the immediate view gives to sensitive man. . . . This aesthetic treatment of topics of natural science presents great difficulties of stylistic composition despite the splendid force and definiteness of our mother tongue. The abundance of nature easily encourages the accumulation of metaphorical images. Such an accumulation, however, disturbs the peace and the total im-

---

[3] The present editors have altered the English of the 19th century translator in a few places.

[4] One of the most influential, contemporary philosophers who connected Kant's rationalistic idealism with the romantic, almost mystic, currents of the day.

[5] *Ansichten der Natur*, Alexander von Humboldt. Tübingen in der J. Cotta'schen Buchhandlung, 1808. P. V-VIII, 1-2, 13, 283.

pression of nature. Touched by emotion and fantasy, writing easily degenerates to poetic prose.

. . . May my descriptions render to the reader a part of the enjoyment which a susceptible mind finds in the direct observation of nature. Because enjoyment grows corresponding to an increasing recognition of the inner coherence of the natural forces, I added to each article scientific explanations and additions. . . .[6] Everywhere I hinted as to the eternal influence which physical nature exerts upon the moral mood of mankind and upon its fate. These lines are first of all devoted to depressed souls. He "who saves himself out of the stormy waves of life" will gladly follow me into the thickest woods, through the boundless steppe and to the high ridges of the Andes. To him speaks the chorus who judges the world:

> "In the mountains is freedom! The breath of decay
> Never sullies the fresh flowing air;
> O nature is perfect wherever we stray;
> 'Tis man that deforms it with his care!" [7]

About steppes and deserts.—At the foot of the high ridge of granite which withstood the inrush of the ocean in the youth of our planet — when the bight of the Antilles was formed — a wide, endless plain begins. If one leaves behind the mountain valleys of Caracas and the lake of Tacarigua, full of islands, where banana trees are mirrored in the near water; or the pastures which shine in the tender green of the thaitic sugar cane; or the stern shade of the cocoa bushes; the eye rests on the steppe in the south which ostensibly rises to the limits of the horizon in unbounded distance. . . .

Out of the luxuriant abundance of organic life the traveller steps perplexed into the desolate margin of the empty desert. No hill, no rock rises as an island from endless space. . . . like the unlimited ocean the steppe also fills the mind with the emotions of infinity. But, at the same time the view of the clear water surface, where the light, gently foaming waves

---

[6] In doing this, Humboldt tried to integrate the two great trends of his age, Romanticism and Enlightenment.

[7] F. Schiller, *Die Braut von Messina*, translated by S. Theodore Morton, Anna Swanwick, A Lodge and others, Boston 1902.

make their ripples, is friendly. Dead and rigid lies the steppe, spread out like the naked, rocky crust of a deserted planet. Nature presents the phenomenon of these wide plains in all zones; but, they have a peculiar character in each of them; a distinct physiognomy which is determined by the diversity of their soils, their climate, and their elevation above sea level.

It is a rewarding, although difficult, task of general regional geography to compare the natural properties of remote regions and to present the results of this comparison with a few strokes of the pen. The reasons for the drought and temperature of the New World are manifold and still little developed. . . .

The impression which is left on us by observation of nature is less determined by the character of the landscape, than by the illumination through which mountains and plains appear —now in the ethereal blue of the sky, now in the shadow of low floating clouds.[8] Similarly, descriptions of nature impress us more or less according to the degree to which they agree with the needs of our feelings; for the physical world is mirrored vividly and truly in the inner feelings. Whatever is essential for the character of a landscape—the outlines of the mountains which limit the horizon in bluish, fragrant distance, the darkness of the fir forests, the forest-streams which rush between overhanging cliffs — all that is in old, mysterious contact with the inner life of man.

KARL RITTER (1779-1859)

Ritter, together with von Humboldt, is regarded as the founder of modern geography. For many years he was professor of geography at the University of Berlin, for a long while the only one in Europe. He planned to write, singlehanded, a regional geography of the world but finished only the volumes on Asia. His knowledge of any pertinent literary document, his diligence, and his imagination enabled him to draw pictures of even those regions which were practically inaccessible in his time. Unfortunately, he never dealt with

[8] This idea of Humboldt's has been taken up recently by Banse in Germany and Granö in Finland.

those parts of the globe which he personally knew from travel. Some of his less gifted students were thus encouraged to attempt geographical research on principle without field work, which was not Ritter's intent. Ritter regarded the earth as an educational habitat of man for a better afterlife. His interest in history made him the founder of human geography proper and the admired forerunner of Ratzel's school. However, he aimed at a kind of regional geography quite similar to that of von Humboldt.

For many years his students filled almost all available teaching positions in geography in Germany and in many other countries. The best known non-Germans among his students were Reclus in France and Guyot, who taught at Princeton in the United States. Ritter's influence, though indirect, is still very strong in France, while in other countries he is usually considered to have been of less importance than von Humboldt. Ritter's ideas on geography must be extracted from all of his works and pieced together from short statements made over several decades.

Letter to Heinrich Pestalozzi[9]

If we suppose that general, topical geography comprises only that which exists, this part has to embrace in the general course of instruction what was, what is, and what will be. The earth is treated therein in its history, as an organized being in the widest sense, which sustains the conditions for its life within itself. The pupil studies this life in its most important facts through the monuments which natural events have

[9] Quoted by J. W. M. Henning, *Leitfaden beim methodischen Unterricht in der Geographie (Outline for the methodical teaching of geography,*)* Iferten 1812. Translated from the reprinted version of Heinrich Schmitthenner, *Studien über Carl Ritter*, Frankfurter Geographische Hefte, Vol. 25, 1925, No. 4.

Johann Heinrich Pestalozzi (1746-1827), a famous Swiss educator, was the pioneer of modern educational methods for Kindergarten and elementary school, substituting teaching with the help of concrete objects for learning by rote.

**Ritter wrote the part on "General Physical Geography or the General Description of the Nature of the Globe" in this textbook which originated in Pestalozzi's circle.*

created and left behind. These very documents gave to the earth's crust its present shape and features. . . . The second material part deals with matter, first as an aggregate, then as a chemical mixture, then as organic life and finally as human being endowed with senses and reason. In this part the geographical distribution of the inorganic part of the earth is taught, and the general rules are found which are present in every branch of nature. Instead of unending detail, the whole being always is presented, as far as it is possible, in its definiteness and limitation. Mineralogy should be followed immediately by the distribution of organic forms; but because every organism is conditioned by climate; and because climate, itself, is caused by the relation of the earth to the sun and its revolution around its own axis as well as by its relations to water, land, and air, the doctrine of the astronomic and physical climate is treated first. Immediately after that the distribution of vegetation, animals, and of man, according to nations, is treated. All this is handled first in simple, then in complicated condition; first in the water, then on the land; first in cold, then in hot, and finally in mixed zones; first in its origin, then in its distribution; first in characteristic forms, then in generalized forms. Man is discussed as a natural being only, driven from the outside by natural conditions and by necessity. At this point history enters development. It is for the historical element to develop in the student all spiritual forces, all mental and emotional motivations by which individuals as well as nations are moved. This is the place where all the outer and the inner motivations in the history of nations are being developed in their main principles and are brought to the conscious knowledge of the student. At that point real history ought to start as a separate subject, and — just as language training helps man to harmonize with his ideas and thoughts — history, which revolves around the whole man, has to help him to harmonize with his political surroundings. It has to show him what he as a citizen of the world should be under every circumstance, and what he as a man can be.

If geography in the narrower sense describes the earth and what inhabits the earth as far as possible in its present condition, then that part of physical geography which contains the physical knowledge of man has to enumerate the races of man and nations which inhabit the world at present, to describe their places of habitation, then to describe their body forms, their cultural level, their habits, religion, language, industry, trade, etc.; finally, it shows the most important places where they live; i.e., their cities, which in the natural order of the presentation are found here. Thus the transition to the third part, that of general geography, is provided.

Letter to Guts Muths [10]

Human beings live in two worlds, both in a visible and in an invisible world. Man lives according to human dignity only if he works on his perfection in both respects. He ought to strive for a clear grasp of his spiritual nature in order to rule himself and at every moment to impress the stamp of his rational nature upon his thoughts, words, and each of his acts. The instruments for attaining this goal lie only in man himself, in the depths of his own soul; he has to educate himself. The more this is the case, by starting at the original sources, the more stable, the more consolidated, and the more securely anchored in himself the individual will emerge from this education.

If man, however, wants to reach the state of determining his own nature out of his spiritual nature and to direct each one of his activities from within outward, he cannot dispense with another, equally important way of education; he has to learn how to absorb nature and understand its inherent orderly course. Nature ought to have the same rational effect upon man as man tries to exert upon nature, in order to enhance the mutual influence between man and nature, which is necessary for the thinking man who believes in an ultimate goal for both.

---

[10] Without date, but approximately of the same period as the first piece, printed in G. Kramer, *Karl Ritter, ein Lebensbild* (a biography), 2 vols., Halle 1864 and 1870, vol. I, p. 258. Here translated from Schmitthenner o. c. Guts Muths was a teacher of Ritter's, another of the pioneers of modern methods of teaching. His stress on physical education was revolutionary for his time.

The purpose in writing the present work [11] was the attempt to perfect the means of instruction in the latter course of education leading to a general philosophy of life.[12] My own desire, still more the request of friends from Iferten,[13] and love of the subject drove me to this labor.

The argument of the whole work can be recognized best from the table of contents containing the order of topics; however, some phases can be indicated only in a preliminary fashion.

The Earth is treated as earth, not as a planet among the planets; the entire mathematical geography is thereby omitted; also the earth is not seen as dominated by arbitrary human action; because arbitrary action is opposed to determination by laws, and political geography should not provide the starting point.[14]

The earth is presented as earth, in its shape, formation, structure, constituent parts, its vegetative cover, its life, the largest living being, covered with hieroglyphics [14a] which tells its history. The beginning is made with the simplest facts. From there progress is made to composite features. Only features existing on the earth are used as criteria; and, thus, a permanent system is found which is not based on arbitrary judgments of the observer, but on nature, itself — a system simpler than any arbitrary one and still more meaningful, because every following step is founded on the preceding. First the most general principles are found, then more specialized ones; and advancing to further specialization, each characteristic form is traced to the very individual, which appears not only in nations, animals, and minerals, but also in everything that nature offers.

Because everything advances from simple to specialized in spatial, temporal, and physical respect; and because in this

---

[11] The title is *Handbook of General Geography*, or *The Earth, a Contribution to the Foundation of Geography as Science.*

[12] Weltanschauung.

[13] Pestalozzi and his disciples had their school in Iferten, Switzerland.

[14] Eighteenth century geography books started out and often did not go further than to present a political-statistical statement of states.

[14a] Signs, hard to decypher.

method rules and laws always result only from presented object lessons, this scientific method can claim to have been conceived in the spirit of Pestalozzi's doctrines and to be suited to systematic training in geography. Therefore, this handbook is the tool by which the geography teacher obtains everything that is necessary for a methodical teaching of geography. He needs only to make a sensible separation of the qualified from the absolute, the general from the specific, the necessary from the incidental, the superfluous from the indispensable. If he does so, he can progress safely to his goal on a road which can be elucidated still better by a manual which parallels the handbook. . . .

The handbook is divided into three parts: the topographical, the formal, and the material; or the knowledge of places, the knowledge of forms (physical geography), and the knowledge of components (biological geography):

1. The topographical part is the introductory course of geography. It contains a preparatory subdivision which gives the elementary course, the natural division of the earth's surface, and notes for the teacher giving only hints to the thinking one, what can be done and what ought to be done. . . .

2. The formal part contains the main forms, the formation of the oceans, the air, and the land in their mutually effective physical conditions; and provides the geographical basis for the remarkable observations and explorations of this last century which has been so full of new discoveries. In this development are encountered all the external influences upon men and nations which gave them the main direction of their historical existence. This second part constitutes, as does the first part, a unit by itself. . . .

3. The material main part contains both the general and the special laws of the geographical distribution of the three natural kingdoms over the earth, besides the characteristic forms, the capacity of spreading out, and the laws of migration of minerals, plants, and animals. It contains at the same time the doctrine of climate, which is the basis for geographical distribution, and those parts of geology which offer clues for the distribution of inorganic beings.

For each of these parts a map is needed. It shall have only

a few names, if any, because the method of the handbook is such that you can find everything on the map without names. The first map contains very little, the second needs coloring, and the third and fourth ones a few names.

Introduction to Erdkunde [15]

The facts which have been gathered in this book had to be arranged around a cardinal point and against an ideological background, so that they could be made methodical and lead to a natural system. Only by such arrangement can the empirical facts be brought into mutual relationship and the manifold assembled into a unity which is missing in inanimate nature. Without such an ideal background hypothesis, or theory, or whatever you may call it — whether made consciously or not — no unified whole will be attained by human beings. Even the very firm conviction of doing research without the help of a working hypothesis is indeed, as Playfair says,[16] in itself a first hypothesis. Lack of a consciously conceived theory, therefore, does not lead to the truth more quickly and does not protect one from one-sidedness; only knowledge of the history of philosophy and science, care in arrangement of ideas, and honest striving for truth can help overcome the human delusions in this respect and, at least, justify the claim for a "disinterested review of facts," which claim every honest scholar likes to raise.

The ideal background from which the author of this book assumes to have derived the unbiased view of facts and their specific arrangement, is in the author's opinion not based upon the correctness of a concept, but in the entire content of all truth; i.e., it lies for the author in his creed. This creed is founded on a general concept which emerged from the author's life in nature and among men. Through a talk with one of the great men of our century this inner concept was lifted into

---

15 Written in 1815, published 1817, reprinted in *Abhandlungen*, 1825, p. 25-26. Translated from Schmitthenner, O. C.

16 John Playfair, *Illustrations of the Huttonian Theory of the Earth*, Edinburg, 1802. Playfair in this book expounded Hutton's theory that present processes explain the processes of the past, and by his lucid style contributed much to the acceptance of Hutton's theories.

consciousness. This basic concept was formulated in relation to science so that, if this concept is correctly handled, it is bound to be reflected in all parts of science and be used in other similar fields. Therefore it is impossible to define the basic idea at the outset, or to limit it; but it can take shape only at the very end by the essence which permeates the whole.

Here, in progressing to the special rules, only as much should be said as seems to be the very essence of perception, in contrast to the discerning and definite quality of concepts. Perception is more inclined to combine and build than are concepts. Thereby the whole form of this work is conditioned.

Letter to Heinrich Berghaus[17]

I do not want to try to justify it (the concept of a territory as an individual) in every respect before the appropriate moment arrives; neither am I wholly satisfied with this concept in each instance where I used it. However, as the reader easily can convince himself, I use it everywhere not directly, but indirectly, in order to designate something in inanimate nature analogous in its physical appearance to living beings; therefore, I, as in common usage, apply it as an analogy of life and organism, although it is in no respect animal life or an animal organism. I used the term earth-individual because I do not know another term for it; but I shall, however, be ready at any time to accept any other more appropriate term which may present itself to me. With this term I refer to what are usually called the big continents, not in the usual sense as spatial subdivisions of the earth, but as definite, big systems of countries or main divisions of the globe. These are delimited by natural conditions in themselves, individual and not casual; they themselves are united in every respect, and

---

[17] This letter refers to an article of Mr. Julius Fröbel. It is from *Annalen der Erd-, Völker- und Staatenkunde*, ed. by S. Berghaus, vol. 4, Berlin 1831, p. 518. Translated from the text of Schmitthenner, o. c. Fröbel is almost forgotten as a philosopher and geographer today, but well remembered as a creative follower of Pestalozzi and the real founder of the theory and practice of the kindergarten. Fröbel's article was published in the same issue. Heinrich Berghaus, 1779-1884, was the publisher of the first modern physical-geographical Atlas in Germany (1937-1848). He was rather close to both Ritter and Humboldt.

quite different from each other. These are characteristics which unite them to a natural unit and which emerge from their formation, and forms (plastique), location, grouping, climate, and organic habitation; these units I tried to describe by the term earth-individual. The objection which Mr. Julius Fröbel raises in connection with his remark on America proves that he did not familiarize himself with what I have said explicitly long ago against the separation of America, arbitrarily in my opinion, into two individuals.

Nature and History As the Factors of Natural History: or Remarks on the Resources of the Earth.[18]

A knowledge of the widely varied resources of the earth, in their diffusion over its entire surface, in their amounts, their kinds, and their relations to special lands and peoples, as well as to the entire system of the globe, would always constitute, if rightly viewed, a real, if not a prominent, part of the geographical science. Up to the present time, however, this has by no means been the case. Blinded by the vastness of its (geographical science) riches, it overlooked their systematic proportions, and never compassed their uses and applications. It never rose above its material possessions, which always remained a lifeless and a useless load. It never pressed forward to a systematic survey of its whole domain, which, without an understanding of its contents, could neither be useful to it, nor to the circle of sciences. . . .

A correct statement of the whole system of connections and dependencies in geography is wanting, the limits of all countries are not definitively designated, their historical expansion and development has not been fully described, no accurate delineation of the distribution of the earth's surface among the different races has been completed, no account given of the course along which commerce, civilization, colonization and all their instrumentalities have advanced in attaining

---

18 (Delivered April 14, 1836). Translated by William Leonhard Gage in: *Carl Ritter, Geographical Studies* (a translation of six articles of Ritter's), Boston, Gould, and Lincoln, 1863. Pp. 281-306.

their present position. The place where all these subjects ought to be fully unfolded is in our geographical treatises. In history we do not have this lack, but find with the statement of results the statement of their causes; in the natural sciences, we find phenomena traced carefully in every direction to discover their entire round of relations and dependencies; but geography, instead of attempting to be the complete mistress of its own domain, and to embrace as truly its own what rightfully falls within its precincts, surrenders its own resources to other sciences, for them to work and to develop.

The diffusion of the gifts of nature over the whole surface of the earth exercises now, and always has exercised in the past, a powerful influence upon the characteristics of the inhabitants of different districts. The very products of the soil have been interwoven, as it were, into the texture of the human mind. Through all zones, and in all stages of the world's progress, the effects of the distribution of natural products have been felt. Even the very nature of human thoughts, feelings, and abstract ideas has been subjected to this influence. We cannot glance for a moment at the characteristics of agricultural, hunting, fishing, and pastoral people without seeing how their occupation stamps the whole of their feelings and thoughts, directs their simple philosophy of life, and gives tone even to their religious ideas. To trace the workings of the agencies involved in this is often a difficult task which defies our most carefully directed efforts to ascertain them. . . .

If, as we have shown in previous articles, we need to employ mathematical figures and expressions in conveying correct impressions of shape and size, and cannot dispense with natural philosophy in elucidating many of the problems of hydrography, we find that natural history is just as indispensable in enabling us to master those provinces of geography which have the closest relations with the products and resources of the earth's surface. We have already attempted to show the close relations between history and geography, and yet there are just as intimate relations between natural history and geography, and the study of the connections between them is no less profitable. . . .

The earth viewed as a whole, or as divided into land and water, which again have their own subdivisions, is the producer, wherever human art has not turned it from its natural functions, of objects of every kind which we arrange and classify in definite groups, deducing from time to time, when our classification is complete, the laws of their organization and distribution. It is thus that we become able to explain and illustrate the play of the great natural forces and gain a systematized conception of the products of the globe.

Grouping all the products of a district together, and tracing certain principles of distribution in their diffusion, the mind is able at last to grasp the whole characteristics of the region, and to determine, with considerable accuracy, what would be the mental characteristics of the people inhabiting it. This would be the more easy were the people in a rude and primitive condition, but it is still possible in the case of the most cultivated. . . .

Thus, whether it is from the contemplation of the forms on the surface of the globe, or the spheres which float through the sky, the influence of nature becomes one of the prominent sources of the individuality of national character, and men take, therefore, from their surroundings a stamp, the peculiarity of which is dependent upon the locality where they live. The nomadic Arab is not only indebted to the country where he lives for the necessity of hunting the creatures which supply him with food from day to day, but the wild deserts and the cloudless sky give him that relish for a free and untutored life and for those quick and soaring dreams of fancy with which he always delights himself. The reserved and meditative Hindu, accustomed to the profuse luxuriance of his country, takes the fantastic ideas of his mythology from plants, flowers, and trees, and believes in the transmigration of souls from men to beasts. This infinite diversity and richness in the forms of vegetation, some of them being of colossal magnitude, the aspects of beauty and terror which daily confront him, in time make him their subject. His surroundings exercise at last the strongest of influences upon him, until, imagining himself under the sway of divine or demoniac powers, he becomes at last an easy victim of tyranny. . . .

This action of the forces and phenomena of nature upon the human race in all its varieties has been one of the chief springs in the education of man and in all historical development. . . .

Analysis must always be the precursor of synthesis. . . . And yet we can hardly say that the time has come for geography to elevate itself to a branch of natural philosophy; and though it is unquestionable that the conception of the earth as a single organism is the true basis of geographical science, yet an attempt to build a system, complete in all its parts, upon it, would, like many geological systems in past times, be imperfect from a want of data. To build a structure which will endure for ages we need a more comprehensive range of materials than have as yet been accumulated. But to sum up, in the manner of most our geographical works, all the products which are met in any province, to connect them together just as they happen to be found and without regard to any general principle, and to make no mention of their uses, effects, and higher relations is not only tedious, but unprofitable for any scientific results. . . . In such masses of isolated facts, no chain of course and relation can be grasped; there is no profitable comparison of analogies, no internal progress, no good results worked out from past inquiries; there is no perception of the great object of geographical investigations, no thought as to how the facts of this science can be adapted to the wants of mankind, no true conception of the great economic functions of the globe. . . .

Efforts have been made in modern times to supply past deficiencies, and to give a systematic shape to the older, stiff, and pedantic catalogues of the products, by introducing some branches of natural philosophy — climatology, for instance — and thus some valuable geographical works have made some progress in disciplining into orderly arrangement the infinite richness of the gifts of nature. By such steps as this we compress the vast range of facts within such limits as to be within the grasp of the mind. . . .

Yet the use of auxiliary sciences to illustrate geography is just in its infancy. Very few physical laws have as yet been applied to generalize the relations of the natural products of the earth. So far as vegetation is concerned, the most dependent of all nature's gifts upon soil and climate, we find certain limits marked out, beyond which only special classes of vegetables can exist. But we are not aware that any attempt has yet been made to study the laws involved in this, nor to classify and group such products according to their natural relations. . . .

* * *

A true and fruitful inquiry into the resources of the earth, or, to speak more exactly, the introduction of natural history into a geographical work, and the tracing of the connections of natural philosophy, climatology, and geology, present three principal questions preliminary to an explanation of the laws of propagation on the globe.

The object of the first is to discover the primitive land, the soil which first supplied the conditions of their existence. . . .

The second question concerns itself with the agency of natural causes, as a means of diffusing the gifts of nature, and of carrying them into regions where the conditions of their existence will differ somewhat from what they were in the sphere where they were indigenous. . . .

The object of the third will be distinctively the investigation of the sphere of civilized man; to trace the agencies which he has brought into play to increase the diffusion of natural organizations. This question concerns itself with what was called in the preceding paper the historical elements; its special dealing is with the world as the home of civilization; it shows how the diffusion of the earth's products has followed the course of human migration, whether by land or by water, and indicates the bearing which colonization, and even persecution, has had in promoting distribution, and how there has been, as the result of movings of men, increase here, diminution there, and sometimes a kind of oscillation in the diffusion of all kinds of organizations. . . .

* * *

After investigating all three modes of diffusion which have just engaged our attention, that of original creation, that caused by inanimate agencies, such as wind and water currents, and that which man directs, and having examined the localities which have exercised a special influence upon the earth as a whole, we shall find that we have gained important knowledge of man in his relation to nature. Such branches of this knowledge as ethnography, physical and political geography, have themselves been unfolded by the new improvements in agriculture, manufacture, mechanics, as well as from advancing commerce, trade and colonization. Still, such is the distance which intervenes between the great divisions of the earth, that commerce is the main agency for promoting the diffusion of the world's products.

MALTHE CONRAD BRUUN (1775-1826)

Bruun, later known in his adopted France as Malte Brun, was a native of Denmark. His first works were poetry, which may explain why he pioneered the writing of geography in a readable, descriptive style, leaving behind the disconnected collections of statistics and data known as geography in the 18th century.

His geography of Poland ranks with von Humboldt's book on Mexico as one of the first examples of modern regional geography. In 1824 he assisted in the founding of the Société de Géographie. Though he must be ranked as less important than his German contemporaries, von Humboldt and Ritter, his influence as the author of the first modern geography which successfully dealt with the whole world was by no means negligible, especially in France. French geography, which he helped found, has consistently aimed at clarity and lucidity, in contrast to the more involved German style of scientific writing.

System of Universal Geography[19]

In exhibiting comprehensively the actual state of the science of geography, generally valid statements ought to precede the

[19] *Précis de Géographie Universelle,* M. Malte-Brun, Paris 1810-1829; translated as *System of Universal Geography,* by an anonymous translator. Boston, Samuel Walker, 1834. Pp. 1, 58, 199, 213.

detail of particular facts.* We shall, therefore, consider the dimensions and physical structure of our planet before entering upon the study of the different countries which cover its surface.

It belongs to astronomy to exhibit to our view the earth balanced by its overweight in the immensity of space, revolving with all the other planets around the resplendent luminary which distributes to each of these celestial globes its portion for light and heat.

As geography exclusively is our province, it is sufficient for us to borrow such astronomical notions as are necessary for comprehending the terms employed in reference to geographical maps and for conceiving the accuracy of the methods used in constructing these representations of the globe.

Having considered the earth in regard to its dimensions, we must now study its physical character. This part of our work, which is perhaps the most interesting of all, will necessarily be the most imperfect; because a good system of physical geography can only be the gradual work of many successive years.

This science, before it can make advances to maturity, requires a continual series of observations, both repeated and varied, made in every part of the world, and combined, as to leave no interval unoccupied.

On the other hand, natural geography is different from mineralogy, or chemistry, or botany. Ingenious arrangement, and exact and methodical classification, are scarcely applicable to it, and for the most part would only retard its progress by loading it with a display of illusory notions. Mountains, valleys, waters, climates and tracts of country present themselves to the eyes under very complicated and irregular appearances, which it is much easier to describe than to bring within exact definitions. The grandeur and majesty of nature defy the subtlety of our combinations and the pettiness of our rules.

The spirit of physical geography unquestionably rejects vague and incorrect language; but at the same time, obviously

*Though essentially a reprint of the 1834 translation, some of the most awkward phrases have been changed.

it cannot be susceptible to the precision of mathematical or chemical terms. What a striking difference there is between the winding or abrupt outlines of our mountains and the regularity of geometrical figures. What an abuse has been made of the appellations, pyramidal, conical, and others of similar kind. . . . In the cabinets,[20] almost everything is irregular in its figure. . . .

* * *

We have for a long time considered the earth as a physical body, having relations to other physical bodies which surround it, or which dwell upon its surface. No sooner, however, has man become the subject of our inquiries, than we have seen *physical geography* gradually give way to *political.* This branch of our science considers the earth according to its political divisions and in its relations to the different civilized societies which are established upon it. It is evident that this department of geography, as well as the others, has general principles of its own, which, taken collectively, form a theory, the knowledge of which ought to precede the study of particular descriptions. Of these principles, however, those which have a foundation in the nature of our being, and do not change with the change of human opinion, are few in number. The other relations vary, if not in different kingdoms, at least in different parts of the world; and this induces us to confine ourselves here to a rapid view of the former class of principles. . . .

The march of civilization is far from being terminated; the wonders we have witnessed may still be surpassed. The Europeans have not confined themselves to the shores of the Atlantic Ocean. . . . The American navigators have already crossed the whole of this aquatic hemisphere — already British colonists have begun to settle the innumerable islands . . . to the south-east of Asia.

Thus, in the history of the human race, the past, the present and the future, are connected with the position of the great seas of the globe, and with the progress of navigation.

---

[20] The museums, which grew out of the private collections, the *naturalia* cabinets, of princes and nobles.

PART II
MODERN GEOGRAPHY
INTRODUCTION

Modern geography is almost 200 years old. The 18th century saw a spectacular growth in the natural sciences. Among them, systematic studies of plants and animals by men such as Linné and Buffon had a significant influence, later felt in geography. Other stimuli came from research in physical processes, and the social sciences made their contributions. The statistician Büsching was the most important exponent of a phase of the science of government which collected material of the type later utilized extensively in economic and political geography. Montesquieu, a philosophical critic of contemporary society, pointed the way for 19th century sociology and sociological understanding of foreign nations. Finally, romantic writing, such as that of Rousseau, popularized interest in the countryside.

Under the influence of this background, modern geography was born in the mid-19th century. It emerged as an endeavor to see the surrounding world as an integrated whole over the surface of the earth.

The founders of modern geography, von Humboldt and Ritter, men of unusual spiritual vigor, dominated geography for the first half of the 19th century, but after their deaths, in 1859, there seemed to be little significant progress for a while. However, in the last third of the century and continuing into the 20th century, a great number of original geographical writers began producing and maintained the influence of German geographic thought throughout the world. From among the leading geographers of the German classical school, eight have been selected to indicate the main trends of geographical thinking. The names of others appear in the introductions and footnotes. A second chapter on German geography is devoted to those who wrote outside the mainstream. For the most part the ideas proposed by these "Dissenters" failed to achieve full fruition, but Christaller contributed ideas which have had and probably will continue to have great impact on a modern philosophy of geography.

Because Germany contributed little to geographical exploration, its dominance in academic and scientific geography is somewhat remarkable. But the great explorer nations, from Portugal and Spain to Holland and Great Britain, have concentrated heavily on this phase of geography and have contributed comparatively little to geographic thought. Indicative of this relative lack of emphasis on geographical thought, only two British geographers, Herbertson and Mackinder, are included in this volume.

Somewhat later than the German classical school, a French school developed which became similarly pre-eminent, in a slightly more restricted field, and only slightly less influential. The selections from the French include ten well-known geographers. As German geography was and is dominated by von Humboldt and Ritter, so French geography was and is dominated by Vidal de la Blache. Only one of the French writers, Reclus, does not follow the pattern; not only because he antedates Vidal, but also because his work shows clearly the influence of Ritter.

Chapter 10 is a collection of writings by geographers from several European countries who write from diverse philosophical approaches. They reflect the influence of German and, to a lesser degree, French geography. However, they also document the vigorous, independent life of geography even in the small countries. The fact that they became known outside their country despite all language barriers is a sign of their independent, creative thinking.

The chapter devoted to Russian and Soviet geography includes samples from the geographic thinking before the 1917 revolution, which shows the influence of Western geographers, especially Hettner. The writers from the Soviet period display an obvious attempt to diminish outside influences and are primarily concerned with the current debate between the physical and economic geographers.

The last chapter presents American geography as written by such well-known geographers as Semple and Hartshorne. but it also includes some less well-known but still significant works, such as *The Earth: As Modified by Human Action,* by George Marsh.

CHAPTER 6

GERMAN GEOGRAPHY: THE MAINSTREAM

During the last third of the 19th century, and to a varying degree in some countries in the 20th century, geography in Europe was dominated by German geography. Though there was a gap of about a decade between the deaths of von Humboldt and Ritter and the renewed upsurge of geographical activity by Richthofen and Ratzel, the influence of the former two was still felt. However, the geographers of the later period were leaders in their own right — proposing new ideas, accomplishing novel studies, and educating a large number of students. Germany was the first country in which a university was not complete without a department of geography, and compulsory geography in all grades of secondary school led the student to a level not much below that of an American college undergraduate majoring in geography. The academic teachers generally succeeded in balancing teaching and research, overseas exploration and theoretical study. There were few countries which were not influenced by the standards set in Germany at that time. There were great differences in approach and interest; however, seen from a century later, the uniformities stand out. Especially obvious were the common background in classical German philosophy, Kant to Hegel, and the feeling that scientific research should be pursued for its own sake; some explorations into foreign countries were undertaken without commercial or political aims. The interest in geomorphology overshadowed all others at times; economic geography was relegated from the universities to a minor place in the business schools. A man like Ratzel stood almost alone. He is, however, characteristic of the sharp cleavage between physical and human geography, based on a one-sided interpretation of von Humboldt and Ritter.

FERDINAND von RICHTHOFEN (1833-1905)

Ferdinand von Richthofen became the leading German geographer after the middle of the 19th century, a period when the great explorations of Livingston and Stanley and their contemporaries made available a great amount of new material. Interest in geography grew accordingly and led, first in Germany, then elsewhere, to the foundation of geographical professorships in all major universities. Many books of that period tried to present the accumulated material in an orderly and readable fashion. Perhaps the most successful attempt in this direction was Elisée Reclus' many-volume work *La Terre* (The Earth). However, a new trend developed under the influence of Humboldt and Ritter which attempted to *explain* the geographical phenomena. The most important representative of this school was Richthofen, originally trained as a geologist, and one of the most successful explorers of his time. His field work was done in parts of China and Inner Asia which few Europeans had seen before his time. His great work on China was important because of his stress on regional geography; but, like his other products, it was even more influential because of his preference for the physical geographical phenomena. Together with Peschel, Richthofen can be called the founder of geomorphology. Richthofen, much more than Humboldt and Ritter, was responsible for the separation of human from physical geography in the second half of the 19th and in the 20th centuries.

China[1]

Before starting the description of China proper, I hope I may be permitted to state the present point of view with a few words in order to make quite clear what the goals and methods of geographical observation should be, because both are regarded very differently. It should always be kept in mind that the object of scientific geography is primarily the study of the surface of the globe, independent of its cover and its inhabitants. That is the only

[1] *China*, Ferdinand von Richthofen, Vol. 1, Berlin, Dietrich Reimer, 1877. p. 729-732.

field which belongs to geography alone. In order to control it, it must investigate, primarily; and it also must accurately fix the geometrical relation in vertical and horizontal direction; the distribution of the surface forms, of the solid and liquid; the distribution of mountains, valleys, and plains; the currents, gradients, and forks of the waters; the distribution of the character of rocks and soils, as far as they determine the surface character; and geography has to find the laws in these factors. It can do so only in connection with geology, since the latter provides understanding of the interior structure of the ground on which those laws rest. In a scientific geography up to today's standards it is unthinkable to omit that geological basis which is arrived at by a painstaking geographical knowledge of the respective countries. This part of what is often called "geognosy" can be regarded, indeed, as the common property of geologists and geographers, and at the same time as the starting point from which these two so closely interrelated sciences depart in their objective. To geology belongs the abstract observation of the constituent elements of the ground, the kind of interrelations they share, and the factors which transform them. The branches of research developing therefrom—petrography, stratigraphy, geotectonics, and dynamic geology — are very far from the field of the geographer. Even farther away from his task is the very own task of the geologist — the investigation of the history of the development of the earth's crust and the inhabiting organisms — although the former receives rich material from those investigations for a better understanding of the problems of his own science.

Study of geography goes off in a different direction from the knowledge of the composition and organization of the present surface of the earth and follows a different method. First of all, that knowledge constitutes only part of its basic dominion. The second type, which appears in cartography in pictorial form, is knowledge of the pure forms of the land. Geographical method rests on the mutual relations of both aspects and its comparative observation according to as multivarious and comprehensive points of view as possible.

Only on these wider and stabilized bases grow those branches of geography — in distinction to pure geography, they could be called applied — which develop primarily from the relations of form and constitution of the surface of the earth, both the solid and the liquid, to a physics of the earth and the climatic and atmospheric conditions. Secondly, other branches emerge from the combined relations of both groups to the vegetation, distribution of animals, races of man, languages, tribes, and nations, transportation systems, settlements, industries, occupations, cultural developments, origins of natural and artificial resources and their distribution through commerce, and finally, to the least stable conditions of political organizations, boundaries, and political institutions. Insofar as these different factors of human existence and activity have a historical development, and the latter is investigated with special regard to the places where it happened, the much tended branch of political geography develops. It cannot, however, dispense with the same bases and methods as the other branches, in order not to fall completely into the sphere of history and philology.

The study of every science is most attractive in those parts which are in contact with other sciences. Thus on the basis of a narrowly conceived, essentially geometrical, and little understood basis the applied branches of geography found the earliest and best care, especially those which refer to man, his settlements and political institutions. However, not without justification, these branches are claimed by the sciences into which they overlap and to whom geography comes, quasi, as a guest — namely by botany, zoology, ethnography, logistics, and statistics, but also by meteorology, geology and others, because the research method originated there. Only if one observes as Ritter did, all the phenomena which are treated in those branches in their causal connection with the forms and the quality of the surface of the earth — if one, therefore, uses the geographical method — comparative geography in the meaning of Ritter can maintain itself as a separate science and an integral part of geography. But, nowadays, it has to go far beyond that point and must follow the concatenation of cause and effect farther than this great geographer did. It must drive its roots into the sphere of geology as Humboldt, Buch, and the far too little appreciated Junghuhn started to do. It is the more necessary to secure this basis in a period in which geography divides into numerous branches. Geography is intent to build on the basis of Ritter but is no longer able to control the material, grown in all directions from all the sciences from which it took something. These branches are barely kept together by anything else than the common coordination in space according to which things are observed. When contact with the basis is impaired or completely lost, superficiality easily occurs; the danger arises that geography may lose its identity so recently won as an independent science branching out logically in different directions. Thus it could, as has happened in statistics, become only the expression of a method to arrange facts from geophysics, climatology, botany, zoology, etc. *Where* it *is* only method, geography loses its individuality; that which gives a science its own character is the fact it *possesses* its own method. That is found for geography, as we characterized it, in the perpetual observation of the mutual causal relations between the earth's surface in its different aspects, geophysics and atmosphere on the one side, and the organic world in the widest sense on the other side. If geography firmly retains knowledge of the form and composition of the earth and their mutual relations as its very own basis, relying on this method geography can invade other spheres, and laden with their material and penetrating them, it will enter even more distant areas. The manner in which geography treats the offered material will secure it; on the other hand geography can allow the clarification of the independence of other sciences, such as political science and ethnography, which are frequently attached in their entirety to geography, and which scarcely can be removed because of established conventional usage.

* * *

Purpose and Method of Contemporary Geography: Inaugural Lecture [2]

Every month increases the sum of our knowledge of foreign areas. However, the geographical material which we have to register in our modern periodicals and handbooks is essentially different from that gathered in former centuries. The methods of observation have improved considerably. We have to investigate afresh what we thought we knew in order to satisfy our claims of knowledge. In a higher degree than ever we are called upon to sift systematically the overwhelming mass of material and to discover the red thread of uniform scientific treatment in the increasing diversity. The points of contact with other well established fields of knowledge have increased so much, and there is such an intricate interlocking of tasks, that frequently it is impossible to discover a dividing line. The question has been asked whether geography can continue as a separate science in such a position between a number of established disciplines. In these vivid discussions about concept and delimitation very divergent ideas have emerged. In a surprising lack of understanding, geography is declared by some to be only an auxiliary to history, while another one-sided concept tries to discern geography as a pure natural science and tries to eliminate anything concerning man. Still others attribute to geography a dualism without uniformity, and this opinion is abetted by some textbooks which know only a division into physical geography and political or historical geography. . . . At present it seems a vain attempt to define precisely the object of geography. In general only few sciences have distinct limits. But in no other science are there so many and so manifold border areas as in geography. Therefore, geography has to assert a firm position in the center within the sphere of variable shifting; it will then be easier to agree with neighboring sciences about contested points.

This firm position is assured primarily by the fact that the

[2] *Aufgaben und Methoden der Heutigen Geographie, Akademische Antrittsrede*, Ferdinand Freiherr von Richthofen, 27 April 1883, Leipzig, Veit and Company, 1883. p. 4-59.

surface of the globe is its own domain. From there the contacts and concatenations go out, with those sciences which deal with what is below the surface of the earth, with what is living on it and occurs there, and with what exists outside in the sky. . . . It is obvious that the surface of the earth, as such, is the object of investigation of no other science . . .

The first task is purely morphographic.[3] It is the measuring of mathematical surfaces which divide the solid and the liquid, first, land and sea, but also rivers and lakes, and delimit them from the atmosphere and the lines which separate them from each other.

From this first basic task involving measures and figures other problems immediately arise. While the lack of regularity in the distribution of oceans and continents seems striking at first, compared with the regular shape of the globe as a whole, the observant viewer soon discovers certain regularities.

A second fundamental task is the investigation of the earth's surface in respect to the stars, especially the sun and moon. This relationship is primarily the concern of the astronomers. They establish it by methods which are foreign to the geographer; but astronomers furnish to the geographer the instruments and means for the mentioned measurements, to establish a grid of longitudes and latitudes on the earth's surface and to fix the position of localities within this grid. . . .

Thus geography enters into close relationship with another science and would be unable to fulfill its morphographic task without it. There exists a still more vivid interchange as soon as geography investigates the material composition of the earth's surface together with the inherent forces and their manifestations. As concerns the atmosphere, the division is simple. The chemist and the physicist investigate the elements and their qualities by exact methods. . . . The geographer observes the "how" in its relation to the "where" on the surface of the globe in vertical and horizontal direction, and this leads to the question of their causation by the laws discovered by the physicist and how they are causally con-

[3] Morphography is the description of forms, in this case, of landforms, to be distinguished from morphology, the genetic explanation of landforms.

nected with the local landforms, the location on the globe. From this derives a further task: to gather the features observed in different places for comparison and to trace them over the whole globe.

While in these subjects the field of geography can be determined fairly exactly, this is no longer true if we conceive the surface of the earth not as a mathematical surface but as a substantial surface layer, and investigate its composition and qualities. . . . The knowledge of the composition of the solid surface layers is increasingly an urgent need for scientific geography and, besides the plastic, the basic need for further research. Because organic beings do not live and move on the mathematical surface, but on and in the upper layer of the earth, in it is rooted thoroughly the existence of man; water and air model it. Without knowing the nature of the ground the earth's surface cannot be understood in a modern sense. Form alone are rigid and dead; they gain life and content only if their physical qualities are known. . . .

In the classical period of "physical geography" . . . (geography) embraced the investigation and presentation of all these kinds of problems. However, before "physical geography" succeeded in integrating itself successfully with the separate science of regional geography,[4] geography was deflected from the direction toward natural science by influences which will be discussed later. Though one occasionally included that which referred to some of the aforementioned stable factors and the movement of the atmosphere and the oceans, the dynamic processes on the continents were used, at most, as an independent introduction in some textbooks. They were not a field of research for the geographer. At the same time the geological surveys started in several countries. . . .

In our period a desire arises of re-incorporating these problems into geography. It is, therefore, permitted to ask whether a moment could be found from whence the effects of the processes which transform the earth belong to geography and from whence, back into the past, they belong to the field of geology. Indeed some have looked for such a borderline. It was

[4] Literally; knowledge of countries and nations.

said that geography started with history, i.e., for the area of each nation from the moment when it enters history. This opinion cannot be accepted. . . . The leading points have to be derived from the surface of the earth. The geologist regards it as something evolving, the geographer as existing. The former is occupied with the formation of the skeleton, the latter thus receives from him the crude form and observes how it was transformed by forces attacking it from the outside. It does not matter whether the original form of a region was completed in the Tertiary period, or in a preceding era, or only at the end of the glacial epoch. . . . If a volcano would emerge today, the causes of its emergence and its connection with other volcanoes would belong to the field of geological investigation; the further transformation of its form would occupy the geographer. . . . In principle they (the dynamic and genetic processes) can be separated in most cases. Practically, the separation cannot always be accomplished. . . . The highest goal of geography is the exploration of the relationship of man to all the aforementioned factors separately and taken together, to the solid surface of the earth and its transformations, to the distribution of hydrographic features, to the atmosphere and its changing conditions, and to the local and general distribution of plants and animals. . . .

Geography has a leading point of view of its own. We have already stressed, as such, the causal, mutual relations of features and phenomena in regard to the surface of the earth. Geography becomes thereby the science of the surface of the earth and causally related features and phenomena. It is not a "science of the earth"; else it would be all-embracing. It would be more correct to call it the "science of the earth's surface". . . .

This dominant point of view dominates also the tools by which our science acquires the material which it is to mold. Basically they are the same as those used by the natural sciences, namely measurements and observation. . . .

(In the natural sciences) observation of facts and features is required, irrespective of whether they exist in nature or are produced by experiment; geography observes facts and features which are given in nature, as far as they have a recognizable relation to the surface of the earth. It combines the objects of several sciences under a uniform point of view, which was not necessarily observed by the other sciences. The more the sciences, which share the objects, make progress, the more the expanse of geographical observation increases and deepens. The desire for perfecting observation expresses itself not only in the extension but also in the desire to use measurements and figures as much as possible and, based on them, to find expression for features and their interrelations.

The material for observations which the geographer has to exploit is infinitely large, as his field embraces the surface of the earth and all realms of nature. He acquires it as well by observing the smallest parts of the surface as by surveying and comparing wide spaces; as well by studying nature as by philosophically studying the maps. . . .

The material gathered by measuring and observation is first methodically attacked and systematically arranged. In this early moment two possible ways separate according to whether regions or facts and features are the uppermost criteria of classification. The first route immediately leads to the descriptive and graphic method which is used in descriptive or special geography; the latter leads indirectly by combination and conclusion to the abstracting method which is used in general geography. We can also call these two methods the synthetic and the analytic method, though with qualification. . . . By combining both methods a third one emerges which is used in the chorological method and consists in combining certain groups of features which are observed in one region and are treated so as to recognize the causal nexuses.

The descriptive and graphic method has two axiomatic presuppositions which are used to determine the criteria of breakdown. The first is that the earth is composed of several regions and that the whole can be understood only by juxtaposition of the parts. . . . The second supposition is that each region is an agglomeration of parts which consist of elements of the six realms of nature, and that it can be presented only by their totality.

The mode of presentation of chorography is didactical, its method essentially progressive, advancing continuously from a given solid basis to those factors which are more changeable, from the causative gradually toward the conditioned factors. Synthesis prevails, though an analytical process is combined in the breaking down of the whole into its parts.

The inherently encyclopedic character which clings to chorography in its purest form, was characteristic for certain periods of geographical literature. It especially developed during periods in which a mass of new information about foreign countries accumulated. . . .

Besides chorography, chorology developed — a science not content to register facts, but which also tries to understand them for each region by introducing a causative and dynamic momentum. Strabo, in ancient times, shone forth as the predecessor of this trend. In our century Humboldt and Ritter were the great leaders. . . .

The chorological interest of these two great men were in different areas. They supplemented each other, though there remain certain *lacunae* even after their combination; for the perfect chrological presentation of a region would have to consider not only the points of view which these two men have validated, but also a number of intermediate factors. The reason is not the frailty of one of them; rather the common goal is too large for the power of a single human being, if he tries to accomplish it with the profundity and accuracy used by both of them for individual points of view and great areas. . . . Chorology has the drawback that it hardly ever can produce a complete scientific structure, because either it confines itself to a small or large region and presents all the causal relations which exist within and relating to its surface — a task so far never successfully accomplished; or it confines itself to a group of causal relations and tracks these down over all individual regions, leaving the derivation of common regular features to general geography. . . .

We called the second method, by which the large content of geography can be handled, the abstracting, or by its prevailing character, the analytical method. . . .

* * *

It is a sign of our period that it has recognized again the

uniformity of the knowledge relating to the surface of the earth. It again attempts an analytical treatment from a geographical point of view and tries to reconcile it with the chorological method which has developed to greater depth. The "Geographia Generalis" of Varenius recovers, thereby, the independence which had been conceded if half a century ago. It is noteworthy that, literally, it lays its roots deeper into the ground than could be done then; and that it is able, by increasingly more accurate methods, to attack problems concerning men which even to a man such as Ritter appeared as hardly attainable ideals. . . .

One after another of the branches which once belonged to geography and since have had only a loose, indirect connection, are again attacked. . . .

The favorable results of the changed position of individual problems cannot be overlooked. As each of them was investigated within the peculiar science to which it was attached, the method of its treatment was according to that science; the goals of treatment went little further. Only since the leading geographical points of view have been applied and these problems were drawn into geography, since problems were viewed in relation to the whole surface of the earth and their causal nexus with other similarly treated features, only since then have they become links between different fields of knowledge.

As far as man is a living creature and, as such, is an object of natural science, it is possible to regard also his relation to the earth's surface in biological geography. Indeed his distribution in races and other features once was a chapter of "physical geography." But to the factors which relate plants and animals with the surface of the earth, others, essential ones, are added. Nature gave man physiological adaptability to different climates only to a minimum degree. The individual with purposeful intent creates the protective means which he needs under varying conditions and changes them according to his own will. By adapting clothing and shelter to his needs, man can adapt his whole existence to changing outer conditions. . . . Man creates tools, and only a few obstructions which the earth's surface offers to his movement are still to be overcome. . . .

Therefore, anthropogeography, as it was called by an ingenious scholar recently,[5] has developed separately into the highest but also the most difficult branch of general geography. . . . One point of view leads to grouping of individuals into categories. There can be different criteria. The ethnical, linguistic, or ethical criteria lead to classifications according to race, language or religion. . . .

If we introduce the genetic point of view into anthropography, we arrive at a field where geography enters a close relationship with history. We try to recognize the development of man in relation to his present distribution over the surface of the earth and the way in which the different dynamic factors have contributed to his relation to the earth's surface. In no other section is chorological research, which has to supply the material, of such varying value.

FRIEDRICH RATZEL (1844-1904)

Friedrich Ratzel a younger contemporary colleague of Richthofen at Leipzig University, is commonly regarded as the latter's antipode because of his importance in human geography, the part of geography which was farthest from Richthofen's interests. Though they shared a common interest, regional geography, the contrast is real and even more obvious among their disciples and followers. Though Ratzel originally was trained in biology, his main work was in the field of human geography, or anthropogeography, as he himself called it. Within this wider field he was the founder of modern political geography as the study of the state. However, German geography followed primarily the leadership of Richthofen and later Hettner, while outside Germany, especially in France and the United States through Vidal de la Blache and Ellen Semple, Ratzel was far better known and more highly regarded. Ratzel's disciples interpreted his teachings as the basis for the doctrine of the state as an organism and for the doctrine of geographical environmentalism, but he was not too outspoken on these points himself. However, Ratzel was most influential as the first geog-

[5] Ratzel.

rapher to investigate the relations between earth and man in a systematic manner.

Political Geography[6]

The state as an organism rooted in the earth

The state in geography and the biogeographical concept of the state.—The distribution of man and of his works over the surface of the earth bears all the signs of a mobile body, which by advancing and retreating is spreading out and contracting, forming new contracts and disrupting old ones, and thereby is assuming forms which have the greatest similarity with the forms of other socially living, mobile bodies on the surface of the earth. In frequently used allegorical expressions, such as "sea of nations" or human flood, national or political island, or political isthmus, some hint of this fact may be inferred; however, the deeper meaning of these expressions rarely occurred to any of those who used them.

These similarities no longer are used in an allegorical way in biogeography: in that field living spaces, islands of life, etc., are real; here also human states are *forms of the distribution of life* on the surface of the earth. The state is subject to the same influences as all living things. The special laws pertaining to the distribution of man over the earth apply also to the distribution of his states. States have never emerged in polar regions, nor in the desert; and those which emerged in sparsely settled areas of the tropics, in virgin forests, or in the highest mountains remained small. States have spread together with man into all parts of the world; and as man's numbers increased, the number of states and size of his states also increased. The uninterrupted changes in the inner and outer shape of states prove that they are alive within their borders, a fact which can only be perceived scientifically as an expression of movement, both organic and inorganic. The same is true in the case of elementary political units whose

[6] *Politische Geographie,* Friedrich Ratzel, 3rd edition, slightly revised by Eugen Oberhummer, R. Oldenbourg, München and Berlin, 1923. p. 1-5. The first edition was published in 1897. This translation was made from the third edition; however, in the translated parts the two editions are literally alike.

coincidence with cellular structure is obvious; everywhere the similarity of all composite living beings is recognizable on the basis of their connection with the soil. Indeed for all of them, whether areas, corals, or man, this nexus is a general property — a property of life — because it is the condition for their life.

The land [7] may either hamper or favor the growth of states, according to whether it hampers or favors the movement of an individual or of families. That is also the reason for the influence of water upon the development of states: they preferably will spread along coasts and rivers and flourish best where nature itself has prepared a system of communications. Such systems are found in great river basins. . . .

Each state is a piece of mankind and a piece of the earth. One cannot imagine man without the earth; neither can one speak of man's greatest product on earth, the state, without mention of it. If we speak of a state, we have in mind a part of mankind and, at the same time, a piece of the earth: the same is true if we speak of a city, or of a road. The state ought to live from the soil. It holds securely only those advantages whose earthly basis it grips firmly. Political scientists express the same idea less strongly when they assert that a territory is an essential characteristic of a state. They call sovereignty *jus territoriale* (right over a territory) and have established a rule that changes of territory can be effected only by law. The life history of states, however, presents us with a much closer connection: we recognize throughout history that all political forces seize territory and become states by this very act. Accordingly, I call a nation a politically united group of smaller groups and individuals, who are not necessarisy connected by common descent or common language, but are united by a common territory.

Thus the political organization of a territory emerges, whereby the state becomes an organism into which a certain part of the earth's surface enters in such a way that the char-

[7] Ratzel uses the word *Boden* which literally means soil. It is translated here according to the apparent context, sometimes as land or earth, sometimes territory or soil.

acteristics of the state are compounded from those of the people and the *territory*. The most important are size, location and boundaries, further qualities and form of its soil together with vegetation and its drainage, and finally its relation to other parts of the surface of the earth. We include in the latter the adjacent seas, and even the uninhabitable (*anecumenic*) regions which are on first glance of no political interest. All together they constitute "the country". When we speak of our "land," those things man has created in it and on it and which are thus buried as memories in its soil are combined in our mind with these natural foundations. Thereby the basically geographical concept is not only filled with political content, but also enters into a spiritual and emotional amalgamation with us, its inhabitants, and its whole history.

The state is, in our opinion, an organism not only because it is an amalgamation between the live substance and the rigid territory, but because this connection becomes so strong through mutual influence that both become a unit and can no longer be thought of separately without losing life itself. Territory and nation both contribute to this end in the degree to which they have the qualities necessary for the impact of one upon the other. An uninhabitable territory does not sustain any state; it is historically a fallow field. A habitable territory, on the other hand, favors political development, especially if it has natural boundaries. If a nation is firmly planted in its soil in this way, it re-emerges time and again with characteristics which have their origin in its soil and will enter into the nation's character time and again: ancient and modern Greeks are seafarers and merchants, inhabitants of coasts and of coastal areas. The *Eidgenossen*[8] of the 19th century cherish freedom in small political units the same as did their ancestors in the 14th century. . . .

The feeling of belonging to the soil is nowhere as strong as where a territory is well defined, can be easily surveyed, dominated and utilized; for this reason people of island countries develop the strongest nationalism and one which is most conscious of its territorial basis. Thus, indeed, the development

---

[8] An antiquated, and therefore difficult to translate designation for the Swiss; approximately, covenanters.

of each state constitutes an increasing *organization of the territory* by increasingly close integration with the people. If the population increases within the same space, the connecting links between people and territory multiply and natural resources are developed more and more and thus contribute to the power of the nation. The nation, however, becomes increasingly dependent on the territory, even dependent to the degree of becoming paralyzed, if the territory is locked in and imprisoned as is the case in Lower Egypt. The larger a territory, the looser is the connection of the people with it. The difference between the state of a civilized nation and that of a barbaric one lies in the fact that in the former the organization of the territory has progressed much farther.

ALBRECHT PENCK (1858-1945)

Penck, a younger contemporary of Richthofen, shares with the latter credit for establishing geomorphology as a branch of geography. It is largely due to Penck's influence, which grew over the many decades of his long life, that in Germany and in many other European countries no one could claim to be a geographer for long without a firm foundation in geomorphology. He maintained close relations with Davis. (The divergent development of Davis' school in America and Penck's school in Europe was based on the work of Penck's brilliant son, Walter Penck (1888-1923).) After Agassiz had established the existence of an ice age, the older Penck — together with Eduard Brückner — established the four glacial periods in the Alps. His influence and suggestions are also responsible for the adoption of the great international collaboration on the 1:1,000,000 map of the world. In later life he became interested in problems of human geography, but he remained basically a physical geographer.

Geography Among the Earth Sciences[9]

All systematic knowledge of the earth begins with the observation of the surface of the earth. The science of this sur-

[9] The Record of the Celebration of the Two Hundredth Anniversary of the Founding of the American Philosophical Society, Proceedings, vol. 66. Philadelphia 1927. p. 623-644.

face — *geography* — is, historically speaking, the foundation of all sciences concerned with the earth. . . . Like the surface of the earth, the atmosphere came in for early attention. Four books were devoted by Aristole to *meteorology.* All the other sciences concerned with the earth were developed in modern times. The eighteenth century brought the beginnings of *geology,* when the experiences gained in mining and through the exploration of the high mountain ranges were utilized in examining the crust of the globe. Even before that, *geodesy* . . . had developed. . . . The *geophysical* science includes meteorology. At present, the two are on the way to be (sic) separated. . . . Besides, forming a parallel science to meteorology, *hydrography,* the science of the water, with *oceanography* as its main part, has been strongly developed and *glaciology* too assumed the character of a distinct science.

Seven sciences are now participating in the investigation of the earth. Each of them has its definite aim and its specific sphere of activity. . . . In the course of the last two centuries *geography* has yielded so much ground to its daughter sciences that to some it no longer appears as an independent science. Yet there is still a wide field left for geography, even when confining it to the most narrow limits of its original content, viz. to the surface of the globe. This surface is of special importance to the whole body of the earth, not as a boundary against the surrounding space — that we are looking for at the upper limit of the atmosphere — but because on it solar energy is converted into a number of different phenomena. To the study of the forms of the earth's surface, therefore, is added the research of the processes taking place on it, in other words, the morphological observations are supplemented by physiological ones. The latter, however, not only comprise the phenomena of inorganic nature, but deal also with those of organic world. All organic life on earth is tied to the earth's surface, and therefore the latter is the actual scene of life, the *Lebensraum;* on that scene man lives and acts. Much closer, therefore, than the relations of geology, are those of geography, to biology. And in geography, too, man plays an active part.

The sciences concerned with the earth are divided and

classified according to different fields of research, not according to the methods employed by them. . . . Undoubtedly, geography more than the other sciences investigating the earth, has to deal with the geographical distribution of individual phenomena, yet the use of such a "geographical" method is not a peculiarity exclusively its own. Both the zoologist and the botanist must give attention to the distribution of animals and plants; and on the other hand, not everything connected with the distribution of phenomena pertains to geography. Measuring methods are not exclusively applied by geodesy, but by every other science as well where dimensions have to be exactly determined. This is particularly true of meteorology, hydrography and glaciology. The geophysicist can no more get along without mathematics than the geodesist, and the more exactly the geographical and geological sciences are treated, the more closely will they get in touch with mathematics. Quite frequently geology and geography have been contrasted with each other as the sciences of time and space respectively. Certainly geology is strongly tinged with history, but tectonic geology cannot do without the chorological observation which has so often been taken as a geographical peculiarity. And geography in its turn, whenever dealing with processes, cannot omit proper consideration of the time for which they were going on. What divides the sciences concerned with the earth is not the methods to be employed but the objects to be investigated.

These objects, however, are not strictly separated from one another, but they are merely individual parts of a large whole. . . . Not even is the surface of the earth separated from its body like a skin; it is merely a surface, varied both in form and in the effects it produces. . . .

What the geographer considers as the surface of the earth is partly the uneven surface of the rigid crust of the earth including glaciers, and partly the surface of the running and standing waters. Underlying are the litho- and the hydrosphere, above is the atmosphere. On it all the changes of energy are going on that are watched by the geographer. Here is the base of all life which rises but slightly into the atmosphere, which does not penetrate deeply into the ground, and which in the ocean is richest near its surface. This *geographical* surface is represented on our maps. . . .

The victory of the evolutional view in the sciences of the earth and of life is the greatest achievement of the nineteenth century. This view is based on the application of a comparative method which in many instances recognized the effects of an historical association in what is coexistent in time. Feeble starts toward such a comparative method may be traced in Karl Ritter's conception of a general comparative geography. Lyell developed it by explaining geographical phenomena through the observation of processes going on on the surface of the earth, i.e., geographical processes. More than is generally known, has geography influenced the development of modern science, and if we are looking for the mutual relations existing between the various sciences concerning the earth, we find geography to be the connecting link. For it is only on the surface of the earth that all the observations regarding its crust and the depths of its interior can be made. They are all dependent on geographical work, since most observations are worthless without a knowledge of the situation of the points where they are made.

This central position of geography among the sciences concerned with the earth is rarely appreciated. The reason is that we frequently fail to realize what we owe to it, and in most cases the required geographical information can be easily procured from atlases. And because it is not realized what an amount of geographical research is contained in our atlases, it may happen occasionally that geography is denied the quality of a science. The knowledge of the terrestrial surface must not necessarily remain superficial. As a matter of fact it is true that the geographical surface, both of the continents and the oceans, can be dealt with by other sciences as well. Geologists cannot be prohibited from giving attention to the surface of that crust which they are investigating, and to the geodesist the surface of the sea, freed from waves and tides, is the visible geoid.

But the circumstance that the same subject is the object of several sciences does not render any one of these sciences unnecessary. . . .

Most intimately intertwined with the surface of the earth is its vegetable garment; in fact, it is an integral part of the surface. The topographical maps of the old world are paying due attention to it. No less a man than Alexander von Humboldt has pointed out that it determines the physiognomy of countries. The shape and the coating of the surface of the earth make up the essential contents of geography. But while the former is due to the action of endogeneous and exogeneous causes constantly operating against each other, the latter is the result of the soil and the climate, in the treatment of which geography and meteorology are sharing. . . .

The fact that organisms became integral parts of the surface of the earth, places geography in a class by itself among all sciences concerned with the globe. In a lesser degree, geology too, dealing so much with the remains of former life, is entitled to such classification. . . . Animal and plant geography belong more to zoologists and botanists than to the geographer. For him there remains a wide field of research on the physical conditions controlling life on the globe, and investigations on its distribution as a whole. The theater of life is part of the earth's surface and pertains to geography, and the manner in which especially the vegetation of the globe spreads over its surface will always be studied by geographers, because in that way they obtain excellent characteristics of individual portions of the surface of the earth.

These characteristics refer to the shape, covering, and situation of individual spots of the earth; they call for a chorological manner of viewing things, which is not a peculiarly geographic one, but is applied also in regional geology, and in botanical ecology. But in no other science does it play so important a part as in geography. It consists in correlating an aggregation of various units, which is tied to a particular spot of the earth, or a definite region; in recognizing a balanced state of processes which are determined by the motion of the underlying piece of crust, the active solar energy, and the accessibility of life. These processes are not only dependent on the locality involved, but processes originating in the neighborhood are playing at part. . . . That is why the *geographic situation* is so very important in the method of regional investigation. In Germany the unit forming its basis has been termed *Landschaft*. Investigations on the *Landschaft* are regarded by some as the real aim of modern geography. The viewpoint however is not new, it has been used for scores of years, and not much has been gained by dividing a piece of surface into individual regions. Its peculiarity can only be fully understood and appreciated by studying the manner in which its individual regions are grouped, by considering what pattern they form, and by endeavoring to comprehend its geographical configuration.

The *Landschaft* (region) represents a state of balance, which is immediately disturbed if even a single one of the factors determining it is changed. No factor is more effective in determining the character of a landscape than man. . . . He transforms *Naturlandschaft* into *Kulturlandschaft*. In many parts of the United States this transformation is still in progress; in the civilized countries of Europe it is practically completed. Harmony has been restored, of a different kind, it is true, than that which prevailed in the virgin landscape and was disturbed there by the interference of man.

In view of the fact that now the cultivated area extends over millions of square miles, there can be no doubt that man, too, by his work is a proper subject for geographical investigation and that, aside from the physical processes, which are bound up by a rigid law of causality, and the biological phenomena not completely subjected to the same law, geography has to deal also with the actions of human will, the causes of which are often difficult to understand. This wide span of different causalities is a fact which, in the view of many, deprives geography of unity. Widespread, indeed, is the belief that it is a dualistic science, part of which should be classified with the natural, and part with the intellectual sciences. This view, however, is not founded on the subject, but on the manner of treating it. . . . Orientation on the surface of the globe is the root of geography, which was primitively the science of the world surrounding man. Herodotus looked at mankind from the viewpoints of space and time. In their beginnings geography and history keep close together; necessarily they diverge more and more, as geography objectively devotes itself to the surface of the earth. . . . If we lose the surface of the globe from our vision we fall back into a sort of anthropocentric view. That is what even eminent geographers have felt as a dualism of geography. It has no material foundation, but it persists in manifesting itself. Again and again it is attempted to remove geography from among the other sciences concerned with the earth and give it the old place by the side of history.

The dualistic character of geography will disappear as soon as geography will give its attention to the great tasks of physical anthropogeography, and will leave much of what it now deals with as economic and political geography to a science of man, which will have to be further developed and expanded. In this connection it may again be pointed out that the investigation of the spreading and distribution of things over the surface of the earth is not yet geography. As it is not the task of geography to trace individual animal and plant species on the earth's surface, so it is not necessarily its province to investigate the mere spreading of man and his works on earth. Undoubtedly it is necessary to do this. But only as long as these important tasks are not taken up by other sciences can they be regarded as belonging to geography. . . . Strictly speaking, geography as a science has to deal exclusively with things connected with the surface of the globe. That is its clearly defined object. Now, as there are geographers who, in addition to one, devote themselves to another of the sciences concerned with the earth, so others could certainly cultivate a science of man in addition to one regarding the earth. While the two objects with which they are concerned are quite different, such scientists are not likely to look upon this as a dualism of geography, but they will simply feel that they are taking up two different fields which are lying near and are in touch with each other. They may do this with propriety, provided they are at home in both of them. A dualism is felt only by a man who sees the lines of demarcation between individual sciences rather than their points of contact, and who more clearly recognizes the distinction between the intellectual and the natural sciences than the intimate connection existing between all the sciences, and the fact that they are all closely related to one another as parts of a grand, universal science. These parts do not lie side by side in a plane, like the different countries on a map, but they are closely connected and intertwined in many ways. Geography is not only in touch with other sciences concerned with the earth, but also with those concerning life and man. That does not deprive her of her character as a science of the globe. Through the uniformity of her field of activity she is enabled to concentrate her research; through the great number of her various points of contact she is able to cooperate in the development of the great, consolidated, universal science.

ALFRED HETTNER (1859-1942)

Hettner held a position in the German geography of his time that was both unique and typical. He was unique because he was the first modern geographer who started his studies with the fixed intent of becoming a geographer, because he was thoroughly grounded in philosophy, and because he had a life-long interest in methodological problems. On the other hand he continued the tradition of von Humboldt that an established geographer should have done field work in his home country, in another European country, and on some other continent and that he should combine field work with library research. Hettner's field of overseas exploration was the Andean countries of South America. Besides his numerous contributions to regional and comparative regional geography, he tried to base geography firmly in the system of sciences by placing it, as a chorological science, in a category distinct from both natural and social science. His influence was widely acknowledged in Germany and even more so in some other countries. In Germany his chorological approach was under attack from several sides. He has been the prime target of criticism from Soviet geographers to whom he remains the principle representative of idealistic philosophy in geography.

The following essay does not give the full breadth of his thought and work; however, it was considered preferable to present an entire piece from his pen rather than a number of very short, disconnected excerpts.

Our Concept of Geography[10]

While I am submitting to you, dear Mr. Philippson,[11] this issue of the *Geographische Zeitschrift,* which contains a part of the articles devoted to you on your 65th birthday by your disciples and younger friends, I do not want to miss the opportunity of adding a word of my own. I want to testify thereby to the agreement which, despite some variety in detail, exists in our basic concept of our science. Today, again, it is questioned and attacked from different parts; I have already dealt with these attacks in the two preceding issues of this periodical, and today I shall try to present briefly our point of view.

The most dangerous opposition comes from an area from which you should least expect it, namely, from the teachers of geography. No philologist or mathematician would expect philology or mathematics as a science or as the subject of university classes to be taught in exactly the way it is needed in high school, but for geography many pedagogues, at least by implication, demand just that. They regard scientific research and scientific theory exactly from the point of view of school methodology. That is wrong and without justification, because scientific research and systems on the one side, teaching in school on the other, follow different rules. Science ought to be led only by the internal connection of things: it must be left to school geography to transform the subject matter according to psychological and pedagogical considerations, and to fit them to the interests and understanding of youth.

Other comments originate from representatives of practical, economic, and political life. They are not interested in theory, only in facts; primarily they condemn morphology, which indeed occupied the center of the stage too exclusively for a while; ultimately geography, like any other science,

---

[10] Alfred Hettner, "Unsere Auffassung von der Geographie," in *Geographische Zeitschrift,* V. 35, 1929. p. 486-491.

[11] Alfred Philippson (1864-1953) is especially known for his studies on Mediterranean countries. Though Jewish, his life was saved from the Nazi fury through the intervention of the Swedish explorer Sven Hedin (1864-1952). He did, however, spend several years in a concentration camp.

shall serve practical life, but only in its ultimate consequences; if it considers only practical interests from the very beginning, geography becomes petrified. Geography became a science by liberating itself from any immediate concern for practical interests, and one demonstrates a lack of scientific attitude if one wants to bring it back to such a state. Even from the point of view of practice it is shortsighted; because the most important applications of science spring from research which has been undertaken without any practical interest. Practical or applied geography stands apart from scientific, theoretical geography; it supplements the other, but does not replace it.

There is an opinion directly opposed which wants to make geography an art, negates geography as a science, or at least assigns to it an inferior position. Geography is supposed to become landscape poetry.[12] However, geography has to refuse that too. There is no order of rank between science and art; quite the opposite, they stand side by side. Science cannot replace art, nor art science; but it is also dangerous if they intrude into each other's sphere. I do not want to give here a definition of art and especially of landscape-poetry, which every student of aesthetics defines differently, but to expound only the task of geography as a science; this task is the discovery of the truth both as a description of facts and as an explanation of them. Of course, it should present its results in a pleasant form; it is wrong to think that neglect of form is a requirement for accurate science. However, a pleasant form is something different from art. Science may also inquire what constitutes the beauty of a landscape; but that is also something different from artistic conception.

Another concept springs from a special metaphysical concept. It would be surprising if the modern slogans of instinctive conception and intuitive conception and unified vision (*Zusammenschau*) had not been applied to geography also. It is not up to me here to investigate their value for metaphysics. To transfer them into science detracts from reasoning. Certainly it is a duty of geography, and especially of regional geography, to integrate the facts and appearances of the vari-

---

[12] Apparently Banse or Passarge are hinted at.

ous realms of nature with that of human life in the same area, but not merely by viewing them. Rather they should be integrated by recognizing their causal connection. It has become fashionable to talk deprecatively of "positivistic" science. But the essence of science is misinterpreted if that expression, which belongs properly in epistemology, is used to indicate the scientific treatment of the visible world, if it is used to say that science ought not to explain or that it ought to employ metaphysical concepts for explanation of concepts which are beyond experience.

I can see in all these things only symptoms of disease — and I think you will agree with me — which have their basis in the disquietude of our time, and the desire for novelty, the striving for originality at any price, and also in a certain lack of energy. Of course, I do not want to say by this that our scientific conception as heretofore propounded is perfect; it has to struggle with many difficulties; nor has it conquered them by any means, but it is on the right path insofar as it treats geography as science for science's sake.

I am less worried about the differences in opinion concerning the delimitation and the system of geography, though they too are of considerable importance for scientific work, than I am about the attacks upon geography as science.

What is the subject of geography? The over-evaluation of the human features and the co-mingling of geography and statistics belongs to a past period in which practical interest outranked the scientific. On the other hand, the reaction of this attitude, the over-evaluation of natural, to the detriment of human, features is a thing of the past. Probably we all agree, both man and nature belong in geography. There exists, however, a conflict in the weight given to every side; several noted colleagues want to restrict geography to the visible, and generally to what can be perceived with the senses, to the picture of the landscape; they do not desire thereby to exclude certain aspects of nature which they introduce by the back door; they rather want to exclude certain aspects of human life, nationality, state, and partly even economy. They exclude, thereby, exactly those features which have been the preeminent concern of geography in the past and, in the popular opinion, still are. They disrupt also the causal connection. There is no good reason, as it is against the logic of science to permit the picture, i.e., the appearance, to be the decisive factor in defining the subject; one imagines only mineralogy or botany or zoology to be satisfied by the external appearance of minerals, plants, or animals. It is possible to observe man more or less deeply, according to whether one has a higher or lower estimate of man's dependence on nature and his influence upon nature. I do not know whether we two agree completely in this respect; but it appears to me inappropriate to make the visibility of man and his products the touchstone for delimitation.

The banishment of general systematic geography as desired by some geographers seems also to derive from an exaggeration of a reaction which is in itself healthy. When nature was introduced into geography and took precedence over the study of man, there was also a trend away from regional to systematic geography; indeed geography became a general science of the earth. The struggle against this tendency has been the main effort of our young years, and today there is hardly a single geographer who considers geology, meteorology, etc., as subdivisions of geography rather than as auxiliary sciences. However, now some of our colleagues want to exclude anything which goes beyond the investigation of individual countries or continents and deliver it to the representatives of the mentioned sciences. But how can the geographer take from geography the inspection of continents and of the whole earth's surface and exclude the large phenomena which are found over several continents? How can he renounce the comparative observation of phenomena which he has to investigate in each separate country and continent? If someone is capable of understanding the landforms, the climate, the vegetation of one country and finally of all countries of the world, why should he be incapable of a comparative view of the whole globe? Certainly, no one of us can fulfill these demands completely; but this difficulty is in the nature of things, and can in no way be removed. On the other hand, meteorology, botany, geology, cannot forthwith undertake geographical observations, because they lack full knowledge of those conditions which lie in other natural sciences, and primarily because they lack the geographical method. A book written by specialists will again turn general geography into a general science of the earth and miss the geographical aim. Without general geography, geography remains a *torso*.

One must always keep in mind that systematical geographical presentation has two tasks to fulfill: the study of the spread and distribution of various phenomena over the earth's surface and their interrelationships in one place. And it would be wrong to say that the first task belongs only to general geography, or that regional geography is exhausted in the second task. It was and is a bad methodological mistake if presentation of a continent traces individual geographical phenomena over the whole continent; then sometimes the individual sections could be identified clearly as excerpts from books on general geography. On the other hand, continuity is lost if one puts landscape beside landscape, locality beside locality, without integrating them with the neighborhood and the whole. I do not believe it is possible to master the subject otherwise than by steps descending from general geography or by a survey of the earth via continent, country, landscape or region, to the locality; how far one has to go, depends on the scope of the presentation. I beg you to pardon me, if I repeat this time and again; it is a basic rule of geographic doctrine. Only if one ignores the systematic approach which is permissible in many cases as a matter of course is it possible to follow another line of presentation. Needless to say, the breakdown of landscapes ought to be derived only from the subject itself. The organization of the subject according to states and political subdivisions completely disregards scientific behavior and springs only from regard of practical interests.

Only within the presentation of a region or a locality is the organization of factors important. The farther one goes in the organization of landscapes, the less the natural realms and their forms are separated, the less meaning has the problem of a "scheme", which has been exaggerated unnecessarily at present. If one writes for a definite purpose and does not take into account completeness of the presentation, it is possible to form the material; on the other hand a complete, systematic presentation will not be able to avoid a definite arrangement of factors and can vary only in detail. The samples which Spethmann gave in his *Dynamische Länderkunde* (*Dynamic Regional Geography*), prove only the fruitlessness of his attempt at reform.

The words *Dynamische Länderkunde* play in a variety of colors. In contradistinction to "static" it can only signify that not lasting conditions, but processes, should be treated in a regional geography. That makes clear how impossible it is. Only in some parts of geography, especially in climatology, can processes as such be observed directly and be presented; physiologists have long employed this method in place of a statistical one of presentation. In most parts of geography, especially in the concept of landform, the processes which of course have created every present form, can only be deduced from the present form and then only imperfectly.

If someone wants to start from the processes, he becomes immersed in an ocean of fog and loses sight of the present conditions, which after all are the main concern of geography. I apologize for saying it, but dynamic regional geography is an empty phrase.

The methodology of every science is a result of its historical development. It originates from experience but has to be examined and clarified by the general doctrine of scientific methods. Neither mere empirical work nor deductive derivative from a one-sided logic leads to the goal. Ideas are easily conceived and a paper or even a book full of resplendent concepts is quickly dashed off; however, if it is neither accompanied by attempts to carry through, nor tried out on the general doctrine of scientific methods, it is of little value for the progress of science. No applause of the multitude can dissimulate that. Of course, I do not want to advocate stagnation of our science; we both are convinced that our concepts can and need to be improved; we have always worked in this direction and accepted improvements by others thankfully. However, we and all serious geographers agree: not dashed-off opinions, only serious, tested work, and only works which are not born from one-sided points of view but originate from the whole body of our science and are directed towards the whole, will be to the credit of our science.

NORBERT KREBS (1876-1947)

Krebs is probably the best known representative of the so-called Vienna School, largely formed by Austrian geographers who studied during the years when Albrecht Penck was professor of geography in Vienna (1885-1906). However, the influence of French geographers and the French School of Regional Geography from Amy Boué and Malte Brun to E. de Martonne and E. de Margerie was more influential in Vienna than in the German universities. Krebs was the most important of the immediate disciples of Penck and later was his successor in the chair of geography at the University of Berlin. His own contributions are mainly in the field of geomorphology and regional geography and, as such, are beyond the scope of this book. However, as the following pages show, he was also a champion of painstaking accuracy in geographical research as a basis for and in connection with vivid description. In his stress on mathematical accuracy he followed Hermann Wagner(1) (1840-1929) to whom the following article is dedicated.

Measure and Number in Physical Geography[13]

Sometimes it is forgotten that geographic description is impossible without exact terrestial measurement, especially since cartography and geodesy became separate fields of knowledge and monopolized accurate mathematical work.

---

(1) Besides pioneering in this respect, Hermann Wagner is also of important in German geography as the author of a handbook which was the most used and most influential textbook for several generations of geography students. The relative uniformity of approach in teaching geographers was mainly the result of a common background in Wagner's handbook.

[13] Norbert Krebs, "Mass und Zahl in der physischen Geographie," in *Hermann Wagner Gedenkschrift: Ergebnisse und Aufgaben der Geographischen Forschung,* Ergänzungsheft Number 209 zu *Petermanns Mitteilungen,* Justus Perthes, Gotha, 1930.

Hermann Wagner represented an ideology which regarded measuring and computation in geography as more than external ornaments; he felt they had a higher value for the understanding and comparing of all geographical factors, whatever one's approach to this science. Actually, he who regards geography as a science of spaces has to prepare by studying geometrical factors and functions. We have to deal in geography with points, lines, areas, with configurations, circumferences, and content, with contact, overlapping, and intersection with forces which work from the center or the periphery. Whether we deal with coastal configuration or rainfall region, cultural landscapes or countries, geometrical problems will always arise. Regional geography will never be completely satisfied with description; it will produce the best and most perfect results by discovering relationships between one region and adjacent regions and their mutual influence. Opinions differ only as to whether we can be satisfied with general statements or whether exact numerical values are needed for which original computations have to be made. It is not a question of such obvious things as evaluation of geographical coordinates, distances, areas of countries, which have always served as auxiliary factors in comparisons. The question is whether more or less measuring should be used in morphometry and of the value of figures in climatology, where fashions alternated between too much and too little. When I started my studies, orometry played a relatively great role in all textbooks and in university teaching. Since Davis' deductions gained popularity, the use of exact figures has been almost totally rejected and all orometrical measuring has been considered a slow and time-wasting toy. This attitude certainly went too far and led the younger generation particularly to neglect accurate training in other respects also, a generation which had not learned exact measuring and was only defectively trained in drawing. Even such a cautious scholar as Alfred Hettner expressed himself unfavorably concerning morphometry, while on the other hand Köppen erected his system of climatic distribution completely on figures, mean values, and limits. . . . It should be investigated to see just how far the "old school" is still valid. From the outset, I should stress my agreement with Hettner's view that computed mean values have no practical use in nature and are rather leading away from our goal of comprehending the landscape and its elements. No doubt, formerly too many computations were made of things which were intrinsically unconnected with the goal of the research. However, these mistakes do not justify casting away the good with the bad and denying the value of good computations. Measure and number retain their value in modern geography.

Slope and relief-energy [14] are the firm basis for every classification of landscapes. Despite a voluminous morphographic literature the definition of basic terms is not agreed upon. We deal with them daily and hourly, but we have forgotten to conceive them as functions of height and slope. A few years ago, Obst [15] could raise the question, what is a mountain? In several recent textbooks no attempt is made to differentiate among a hill, a high plain, a plateau, or a sill. Only Passarge in his *Principles of Landscape Geography* (*Grundlagen der Landschaftskunde*) and in his small *Morphology* discusses these terms. However, he says in the first of these publications that "the uncertainty is very great, because one thinks of one value, another of another one." He himself, further, does not devise a classification which accounts for all three factors (absolute and relative elevation, and slope) but gives terms which refer to only one of them. No doubt, there has to be undertaken a sober, perhaps boring, but necessary work in this field. There is no wonder that in the face of all this uncertainty among scholars themselves, popular publications of wide appeal are found wanting or, what is worse, evoke wrong ideas.

CARL TROLL (1899-)

Troll is regarded as the most prominent living German geographer. Not only did he have the courage to assert openly his rejection of Hitlerism at a time when it was extremely

[14] In America usually called local relief.

[15] Erich Obst (1886-) is one of the better known, living German geographers.

dangerous to do so, but he also became the spokesman of German geography in the allied countries after the war, when many people were inclined to see German geography as an ally of Hitler through its involvement with geopolitics. In an article which was published in the *Annals of the Association of American Geographers* [16] he showed, among other things, that the majority of German geographers never followed the lead of geopolitics. As founder and editor of *Erdkunde,* the leading post-war German geographical periodical, Troll has remained the spokesman for German geography.

Troll began his professional life as a botanist and as a geographer has retained his interest in plant geography. He soon branched out into climatology and geomorphology, which led him into mountain geography, especially of the tropics. Extended field studies in the Andes, the volcanoes of East Africa, and as the scientific leader of the Nanga Parbat expedition in the Himalayas have provided him with a wide background. His travels led him to realize at an early date the possibilities of aerial photography in little-mapped countries, a recognition which was not very obvious to "Europe-bound" geographers used to working in well-mapped regions. The introduction and development of air photo interpretation owes much to him. The following translation is an abbreviated version of his philosophy of geography.

Geography and Landscape Research[17]

Occasionally geography is still considered a mere description of countries and enumeration of their mountains, waters, boundaries, settlements and products, as it used to be treated in the topographies of the 18th and even the early 19th century. For about a century, by enlarging its problems and methods, geography has grown to encompass a field which has no equal in breadth and comprehensiveness. The evolution of

[16] Troll, Carl, translated by Eric Fischer, *Annals of the Association of American Geographers,* vol. xxxix, June 1949.

[17] Carl Troll, "Geographie und Landschaftsforschung," Introduction to *Bonner Geographische Abhandlungen,* no. 1, pp. V-X, edited by the Geographiches Institut der Universität Bonn, Ludwig Rohrscheid Verlag, Bonn, 1947.

physical geography, which was made possible by the progress of the natural sciences in the 19th century, was followed by Fr. Ratzel's system of teaching cultural geography and anthropogeography. Probably, for a long time to come, it will be necessary to elaborate its structure. It proved to be very fruitful to center geographical attention upon the landscape and to investigate prehistorical and historical development of the natural landscape into the (present) economic and cultural landscape. The development of the cultural landscape can only be understood, if — besides the natural, physical and biological mutual relations, which we call landscape-ecology — economic and sociological processes and spiritual contacts also are considered and brought into accord with the results of the social and economic sciences. Present day geography took its intermediate position among natural, social, and economic sciences and tries to obtain its goal in close contact with the corresponding sciences and to understand the phenomena of the outer globe in their local diversity and causal, mutual connections. Therefore, geography fits into general trends of contemporary scientific thought without difficulty.

In modern research there is an extremely vital striving for a comprehensive, holistic landscape-research, and at the same time a striving for the utilization of this landscape research for national economy, landscape conservation and regional planning. Thereby, frequently and consciously boundaries of traditional disciplines are pierced. They have been maintained for the moment by the traditional practice of science as shown in the delimitations of university faculties and institutes, curricula and textbooks. However, in recent decades a far-reaching division into partial disciplines has occurred. The very problems and branches of science which are straddling the border between two basic sciences are in the center of attention today.

Among the daughter disciplines of modern landscape research are especially the following branches: *soil science* which investigates the dependency of weathered soils on rocks, climate, groundwater, vegetation, and human agriculture; *geomorphology*, or the doctrine of the surface forms of the earth, through which the phenomena of the geological structure are integrated into the landscape; *topographical plant geography* which fosters mapping of vegetation; *plant sociology,* the doctrine of plant associations and their development in succession series; *biocenology,* which tries to comprehend plant- and animal-life in their mutual dependency and harmony as units of life; *microstratigraphy* and *micropalaeontology,* which, primarily by the use of pollen-analysis and the present distribution of plants and animals, tries to clarify the history of the recent, glacial and postglacial landscape; *micro-, soil-* and *agro-climatology* which study the climatological conditions in the lowest layers of the air, in the vegetation cover, on the surface of the soil, i.e., the climate effective for the vegetation; *hydrology* and the *doctrine of the water balance,* which do research on the water, the hydrological cycle, and also on the balance of water as the basis for our water supply; *limnology* which occupies itself with physics, chemistry and biology of the water bodies on the land surface and which was the starting point for biocenology; and *agro-ecology, forest-ecology,* and *agro-geography* which convey the understanding of the natural conditions for agricultural and silvicultural use as they change from place to place. The very cooperation of all these branches of science leads to research on natural landscapes, to a landscape-ecology. The most recent research tool for such a holistic *landscape-ecology* is air photography, or more accurately, the scientific interpretation of the picture of a uniform landscape as it appears on an air photo or a photo-mosaic-map. The great successes of air photo-research for forestry, soil science, plant geography, recognition of mineral bodies and archæology are based on the fact that in an air-photo, not the individual features of the landscape, but a composite of vegetation is visible. From the spatial-topographical structure of the vegetation emerges the locational variation of the individual components of the landscape.

The special contribution of geography to all these branches of science is the understanding of the locational differentiation of natural phenomena. The best starting point is offered by geomorphology and vegetation geography. Geography also contributes the transition from the partial geographical sciences to the social science by way of an indisputable characterization and delimitation of the natural landscapes within countries. The practical-scientific importance of such a landscape-science primarily affects three areas: agriculture, forestry, and water management.

Agricultural land use and distribution of crop types has heretofore been considered by agricultural science either by starting from the individual farm, employing the theory of agricultural administration, or by statistical surveys, using administrative units (counties, communities, etc.) as a starting point. The true pattern of distribution, the arrangement and structure of the agricultural landscape, can only be understood, however, if in addition to the economic ties, the equally important ecological ties to the various locations are also taken into consideration. It is the goal of agro-ecology and agricultural geography to observe and map agriculturally-used surfaces, as it has been done for about two decades. For the many-sided agricultural landscapes of the land Nordrhein-Westphalen, such a contiguous mapping of utilized surfaces was only recently started.

Present-day forestry can not be imagined without a soil science related to forestry, a vegetation science related to forestry, and a microclimatology which, indeed, originated from forestry. Appraisal of forest values can not be considered any more without air photography. Forest conservation, which has to look far ahead, has to look for natural associations that are the smallest units of the landscape, the biotope of the biologists. This has to be done even more in this case than for agricultural land use. It is not by chance that the best research products in the British Empire concerning landscape research and land classification have grown in recent times out of air photo research on forests in Burma, Rhodesia, and England.

Water management is affected similarly. Its geographical exploration assumes increasing importance in the highly developed countries as the water supply is more extensively utilized economically and as a growing population and industrialization consume, or at least use, water through more intensive agriculture and through electric powerworks, and as artificial waterways are added to the water cycle. Hydrology can no longer progress in regional research without looking to soil science, vegetation research, agricultural and forest ecology. It has to base its calculations on natural landscapes. . . .

Finally, landscape research has to be used for questions of regional history. For a long time our landscapes have not been natural landscapes, but have been changed into cultural landscapes through the influence of peoples and civilizations, a process that has lasted through millenia. But they are subject also to progressive changes. The present (integrated) landscape structure and the present (individual) landscape can not be understood from the present alone, but only with the background of historical development. In order to understand these changes better, ecological landscape research is indispensable to a physical geographical total view. In such historical studies of landscape, the experience has been repeated time and again that, with increasing land use, natural landscape boundaries are not blurred; indeed, the natural differences of landscapes often are stressed by agricultural specialization which was made possible by modern transportation. Thus landscape ecology has the task of widening the understanding of the landscape of our homeland and its changeability for the prehistorian, the settlement historian, the economic historian, and in part even to the historian of art.

HANS BOBEK (1903-)

European — and especially German, French, Polish, and Austrian — geography suffered grievous losses during World War II. Many younger scholars died either in the armies, or as victims of Nazi persecution, such as Ancel of France and the younger Albrecht Haushofer; a few emigrated and others were discredited and excluded from the universities after the war. Fortunately, several of the older generation, already elderly men and well known for their accomplishments, not only survived the war but continued their work to a ripe old age. In that way the loss of a generation was partly bridged, and a few promising young geographers have appeared in the years since 1946. Also in each of these countries a few young geographers survived the war unscathed and were able to carry on. Among them is Bobek who after having spent his formative years mainly in Germany has returned to his native Austria as professor of physical geography. The excerpts from the following article, show his wider interests. His co-author, Josef Schmithüsen is teaching at the University of Saarbrücken.

The Landscape in a Logical System of Geography[18]

I. The subject of geographical research is the litho-bio-atmospherical space on the surface of the earth in its entire endowment and formation — both in its individual regions and as a whole. Geography does not restrict itself to the description and determination of the visible, although it starts from it. On the contrary it tries to perceive the essence of all the parts of this sphere, which we call for short "the surface of the earth," although this is actually wrong.

To the essence of a region on the surface of the earth in this sense pertain:

A. Its perceptible material and spatial appearance or more accurately its size, form, material quality, internal articulation or structure.

B. The acting structure which is its basis and is accessible to immediate observation only in its smallest part. It can have its origin also outside and, therefore, include spatial and positional designations.

C. The historical development, which leads to the present phenomenon and beyond into the future and through which forms may be inherited, can not be explained through the present dynamics. It is the sum total and the result of the acting forces of the past.

To perceive the essence of such a partial area of the entire surface of the earth is to explain it.

Taken as objects of geographical research, the regions of the surface of the earth should not be perceived three-dimensionally as spatial formations of only immediate import, but

---

[18] Hans Bobek and Josef Schmithüsen, "Die Landschaft im logischen System der Georgraphie", *Erdkunde*, vol. III, no. 2/3, 1949, pp. 112–120.

four-dimensionally as spatial-temporal phenomena-wholes, formations or shapes. As a whole as well as in their individual essential elements they constitute the "geographical substance." Three different domains of existence participate in their structure and formation:

1. the inorganic world,
2. the biological world,
3. the cultural world, i.e., mankind and his works.

Different types of determinism prevail in the functions and phenomena of these three domains, namely:

1. physical causality,
2. biological "determinism" which, so far, is not certain to be a part of physical causality,
3. the internal determinism of culturally oriented beings, especially when in society.

A complex ("geographical") determinism and a difficulty in perceiving fully the quality of geographical objects are apparent through all of these categories.

Within the inorganic world, that is, the landforms are the result of combined forces of tectonics, atmospheric forces and the material of the crust; but these forces may not be only the presently active ones; the landform may be inherited from combined landforms of the past. In addition, they may be shaped also by such human action as forest destruction, lowering of the watertable, diversion of a river, etc.

In any biological association, e.g., that of a forest, not only are the conditions which are created by the physical environment important, but also those which have been caused by the biological association itself as an entity of a higher order. The factors of biological nature, which so far could not be explained by physical causality, further condition the environment.

The conditioning factors are present also in man as a physical being. Further, according to his stage of development, in varying degrees man is dependent on the sum of effects originated by the inorganic and biological world. Man, by the force of his spirit, is capable, by himself, of interfering productively with the structure of the surface of the earth creating, at least partially, his environment himself and creating objects which, however determined as matter by physical and biological factors, are autonomous creations of the human spirit.

Therefore geographical objects are created not only by the fact that components of all three spheres combine or even mutually interpenetrate spatially, but because a very real integration occurs. This means that by the collective action of the heterogeneous fields of action new products emerge which belong to two or all three spheres at the same time and participate in their particular determinism. In particular, cultural phenomena are not simply superimposed over natural elements or just added by summation, as appears to be the case in some presentations. Quite the opposite, nature and culture are integrated indissolubly in many primary geographical objects, such as every agricultural or silvicultural area and every settlement. In the main, the formative forces of all three spheres do not operate independently, but are interwoven from their origin in their mutual effects and connected with each other in complicated spheres of action.

II. Organic and inorganic nature and spirit are melted together in the geographical substance. That is the cause of the intimate unity of geography and the fact that it can neither be natural science nor social science. It has to unite the methods of both in itself if it is to do justice to the explanation of its objects. Seen from the objective (of geography), dualism in the older, often-quoted meaning, does not exist; however there is a tripartite division relative to the applicable determinisms which have to be used for explanation.

On the other hand, dualism exists in the method, if its goal is taken into consideration; idiographical and normative methods are equally justified in geography. Upon this fact is based the difference between regional methods and methods based on the doctrine of landscapes.

Regional geography considers and evaluates a geographical object idiographically, i.e., as something unique in time and space. The geographical object that is conceived in this way, individually, as unique form, is called a *land* (country, region). What makes a part of the surface of the earth into a region in this sense are its specific location and its special historical situation. It is possible to speak of its fateful location and of its individual fate in time. The regional concept as such is independent of size and may refer to the whole surface of the earth, to continents, their parts down to the smallest units at the lowest limit of the geographical scale, and to localities.

As landscape research we designate the normative method which, in contrast, arranges the parts of the surface of the earth into species or types respectively. It neglects consciously the unique within the object in order to put into relief the regular in its phenomenon, structure, and historical development. Such a spatial unit in scientific geography is called a landscape; this concept is also independent of scale.

Whether we speak of region or landscape, it is always a piece of the surface of the earth in all the complexity of its phenomena.

III. (omitted)

IV. If we observe the different elements of a landscape and the manner and kind in which they combine into partial structures and gradually integrate to the complete structure of a landscape, we recognize, first of all, that basic tripartite articulation which is caused by the different kinds of prevailing determination. The inorganic world, the organic world and the spiritually determined world of man stand side by side.

But their attitude toward space allows only a dichotomy which is of the highest importance for the later composition of the landscape.

The inorganic and biological components are completely, or to a high degree, determined on the basis of their fundamental causality in relation to their spatial arrangement or their habitat.

On the other side is man, primarily determined spiritually, and his creations which are largely autonomous in their spatial distribution.

The actual landscape grows through the combination of both groups. This gradual integration is shown in the following table.

Inorganic world	Biological world	Spiritual order and biological determinism
Physical causality	Biological determinism	Spiritually determined world
Spatial determinism		Ordered distribution in space

Landscape and parts of landscapes, respectively

Geographical character		Societies (localized social combines)
Local non-biological combined units	Biocenoses	Human groups
Non-biological individual phenomena and partial units	Biological elements	Humans

Some of these terms have to be explained.

The non-biological individual phenomena and partial units.—In the inorganic sphere, the geographical interest does not extend to the elements, but stops at greatly compounded systems and complexes which, however, in the life of the landscape play the role of elementary units: e.g., air is such a complicated system which plays the role of an elementary unit.

The biological elements.—Contrary to the inorganic individual phenomena and partial units, individuals of the organic sphere can be regarded as genuine elementary units in relation to the landscape into which they enter as parts of it. Being organisms, they are genuine wholes, closed integrations. Therefore, the individuals of the organic world are basically different from the inorganic sphere. They are determined not only by the causative happenings of their environment, but partially from principles of development, the ultimate regularity of which research has not yet been able to discover.

Living beings are not just a product of their environment. They are opposite to it to a certain degree as subjects, without being really autonomous, because, as ecological-biological research has shown, they adapt themselves to the conditions of the given environment. The biological types (biotypes) are adapted to their habitat (biotopes). That is true also for man on its lowest cultural level, as long as he does not rise over the purely biological life by spiritually determined products.

The biocenoses.—The biocenoses are the associations of organisms living at the same place. Biocenoses are biological units of a higher order, i.e., relationships which have properties not to be found in the participating elements as such, and in which the individual members influence each other, even if sometimes only indirectly. The unity of the biocoenoses (unity in manifoldness) is created through the common adaptation of several animal and plant species into the same non-biological whole, also by direct influence of one organism upon another organism and through indirect effects via biologically created (in the process of life) changes of the outer conditions of living, and finally by purely biological determinisms that lead to a certain harmony, i.e., to an equilibrium in the whole of the biocenosis. Relative to the structure of the landscape, the biocenoses are a more advanced degree of integration than the biotic individuals of which they are built. But they are less integrated within themselves. Biocenoses are not organisms, not genuine wholes, but only communities of wholes in a partially self-created environment. In biocoenoses, members are exchangeable and can partially move out, e.g., higher animals which change their habitat without destroying the biocoenosis. The lower degree of integration shows up also through the fact that automatic regulation does not have the same importance with biocoenoses as with individual organisms. There exist such phenomena in the biocoenoses, as the regeneration of destroyed parts by resettlement processes or succession, or new formation of the characteristic soil, water economy, etc. But if an animal species emigrates or a plant species dies out on a place, the respective biocoenosis never can regenerate its totality of species by itself.

The biocenosis is influenced by the non-biological local complex of its habitat. It has adapted itself to it and has developed with it. But it is not its products or necessary conclusion.

HERMANN LAUTENSACH (1886-)

One of the leading geographers of Germany. He is best known as the foremost expert on the Iberian Peninsula, even considering the Iberian geographers of Spain and Portugal. Lautensach has published studies on every aspect of Iberian geography from place names to morphology. He also thoroughly studied Korea, in the field as well as from the literature. From the detailed study of these two peninsular regions he has formulated his theory of regular changes which is not meant to be a physical law, but a practical methodology. As such it has influenced several German geographers of the post-war generation. The parts translated here convey the essence of the theory of regular changes.

Variation of Geographical Forms: Studies for a System of Landscapes[19]

In recent decades reforming ideas have been brought to the study of geography repeatedly. The revolutionary ones among them did not exert a deep impact because they opposed the existing research system only with sharp reproach and blunt rejection. Evolutionary suggestions and countersuggestions which recognize the given trend and try to divert it into a new direction have been of great influence time and again for the development of our science, which needs such suggestions more often than some other sciences whose characters are not questioned for long periods at a time. The work of Hartshorne shows that they have also been considered in other countries.

Methodological discussions require, of course, completely exact and clear definitions of terms, the same as research in the subject. However, such definitions are seldom made. I am putting the definitions first. They are derived, to a large degree, from the system of Bobek and Schmithüsen.

---

[19] Hermann Lautensach, *Der geographische Formenwandel: Studien zur Landschaftssystematik.* Colloquium Geographicum: Lectures at the Geographical Colloquium in Bonn in memory of Ferdinand von Richthofen. Vol. 3. Ferd. Dümmlers Verlag, Bonn, 1952, p. 3-7, 179-181.

Geographical substance: all geographical material that can be perceived physiognomically on the surface of the earth or on parts of it, regardless of whether its constituent parts belong to the inorganic world, the biologic one, or the cultural.

Geographical form (geographical phenomenon): every part of the geographical substance including its material, therefore not just the geomorphological form. The term form is used because it is shorter than the frequently used word geofactor. The term geographical phenomenon is applicable especially for geographical forms expressed in movements, e.g., traffic, fishing, movement of air or water.

Geographical area: part of the surface of the earth of any size, regardless of the point of view from which its geographical substance is inspected.

Geographical region: The area of distribution of the individual geographical forms of phenomena.

Geographical character: The whole entity of all inorganic and biological, but not cultural, forms united within the same area.

Land: Individual space of any size, perceived idiographically as an organic unit, in all the complexity of all its geographical forms and phenomena.

Landscape: Type of space, in the complexity of its geographical forms and phenomena, as far as they are regular, and of any size.

The geographical substance of the entire dry surface of the earth constitutes a continuum (an uninterrupted unit), as Schmitthenner has stressed recently. The same applies, without counting the relatively small water surfaces within the continents, to the geographical substance of the liquid surface of the earth. The seashore is perceived at the same scale as these two spatial groups, a linear border between the two basic forms of the geographical substance. In this study, we confine ourself almost exclusively to the continents. On the continents the structure of any chosen space (of a small space in the beginning) has a definite order. It originates with the interrelationships of the inorganic, biological and cultural worlds. In an adjoining area, the combination and structure of the geographical substance is changed. But this variation is not so much an individual change, as it is an exhibition of a definite regularity. *Thus I understand variation of geographical forms (Formenwandel) to be the definable changing of the geographical substance in space to the extent that it appears as a continuum.*

Up to now too much attention has been paid to the different development of the geographical substance in different areas. This point of view put area wholes in sharp opposition to others, e.g., "natural continents," landscape wholes, and "landscape belts." Thereby the idea was fostered that the basic features of the geographical substance within each were developed in the same way. Often too little attention was paid, e.g., by Passarge, to the fact that regular changes also occur in definite directions within the larger areas studied, and therefore the development of the geographical substance, e.g., along southern and northern borders, is very different and is much closer to the adjacent areas beyond the respective borders. Here the attempt is made *to view the continuum as changing, now faster, now slower, but regularly in fixed directions, as it offers itself to the unbiased observer, and to construct in most cases a system based on this mode of observation.*

Therefore, the term "variation of forms" is restricted to regular spatial variations. True, the regular variation in space cannot be understood by a dynamic observation of the *present.*

The structure of the substance of every area is rooted largely in its *past* and therefore is in need of genetic investigation too. Thus *time* enters the investigation. Dynamic and genetic investigation have to interpenetrate each other if one is to understand the variation of forms of the substance. Nevertheless, I do not want to join Winkler and Bobek and Schmithüsen in designating geography a space-time-matter-science. The same could be said of history, with only a slight change of the accent. Temporal consideration enters every natural or social science which deals with growing or grown things. As it is for most geographers, geography is to me knowledge of the present.

The structure of the variation of form of every area is a function of its geographical location. . . . The basic locational types for a systematic arrangement of the landscapes of the entire surface of the earth are the following: 1. the *planetary location*, i.e., the location in regard to the degrees of latitude, 2. the location within the continents or oceans, i.e., either a *peripheral* or *central location*, 3. the *easterly* or *westerly location* within the continents or oceans, 4. finally, within the location, regarding the relief, which we can call the *hypsometric*, a term which was used frequently by A. v. Humboldt. These four locational types constitute a suitable basis for explaining the individual forms and phenomena as well as their causative forces and actions, which by their cooperation give the imprint of the surface of the earth to the landscapes, and they allow, therefore, the interpretation of the regular part of the substance of each area.

The concept of location stimulates the comparison of the geographical substance of an area with that of the adjacent areas. Let us imagine a series of points at sea level ordered from the Arctic along a meridian, and let us register the mean yearly temperatures or monthly temperatures of each point; we shall establish an increase to the thermal equator and then again a decrease. If we observe a series of points aligned from the periphery toward the center of any continent outside the central tropics, an increase of the annual range of the temperature will appear. If in the middle latitudes, if you draw a cross section from west to east through the continents, it becomes obvious that in the areas of western coastal lands winters are cooler and summers warmer than in the areas along the east coasts. Areas of increasing elevation present a decrease in temperature uphill. What is true for mean values of temperature is true also for the mean values of other meteorological elements in space as they are integrated with each other on the earth's surface; that applies to the annual averages as well as to the seasonal and follows definite rules. Briefly, *the climatic conditions of the whole surface of the earth can be perceived in their basic traits under these four categories of continuous spatial variation. They constitute, therefore, in their regular features a composite picture combined from the pictures of the individual categories.* Every landscape has definite regular climatic features according to its location, considered under these points of view.

Therefore, categories, according to my definition, are the four directions in which forms vary. . . .

On the continents, climate and the biological and non-biological components of the landscape which are partially climatically caused have corresponding regular variations, especially the climatically conditioned forms of relief, soil types, water, plant associations, and ecological communities of animals. Not only typical conditions, but also the modifications of the nature of the area (Passarge) can be perceived in this type of observation.

The great surface forms of tectonic origin, the rocks and soil types, of course, can not be fitted into such a system smoothly. Correctly, Hettner time and again stressed that the main features of climate and relief are two completely independent groups of facts. But at this point it must be emphasized explicitly that the concept of variation of forms is not restricted to the climatic sphere and to the phenomena depending on it. The doctrine of the variation of forms is not a climatically based science of landscapes. All phenomena are subsumed among the four categories which are changing regularly with the change of one of them, regardless of whether there exists a causal relation or not. I am speaking only of regular changes (definable, not capricious), not of those subjected to a strict law. The phenomena are comprehended first according to formal, physiognomic criteria and not according to causal criteria. Within an area subjected to investigation by the categories of the variation of forms, the geological structure may change regularly, parallel to one of the categories of climatic change. For the application of the idea of variation of forms it is irrelevant that no primary causal connection exists between these two changes. The causal relations appear immediately in those phenomena which depend on climate as well as on rock types, e.g., soils and natural vegetation.

Many forms of cultural regions fit the character of the area very well. . . . In interpreting any form or phenomenon of the cultural region, therefore, as well as those forms which are subject to the variations of forms, only the social principle of empathy of the basic phenomena is meant, an interpretation by different types of motivation according to W. Wundt, not the principle of the natural sciences of physical determinism. The time is gone when chorological dependencies were derived simply by a logical short circuit from the local coincidence of phenomena. . . .

The system, as it is here developed, serves the coinage of terms for types of landscapes. Instead of speaking of variation of forms it would be possible to speak of variation of landscapes and introduce a term which has been used before by Passarge with the connotation of planetary variation of the natural landscape. If I prefer the first term, I do so only in order to stress emphatically that the four categories of areal change have to be defined with the help of regular synchoric [20] changes of the individual forms. The term doctrine of landscape, in my opinion, should remain reserved for Passarge's system. It is to be regretted that this clear expression was watered down by later authors. Many speak of "regional and landscape geography" and have in mind only the geography of large and small areas. In opposition to the systems of Passarge and of Obst, my system is not derived from a classificatory order of ideal types (classes, orders, families, etc.) but from the regular variation of the geographical substance

[20] Synchoric=at the same place.

in space. That is a fundamentally different point of view, and its consequences extend into the minutest details.

There is the final question of how the doctrine of the variation of forms can be integrated into the general system of pure or scientific geography. The following system constitutes the logical order of consecutive operations which in the presentation should not always be treated in separate chapters. . . .

The first stage is the *isolation of the geographical substance from the entirety of facts given in the different regions of the surface of the earth.* At this stage, as Ritter says, the observation of the whole offers us the scale for the parts. On this preliminary stage the forms and phenomena of the geographical substance are collected and described. Personal intensive travel over the selected area, collection of official sources, such as maps and statistics, as well as an accurate study of the literature forms the fundament. The travel serves not only for an intensive familiarisation with the area, but most importantly for a critical check of the data in the literature and the emendation of gaps in the perception of the geographical substance. In geographically little known countries travel observations will have to provide the main body of the total material.

The second stage is the *topical investigation of the different groups of geographical phenomena in the individual areas.* The type of development and the distribution of the different forms and phenomena is presented in textual and cartographic form. In genetical research the processes, in dynamic research the forces, are isolated on the basis of the individual forms and phenomena and their distribution. This results in the production of topical regional monographs, such as a climatic geography of the Iberian Peninsula,[21] a plant geography of Anatolia, or a cultural geography of China, etc. In such monographs it will become obvious which features of the geographical substance can be described under the four categories of the variations of forms and which escape such a treatment and constitute individual characteristics of the area. . . . It would be worth while to reinterpret the concepts

[21] Lautensach published such a monograph.

of type and individuum from the point of view of this book. Indeed, in the question of what is to be regarded as typical and what unique there will always be a certain margin which has to be decided subjectively. Of course, it can not be expected that monographs will be published on all topics of all regions. But geographical country atlases, such as the *Atlas des Deutschen Lebensraums* or the *Atlas de France,* for as many regions as possible would give a basis the value of which can not be overestimated for the next stages of geographical research.

The first two stages create the basis for the third stage, the special or regional doctrine of the variation of forms. It uses all results of the second stage for elaboration on the variation of forms in the individual areas. They are analysed as in the examples [22] according to the four categories. The main result is a comprehensive view of the character of the variation of forms in the investigated areas; an additional result is their arrangement into landscapes. . . . Following such an analysis of the variation of forms, a synthesis is easy. It consists of determining the phase of each category and elucidating the effect of its interference for each topic. Thus the typical character of every landscape and its position relative to all the landscapes of the region is found. . . .

The fourth stage contains a regional and a general division. In the regional division the landscapes which have been separated at the third stage and synthetically characterized are named, of course with proper regard for the national usage. Thereby every landscape is marked as a *land.* The problem has been carefully weighed as to how far the landscapes developed by the method of the variation of forms are coincident with the locally used designations. Its consideration may furnish valuable clues for regional geography. Then, on the basis of the defined position of each of these small countries, its individual character is evolved. The completion of a regional geography is the elaboration of the individual features of the total area on the basis of all preceding results. In working on a regional geography one has first to pass through

[22] The examples are omitted here.

stages one to three. The presentation can start with stage two. Therefore, a complete regional monography consists of five chapters, each based upon the preceding one: 1. Presentation of the causation of the forms and phenomena of the topical material of the whole area accompanied by analytical maps. 2. Analysis of the variation of forms. 3. Synthesis of the variation of forms. 4. Regional treatment of the areas defined by the method of variation of forms. 5. Presentation of the regional character of the total area.

In recent decades general geography, under the influence of Hettner, was usually defined as regional geography of the whole globe. This way a *geographia universalis* was put beside the *geographia generalis*. That was correct in order to emphasize that general geography ought to perceive its problems under the point of view of the orderly development of forms and development over the whole globe, and not only under that of the classificatory formation of types of the topical material. From the point of view of the doctrine of the variation of forms, which makes a sharp distinction between landscape and land, type and individuum, this concept can be tolerated only insofar as type and individuum become the same in this largest possible area of geographical research.

CHAPTER 7

GERMAN GEOGRAPHY: THE DISSENTERS

German geography had its brilliant, classical period in the last third of the 19th century. The geographers of the 20th century were able to build on a solid basis, and they accomplished results in no way inferior to those of their world-renowned predecessors. However, it is perhaps a sign of the vigor of German geography that there was also room for men who went their own ways and strove for new solutions. Whether their work was accepted by their contemporaries was not the main criterion; that of Haushofer and his school, for example, has been widely rejected. Nevertheless he and men like Passarge, Banse, and Spethmann had influence inside and outside of Germany. The same is true for an earlier predecessor, Gerlach. All of these men did some solid, generally accepted research. The opposition to them might be partly explained by the novelty of their ideas and partly by personal traits, especially in the case of Banse, but largely by their mixing of political with scientific aims. In the end the geographers who followed the mainstream of geographical development remained the representatives of German geographical thought.

The ideas of Haushofer, Passarge, Spethmann and Banse were significant variations from the mainstream of German geography, but none of them has been continued to the extent of altering traditional geographic thought. The fifth man included in this chapter, Christaller, is probably the most significant of the "Dissenters", because his ideas have been studied and further developed by succeeding generations of geographers. Most of the new trends in theoretical geography show the influence of Christaller's work.

KARL HAUSHOFER (1869-1946)

Haushofer was the most important geopolitician of Germany — or anywhere. Although preceded by Kjellén, he was primarily responsible for the separation of geopolitics from political geography. (According to Haushofer, geopolitics is more than a science: it is the art of applying geographical knowledge in politics.) In addition to Kjellén, Ratzel and Mackinder furnished him with some of his basic concepts, though he developed them to a greater extent than had his predecessors. Expanding on Ratzel's concept, he regarded the state unequivocally as a living organism. Similarly, he carried Mackinder's "heartland" theory to practical conclusions in attempting to influence Germany's political and military attitudes toward Russia.

Haushofer was an officer in the Bavarian contingent of the German Army, where he received a less militaristic outlook than the prevailing Prussian tradition impressed upon the average German officer. However, he far surpassed his fellow officers in his serious interest in science, especially geography, and in his artistic talents. His appointment as military attaché to Tokyo and his leisurely voyage to that post led to a lasting interest in East Asia and to his writing a book on Japan, probably one of the best and the least controversial of his books. Although he certainly had some influence upon Hitler through his student, Rudolf Hess, the amount of this influence was vastly exaggerated during the war years. With Germany's collapse in 1945, his influence in Germany ceased completely. Haushofer committed suicide. Outside Germany geopolitical schools — Ancel in France, Walsh in America — have carried on, of course without the German bias.

Geopolitics of the Pacific Ocean[1]

How few realized the *value of the wide spaces*[2] and their

---

[1] *Geopolitik des Pazifischen Ozeans,* Karl Haushofer. 2nd edition, Kurt Vowinkel, Berlin-Grunewald 1924. Pp. 320-344.

[2] No attempt has been made to render Haushofer's sentences literally. Haushofer's language is so involved, opaque, and vague, that the meaning of many sentences, even in the German original, often has to be guessed. Poetic and allegoric expressions abound.

regenerating power and broadening force for the world concept of Germans, who come out of restricted spaces. . . . We did not recognize the sea as a source of greatness of nations at the right time, although Ratzel had shown it to us and Richthofen had held it as an example before our eyes, admonishing us to study Japan, when he depicted the early and the mature stages of island empires. We want, first of all, to redress this fault and create the basis from which first some individuals and later many can start out into the wide world with open eyes and safe knowledge that they are able to undertake the great adventure, backed by well-founded knowledge and not starting in ignorance. . . . Primarily we are concerned that the leaders, and later also the great masses, recognize again the conditions for the existence of sea-girdling power which can be recognized in their purest form in the Pacific in the form of cultural and economic bodies. The preliminary conditions for such an understanding lie, of course, in penetrating the very way of life of oceanic nations, of island nations, and island empires. This means that we must become familiar with foreign ways of life, starting with that of oceanic nations. This understanding is indispensable to the foreign policy of landlocked countries.

In this area of Pacific imponderables of political sentiment, there are pacific types of patriotism and of the concept of power which can be recognized by geopolitical methods — perhaps in the manner in which E. Demolins treated the European types in their regional aspects. Would this perhaps be a synthesis, an integration of the Anglo-Saxon ideal of life — which is based on the concept of wide spaces, but is nevertheless concerned with the independence of the private existence — with the most ancient cultural traditions of the human concentrations of south-eastern Asia, and their prototypes of growth which so often appear impersonal to the western mind? Might there even be an ingredient of German state theory, for example, in Japan? The result of all our work up to now answers this question in the affirmative. . . .

The reader who has followed us so far will be able to find without any further difficulty countries which react like manometers or seismographs all over the Pacific area:

(1) Such indicators exist in their most explicit development in the ways of life within the Australo-Asiatic island-arcs and tension-belt: Japan, Philippine Islands and Australia;

(2) Some areas especially sensitive to happenings far away exist along the borders of the great continents which are only weakly influenced by Pacific occurrences, i.e., the drainage divides between Eurasia and the monsoon areas and the Pacific drainage divide of America;

(3) Indicators also exist in areas of political growth. Referring to the first point, we want to make clear an additional distinction of countries acting as indicators because they are themselves under pressure. They may either collapse under the pressure, or withstand it and overcome it finally. Other countries may be observed which are like seismographs. They react very sensitively to changes in political pressure upon other places — near or far away — and indicate them accurately. These countries need not be under direct pressure themselves; because of their sensitivity, if put under pressure they might break or explode immediately. . . . We consider different political formations as primary indicators of political pressure — all within the same grand physical environment of the great island arcs. Some examples are, on the one hand, the proud island empire of Dai Nihon (Japan), which never was trod by an invading enemy; on the other side the Philippines, the rich political unit, which of all in Eastern Asia, even in the entire Pacific area, has been deprived longest of its self-determination, but nevertheless has proved its right to lead a life of its own; and there is finally the Commonwealth of Australia, the most important Anglo-Saxon adaptation to Pacific conditions.

In order to recognize the Pacific influence upon remote areas, we might choose profitably such regions where Pacific influence fades out into other spaces. . . .

Among the autochthonous, national, pure civilizations of the Pacific only Japan remained untouched by Atlantic and continental influences, at least outwardly in its way of life, which is bound to its soil; perhaps we may add the tiny island kingdom of Tonga (Friendly Islands), at least as far as its internal organization is concerned. Japan, alone, is, therefore, capable of serving as a pressure gauge which, up to now, has remained free from foreign oppression. The heaviest, most prolonged pressure was weighing down upon the adjacent area of the Philippines. In these two island countries, therefore, the greatest political contrasts almost touch each other; and other influences, radiating from a distance, are added, originating from the most powerful island empires[3] and bulkiest continental powers.[4] Because of these circumstances, the value of the problems of the Japanese state as a pressure gauge should be without rival; its sensitivity to distant influences, which is raised almost to a telepathic marvel, is practically unequalled in sensing even potential dangers to its self-determination; equal is its enviable capacity to subordinate all other vital activities to the preservation of its self-determination in every case in which it senses such dangers. . . .

* * *

. . . The geopolitical pressure gauge of the Philippines presupposes a totally different construction, located as it is at the point in the Pacific which is most under pressure. This geopolitical body is under the heaviest pressure and not, like Japan, just near it. It suffers by it, it reacts to it, but nevertheless it is able to preserve the capacity to indicate the degree of the experienced pressure. . . . In the midst of all these conditions, the value of the Philippines lies in its position as an especially tried instrument, a pressure gauge for all Pacific tensions, which is shown in its internal conditions, its public opinion, and its armed or passive resistance.

The Philippines have value for the recognition of pan-Asiatic pressure conditions and the psychology of peoples because of their exposed focal location; this value has not been recognized so far in international relations and laws. They are located at the point of contact of the Malayan cultural region with both the Chinese and the Malayo-Mongolian-Japanese regions; at the most important bridge link between

[3] Great Britain.

[4] The U. S. A. and China.

the northern and southern parts of the Eastern Asian island arcs; at the only part of the ancient East Asian cultural realm which is ruled by racially foreign elements which extend from the New World across the wide ocean. Geopolitically, i.e., by their soil, climate, race, and settlement, they are oriented toward Southeast Asia but necessarily must look toward the Anglo-Saxon world in questions of power, international communications, and economic problems. They stand against the secular power of the Church, but are distinctly Catholic, and they are most closely related to Spanish speaking South America culturally. They have developed into a connecting link in international Southeast Asian organizations, embracing all the essentially related countries of the monsoon region — first in respect to legal protection — and have become important standard-bearers of the idea of To-A (East Asia) and of pan-Asian ideals (Asia for the Asians). The Asian Society for Legal Protection received its strongest impulses from the Philippines. It met first in Manila in 1919, in Tokyo in 1920, and in Shanghai in 1921. . . .

We must always watch the microcosm of the Australian-New Zealand power area as a third geopolitical indicator for the Pacific areas; it turned its back — the sparsely settled spaces — toward the main areas of disturbance; and, by the same token, it is remote from the genuine cultural centers of this region. Its social egotism can be explained convincingly in geopolitical terms by its geographical location, its center of population gravity turned away from the other Pacific areas, its ecumenic security belt, and its colonial, historical past; but it cannot be explained either by morphological causes alone or by political motives, emanating from human will. This has been shown when the center of gravity of population of Australia was so carefully determined, when the scientifically and biologically best location for the federal capital was investigated. This process demonstrates the great difference of a scientific approach to geopolitical problems with biological methods in the Pacific sphere of life, in contrast to western, Eurasian methods; it shows also the advantages of their scientific method, namely, the freedom from passions and from presentiment,[5] but also the absolute impossibility of proceeding the same way as was possible in Australia in areas encumbered with old traditions.

* * *

Finally, it would also be possible to use the manifold types of colonial outposts because it is quite obvious that they reflect both the pressure and vitality of the political organisms which sent them out and of those into which they intrude.

The characteristic trait of such overseas outposts is their location beyond an uninhabitable stretch, oceanic or anecoumenic, on the opposite shore of the area of their biological origin or where they get their lifeblood. If we consider such outposts as pressure gauges on a small scale, whether they are harbor colonies, trading posts, or naval bases it is impossible to arrange them according to their degree of vitality. We have perhaps to distinguish: 1. burnt out, passive, or immured places (Deshima near Nagasaki,[6] Malacca,[7] Port Arthur [8]) ; 2. stagnant or retrograde outposts (Macao,[9] Vladivostok,[10] Weihaiwei [11]) ; 3. and the rare neutralized or latent outposts (perhaps Shanghai or Tsingtau [12]) ; 4. growing out-

---

[5] The Australian Capital Territory was chosen as the seat of the federal government after prolonged discussions in 1908 and acquired in 1911. The discussion was not purely scientific, but marred by the conflicting interests of New South Wales and Victoria. The actual building of Canberra started in 1923.

[6] The tiny island in the bay of Nagasaki, where the Dutch were permitted to keep a small factory during the period of Japan's seclusion.

[7] The main harbor on the Strait of Malacca under Arab, Portuguese, and Dutch occupation, until replaced by British Singapore.

[8] After the Russian-Japanese war of 1904/5 it appeared as if Port Arthur would be completely superseded by Japanese favored Dairen.

[9] The Portuguese relic colony near Canton in Southern China.

[10] In 1924 it appeared as if the Russian port was completely walled in by the expanding Japanese Empire.

[11] From 1895-1930, British harbor on the north coast of Shantung, opposite Port Arthur, acquired as counterweight to Port Arthur and also the German Tsingtao. It remained without major significance, however, and was given up without struggle soon after this was written.

[12] German outpost in China, conquered by the Japanese in the First World War, but developed by them only after the date of this book.

posts but growing at a decreasing rate (Hongkong, Tientsin[13]); 5. very active accroaching places (Singapore, Dairen with Liaotung[14]).

It is extremely instructive to observe such well-known entities through their sudden vicissitudes; to ponder the slow shifting of their vitality and political importance; to draw conclusions from their different stages; and to determine the situation of their emitting living spaces, and the proportion of the force of the metropolitan areas to that of the temporary or permanent host nations.

In general, the strongest political and national powers do not feel it necessary to fortify their colonial outposts, or they do it only late and superficially.[15] They instinctively are afraid of impeding further growth; only when the living spirit is slackening, does the need of protection behind fortifications arise. The naval bases of the strongest powers most value free exit possibilities and wide oceanic spaces; protection by localized strength and seclusion is looked for only when self-confidence is waning.

SIEGFRIED PASSARGE (1867-1957)

Passarge is significant not so much for his several valuable topical studies, e.g., on deserts in Africa, as for his insistence that the object of geography should be the study of landscapes as types (*Landschaftskunde*). In general he excluded man and animals from the concrete landscape. Natural vegetation is the basic feature which helps to define an individual landscape, in contrast to the region, for which the interrelation of many features is important. On this basis he thought a classification of landscape types was possible. For a long period of his life, Passarge thought of geography as the study of relationships, not of regions. He was also close to those who tried to establish an aesthetic approach to geography;

---

[13] The harbor of Peking, where most western powers and Japan owned extra-territorial rights.

[14] See note 8.

[15] Before World War I neither Singapore nor Hong Kong were fortified; neither was Dairen in Japanese hands, as opposed to the strong fortifications with which the Russians had surrounded Port Arthur.

but, nevertheless, he maintained in his work an irreproachable accuracy and high standards. His abundant use of photographs and colored pictures was a pioneering step for his time.

His influence was felt more in England and America than in Germany, where he was involved in acrimonious debates with Hettner. The overwhelming majority of German geographers sided with Hettner.

Essence and Limits of the Science of Landscapes [16]

The Science of Landscapes (*Landschaftskunde*) is the doctrine of the distribution and mutual penetration of spaces and their integration to uniform component parts of the landscape. The smallest uniform component parts are the "Landscape divisions" (*Landschaftsteile*), the building stones of the landscape. "Landscape constituents" (*Landschafts-bildner*) are elements which together constitute the landscape, such as climate, surface configuration, rocks, vegetation, weathered soils, and drainage features. Added are man-made culture features of the landscape, such as those pertaining to economic life, traffic, settlements, and installations connected with political boundaries. The contiguous areas of these landscape constituents are the single regions.

In contrast to these physical and cultural landscape constituents, which are immobile and change only slowly if at all, animals and man move easily from place to place and do not constitute "single regions," but have non-contiguous "areas of distribution." To be sure, there are exceptions concerning some animals—e.g., the reef-builders—but for the majority the above statement is true. The landscape constituents unite, therefore, individual regions and constitute the "landscape regions." (*Landschaftsräume.*)

The following fact is important: The physical landscape constituents are not scattered around indifferently side by

[16] "Wesen und Grenzen der Landschaftskunde," Siegfried Passarge in *Herman Wagner Gedenkschrift, Ergebnisse und Aufgaben der geographischen Forschung*, Ergänzungshef no. 209 zu "*Petermanns Mitteilungen.*" Gotha, Justus Perthes, 1930. Hermann Wagner, 1840-1929, was highly respected as an academic teacher and author of a widely used textbook.

side, one on top of the other, or indiscriminately mixed, but they influence each other. It is this mutual influence which renders the whole picture so complicated. There is hardly a "single region" which is not under the influence of forces radiating from others. One example of constituents may explain the situation.

a) Rainy climate — a concave landform — impermeable rocks — water gathering in the cavity — development of swamp with swamp vegetation and muddy soils — influence of the swamp upon the local climate — refuge area.

b) Tropical rain forest climate — mountains — rain-forest on the weatherside, steppe basin leewards — accordingly different soils, drainage conditions, springs, and bases for civilization in the drier basin.

c) The following example illustrates the human influence: Tropical mountain cloud forest — permanent streams — thick layer of brown weathered loams, wet and colloidal — earth slips, leading to occasional damming of streams — little denudation — rain falling as drizzle, not as heavy downpours.

Now deforestation starts, accompanied by drying of the soil, increase of run-off, denudation, and gullying. Climatic changes follow: storms replace drizzles, greater heat in daytime, cooler nights, thereby changing vegetation and changing conditions for cultural life. Hettner describes such changes in the cordillera of Bogotá, and Sapper in Central America.

Such mutual influences are, therefore, characteristic for the "landscape constituents" and their part in creating the landscape regions. In the process of creating a landscape the "landscape constituents" develop a certain formative force. This force varies in different landscapes; i.e., there is no definite hierarchy or order of force, rather its gradation varies in the different landscape zones.

In the tropics, for example, the formative force of the landforms is more pronounced than it is in Europe. In the tropics the rainfall is often so strongly influenced by the landforms, that windward and leeward have totally different landscape character: rainforest slopes vs. steppe slopes or steppe basins. Mountains enforce a differing development of the landscape. The force of the relief in creating landscapes is, therefore, greater than that of the other "landscape constituents." The order of the "landscape constituents" would be tropical rainforest climate as the primary concept in the whole area. The landforms are the cause for different rainfall amounts — that again is the basis for different development of the vegetation (rainforest or steppes); therefrom originates differentiation of drainage features, soils, conditions of denudation and deposition, cultural conditions, etc.

The following examples show something entirely different: tropical rainforest climate and mountains together with low hills or even plains. Despite the rainforest climate, a savanna is dominant, which is green in the rainy period only and in some places there is even grassland with scattered trees. Why? The lithological character is responsible, a very porous limestone, perhaps coral chalk. It causes the development of savanna and even of steppes through the dryness of the soil. This type of forest and the steppe vegetation respectively are the basis for the development of drainage features, soil conditions, denudation, cultural conditions, etc., which do not belong into the tropical rain forest climate.

Still a third example: tropical dry forest or steppe climate with a five month dry period and very high precipitation in the rainy period. Instead of dry deciduous forest or steppes with intermittent rivers, strong denudation, and desiccation of the soil, an evergreen rainforest covers the country — regardless of its character as mountain, tableland, or hills. Which is the overweening landscape constituent? It is the soft, cellular laterite which absorbs the water like a sponge. The soil is dominant. It causes ample nutrition of the stream in the dry period, development of perennial streams, and hinders denudation — in brief it causes the development of a rainforest landscape, e.g., in Upper Guinea.

However, man penetrates into the rain forest. He destroys the forest; the soil is desiccated and a crust of many meters' depth develops, forming hard, cellular brown hematite (Dekkan). A dreary steppe replaces the luxuriant rainforest, its value for cultivation becomes nil, and the climate also changes. It becomes drier, and heavy downpours replace the soft long lasting rains. Perennial streams persist in valleys, where gallery forests persist, indicating that the creative dominance of the water-giving soils has not yet been absolutely destroyed (Lower Congo area).

All these examples lead to the formulation of some important concepts and ideas of the landscape theory. They will be discussed in order:

1. *The potential power of individual regions to create landscapes.* It is impossible to give a fixed scale. In one landscape one constituent factor prevails, in another another factor. One factor, however, is predominant — the others follow in a definite order.

2. *Arrangement of landscape regions.* Such an arrangement, of course, is oriented according to the scale of the landscape constituent factors, and at the same time such analysis of factors is connected with instituting an order of the landscape regions according to their magnitude. The individual landscape areas are only partly adjacent; some smaller areas are included within the larger ones in many instances. Many different orders of magnitude exist accordingly. . . .

3. *The delimitation of landscape areas.* A landscape region can frequently be broken down into a great number of smaller landscape divisions partly boxed one into the other; but their exact delimitation is difficult. The cause of this difficulty is that in many instances the boundaries of the individual areas do not coincide. An example:

A mountain range terminates rather abruptly along foothills, and these along a plain — there are, therefore, three distinct orographical units. The weathered soil uniformly covers all three orographical units, but terminates within the plain, where peaty soils begin. The vegetative cover consists of a) forest on the highest slopes of the mountains; b) vineyards on the lower slopes and on the foothills; c) mixed fields and vineyards in the plain on alluvial clays and sands; d) meadows on the peaty soils.

How should the boundaries be drawn? . . .

4. *Norms and modifications.* The general landscape character is determined by the climate and its effects: climatic plant formations, drainage character, and climatically determined soils. If the landscape constituents develop a certain

average strength, the normal landscape character, as determined by the climate, is preserved. In moderate altitudes on moderate slopes, over average permeable rocks or soils, the rain forest prevails undisputedly in the rain forest climate. If the slopes become too steep, the rocks too permeable or too impermeable, the soils too infertile, rain forests are replaced by savanna or steppe, or vice versa by a swamp if there is abundant water.

An example of modifications in a landscape zone are the tundras. Norms on clay soils are: permafrost soil, weak development of podsols, moist soils in summer, lichens and heath or dwarf shrubs. Modifications are: a) if the soil is too dry; stunted tundra and stony soils; b) if the soils are too wet and there is stagnant water: bogs and marshes; c) if there is irrigation and strong sun radiation (e.g., reflection from large water bodies) : gardens on slopes; d) rock glaciers with lichens are soil modifications; e) if there is superabundant water on gentle slopes: mudflows.

Despoiled landscapes (*Raublandschaften*) frequently resemble natural landscapes and it is uncertain in many cases whether a landscape is natural or despoiled. In some cases — for example, fruit grown on plains in the midst of rain forest mountains — the situation is obvious, and it is possible to point out man-made modifications.

It may be advisable to regard small islands of cultural landscape — fields or plantation clearings in virgin forest — as modifications. The case is different where the cultural landscape covers entire groups of landscapes (Europe). In such instances it best serves the purpose to treat such cultural landscapes in the same manner as natural landscapes and to determine norms and modifications within this landscape. In this process in the cultural landscape the *cultural stage* has to be taken into consideration. The "norms" are different in different economies. The neolithic peasant of Central Europe changed "as a rule" only steppe and heath to fields; today as a rule the fields expand over former forested plains, and meadows on wet lowlands and forests on steep slopes are modifications.

Using the concepts "norms" and "modifications", one can often clarify conditions in the same way that morphological conditions are explained by the categories of "recent" and "inherited" forms. "Exotic forms" (*Fremdlingsformen*) are modifications caused by forces originating in another landscape zone.

5. *Climatic and edaphic features.* The concepts of "climatic and edaphic plant associations" were invented by botanists. Whether they suffice for them can remain unanswered; here it should be stressed that they do not suffice for the science of landscapes. The goal of the geographer is different from that of the botanist in many respects. The latter is usually concerned with the flora, i.e., with the association of genera. . . . On the other hand the geographer stresses the following factors:

a. The physiognomic picture is more important than the floristic composition. Therefore, the plant-geographical maps of botanists are unsatisfactory for the geographer;

b. the geographer is interested in distribution, and together with it the effect upon the landscape;

c. the concept "edaphic", i.e., conditioned by the soil, is insufficient for the geographer. He has either to split this concept or to generalize in other respects.

Regarding these requirements it seems advisable to introduce the following concept based on spatial extent. The *landscape zones* depend on climatic conditions which are *theoretically* alike over wide areas. They have a fixed "normal" climatic plant association, climatically caused soils, climatically caused drainage character.

Regional areas are wide areas, perhaps of the magnitude of groups of landscapes, in which lithology, regional climate, drainage conditions, and human influence created "modified regional plant associations," regional soils, regional natural or despoiled landscapes.

Local areas or *localities* are modifications in restricted space — local associations of plants, localized soils, local features of the cultural landscape. *Dwarf areas* or *microareas* could be the designation for very small areas of distinctive climate in a small space of frequently less than 100 square meters (350 square feet), e.g., windprotected ravines, a sunburned corner on a south facing slope, or a sphagnum bog in a trench. . . .

6. *Landscape structure.* That can be defined briefly. Using "modifications", regional and local areas, parts of landscapes and partial landscapes, etc., the inner structure can be defined, and can differ widely according to number, size, and distribution of the different structural elements.

7. *The science of landscapes and geology-morphology.* Although the essential facts are obvious from the preceding discussion, because of its basic importance this question shall be discussed again briefly. In some respects the *science of landscapes* breaks completely with geology and morphology, eliminating their hitherto almost absolute domination. It seems that this devaluation of morphology, as founded by von Richthofen, is resented by many geographers. As every landscape constitutes among other things a part of the solid surface of the earth, the latter never can be omitted, just as climate cannot be eliminated. One must determine in each case individually the rank of the formative forces exerted by the earth's surface among all the formative forces to know whether the landforms as such are decisive or the rock types. These are usually the most prominent, while problems of tectonics and development are secondary. That says that morpho*graphy* is more important than morpho*logy*. . . .

8. *Relation of landscape zones and landforms.* In some zones landforms can be subordinated to the zonal arrangement without difficulty, e.g., in our country, where the three great landforms — plains, rounded low mountains, Alps — determine the regional breakdown within the framework of the temperate mixed forest zone. In other areas — tropics, steppe areas of the temperature zone which suffer from aridity — relief causes such strong modifications of the climate that the area resembles a mosaic of landscape zones. Thus blocks of landscapes develop — i.e., within an area well defined orographically regional climates cause development of regional landscapes, each of which is really a landscape zone — the Alps, Danubian countries, Abyssinia, Central America.

9. *Landscape description.* The next goal of landscape research is the description of landscapes -- that part which is, as experience shows, by far the most difficult and which, sorry to say, so often is overwhelmed by explanatory hypotheses. Of course, they are more exciting than a single statement of facts. That is true not only in the science of landscapes, but in all sciences. However, the ascertainment of fact is the basis of all scientific perception and has to proceed without compromise. By a good, reliable description, i.e., statement of fact, the road is opened to attempts at explanation. They should be based, in principle, upon *differential diagnosis.* Such differential diagnoses, as a rule, impel further research, and thus science gradually advances.

In landscape research two methods exist; both have advantages and disadvantages. The first method, which should be employed by everyone without hesitation first, is *observation in a small area.* This method was used in regard to "physical morphology" even before the war (World War I). The first model of such a "landscape analysis" was published as early as 1911 for pedagogical purposes. . . .

Thus the building stones of a landscape are made apparent by analysis and construction; but one cannot observe more than a small portion of the countries. Even if the observed features of one small area can be found again in other areas of similar landscape character, and if, therefore, cautious generalizations are permitted, the second method — *study of literature* — cannot be omitted. . . .

The difference is tremendous. Study of literature renders, it is true, a general view; but it remains uncertain, and subdivisions of landscapes seldom can be recognized. Despite that, such a study of literature is extremely useful. It gives a clear picture of our previous knowledge of countries, and direct field exploration is made easier by literary preparation.

10. *Landscape explanation.* Description is the basis of all scientific research, but not its final goal: it is also desirable to explain the phenomena. However, thereby many difficulties are met in the Science of Landscapes. While botany, zoology, mineralogy, etc,, are based on chemistry, physics, and mathematics, in the science of landscapes so many different sciences

come together that extremely complicated conditions emerge. Even man and his culture participate quite often in this interplay of forces. . . .

Thus every landscape region is an area for research by several sciences: geology and mineralogy, morphology, climatology, pedology, botany, zoology, and many social sciences. Geochemistry and geophysics should not be forgotten.

The situation is obvious. No individual can explore and explain a landscape region without residue, because no one can be an expert in all sciences. The explanatory duty of the geographer can, therefore, only be restricted. Delimiting and describing independent landscape regions is his first, largely disinterested, work, because all natural sciences are furthered thereby, first of all plant and animal ecology, pedology, morphology, hydrology, and as far as relation exists to landforms, also geology. Added are human civilization, human economy, settlements and transportation. Insofar as local and regional climate is better understood with the help of landscape regions, climatology is also furthered and suggestions for its study are given. . . .

11. *Terminology for landscape.* . . .[17]

12. *The cartographic problem.* If you explore a large landscape and its divisions, and if you map a small unit separately, a confusing mosaic emerges which is not usable. In comparing individual landscape units, however, stressing the common features and neglecting "individual" peculiarities, mutually comparable types emerge which can be unified in the symbolism. These types also receive separate names. . . .

13. *Real and ideal landscapes — real and comparative sciences of landscapes.* The real science of landscapes explores the actual landscapes; the comparative deals with landscape types. The latter are, like isotherms and isobars, reduced to a common level and thereby comparable. The following "individual" features have been omitted in describing the landscape types, though they are of particular significance in dealing with real landscapes.

[17] As this paragraph is closely bound to the structure of the German language, its translation would be of little interest.

a) Absolute figures for area and elevation, b) the composition of landscapes from smaller units, c) the botanic, mineralogic, geologic, etc., incidental forms, d) location on the earth and in relation to adjacent landscapes, e) many incidental phenomena. In a real landscape as in mapping it is possible and necessary somewhat to reduce real landscapes to types; otherwise it is impossible to stress the characteristic traits; neither is it possible to bring order into the presentation. . . .

Totally different is the comparative science of landscapes which deals with typical landscapes. It strives to describe non-existing *ideal landscapes.* However, as these ideal landscapes are without individual traits, they can be traced across real landscape zones and the peculiarities stressed as long as they belong to equivalent types. Because of the compass-like nature of the *science of landscapes* the real and comparative sciences of landscapes form a unity in the last analysis despite all differences. These two branches are like the two legs of a compass. Just as the legs are bound together in the hinge of the compass, the real and comparative sciences of landscape come together in the landscape zones.

The landscape zones are theoretical spaces of — *theoretically* — uniform climate. Within, one should neglect all modifications which are caused by surface configurations, types of rocks, soils, and distribution of drainage. The landscape zones have, therefore, an ideal climate, and on this depend the climatic plant associations, climatic soils, climatic drainage characteristics, etc. From these idealized landscape zones, which are, however, *real* earth spaces, the same as isobar-isotherm regions, both the real and the comparative science of landscapes branch off. Both originate from the condition that the crust of the earth is breaking up the landscape because of differences in elevation and landforms and is dissolving them into landscape spaces each smaller than the preceding one — landscape regions, landscapes, landscape divisions — each of a different order of magnitude. In the real science of landscapes the actual landscapes are discussed; in the comparative science of landscapes, however, only idealized types of landscapes are discussed.

14. *Science of landscapes and regional geography.* Their

objects are different. The science of landscapes investigates uniformly defined areas, i.e. "landscapes," in which certain landscape constituents dominate. "Countries or regions," on the other hand, cannot be uniform by definition. A country may be an island, a peninsula, a drainage basin, a cultural or national unit, an historical unit, a political unit, a scientific abstraction. Quite different landscape zones may form a "country" — such as Russia; uniform landscapes may be separated. . . .

HANS SPETHMANN (1885-1957)

Spethmann is another German geographer who was captivated by the organism concept. For him neither the state, as with Ratzel or Haushofer, nor the landscape, as with Banse, but rather the region was the individual organism. He tried to stress the genetic development of regions above all other considerations, denying the value of any other relationship. He called his method dynamic geography. He ranks with Banse in his strong opposition to Hettner.

The Ruhr region [18]

The Ruhr region offers probably the most complex challenge any landscape in Europe or elsewhere can present (to the geographer). The most varied forces on the ground, above the ground, and underground, contribute to its formation, including the purely agricultural forces of the past and the highly developed industrial agricultural practices of the present, from physical factors of nature to the most refined expressions of life as represented by leading personalities. Furthermore, these processes and conditions are displayed within the framework of great events. Such a colorful diversity makes difficult an interpretation of the Ruhr region. On the other hand, it presents a challenge to attempt an understanding and presentation, just because of this abundance of problems.

In order to understand such problems, one must resort to investigations in many fields. First, it is necessary to know

[18] Hans Spethmann, *Das Ruhrgebiet.* Reimar Hobbing, Berlin 1933. Vol. II, pp. 603-613, vol. III, pp. 613-616.

the Ruhr region from personal experience. Although this precondition is a matter of course, it must be stated openly here, because so many who have never seen it, or who think one is able to appreciate it after a superficial visit, are writing about the Ruhr region and judging it. . . . *Observation and study are insufficient bases for the knowledge of a landscape; primarily taking an active part in its economic life is necessary if one attempts honestly to appreciate the whole human behavior in the development of a segment of the earth's surface.*

Only such a participation enables one to understand how very complicated processes frequently may be, processes which some scholars think can easily be explained; and it also makes one aware of the number of different factors which in conjunction contribute to the emergence of some feature on the face of the earth. On the other hand it should never be forgotten that research and deliberations in natural sciences, namely, in morphology and geology, are also necessary to reach that goal. . . . In the context of the landscape, however, geological or morphological observations, as such, are not needed, but rather it is necessary to correlate them with other things, and in doing so, to delimit their importance correctly and then fit them into the appropriate place.

Further, in order to view the broader frame of the Ruhr region and to depict its peculiarities, I undertook comparative studies in regions which have similar natural conditions, but look quite different. . . . The personal inspection of comparable regions allows one to see more clearly the common, as well as the contrasting, features of landscapes with similar natural conditions.

Therefore, in my presentation of the Ruhr region I have always stressed the development rather than the end result. Everything is changing. Combined forces flow from one point to another and, once there, are displaced by others; foreign objects intrude from without, others strive to escape and are lost. The totality (of forces) strives continuously for reconciliation, or harmony, but can obtain it no more in the Ruhr region than in any other landscape, because such a harmony is possible only in connection with adjacent spaces. However, the very next moment the sum of forces has changed its composition, again something out of equilibrium has developed, which desires reconciliation, melting of everything into a unit, becoming one in itself, i.e., quiescence in motion. However, this quiet is never reached; such a moment would mean the death of all forces. *The landscape is alive;* that is the basic motto of this study.

In order to understand the processes, I tried to penetrate their actuality as far as possible. For this purpose it was necessary from the beginning to avoid adherence to any firm system and to eliminate any bias, though often there was an unconscious one. So in my *Ruhr region* in which economic problems are so prominent I avoided basing my research upon the often used outline which follows the progress of production, though I did use it myself in *Grosswirtschaft an der Ruhr* in 1925. This method shows processes in a more external connection and not in their causal nexus. *It sounds very simple to start with the production or procurement of some raw material, then to follow the progress of its utilization together with questions of pay and length of labor hours, and to conclude with the markets. However, this does not explain the genuine relationships, as we have learned only too well through the events of the last years when the marketing conditions determined the entire production process.*

The same is true in respect to the regional geographic scheme, which Gradmann [18a] already has regarded as rehash. Time and again a regional geography offers the same order in its individual chapters: geology, morphology, climate, hydrography, plants, animals, men. In addition this scheme does not reveal true causality. As late as 1919 the leading geographical methodologist, Hettner, thought he could present such causality in a model example, explicitly stating that one should recognize "how the features of the various natural realms, which are united in the same place (or in the same landscape), are connected with each other in a causal order, so that no doubt can arise about this basis of geographical

[18a] Robert Gradmann is one of Germany's best-known georgraphers. He concentrated on Southern Germany and drew general conclusions from his studies concerning the original landscape and its vegetation, based on the interrelations *(Zusammenhang)* of phenomena.

perception." [19] It is true that Hettner also stressed, repeatedly, that which had been stated clearly for 130 years, that actually a mutual reaction exists. However, until now people were satisfied to state their fact; or they altered statements such as what was needed was to penetrate deeply into one's subject. But then they halted before the gate of mutuality, instead of opening the gate and exploring a new field of knowledge. Progress is only possible if one reveals mutual causations. This has become the starting point for a new method, the dynamic.

This method does not proceed in its concept — or in its presentation — according to the schematic blueprint of some theory of science; neither does it prefer, one-sidedly, morphology or geology, as is still being done elsewhere; rather it brings into the limelight at any given time that feature which impresses the observer most, such as the virgin forest and the untamed Rhine in the pre-Roman period, or the landscape of clearings in the time of Charlemagne. It tries to understand this outstanding characteristic of the landscape through its connection with other contributing features, for example, the virgin forest together with the forces which originate from climate, drainage, and vegetation, and even from human interference. Every landscape can, therefore, be conceived as a field of forces containing one principal dynamic (force) and several secondary ones. It is a clockwork of propelling forces which is turned by the major wheel of the main force. It is regulated by the velocity of the smaller wheels, although they are individuals in their own right and are capable either of accelerating or retarding the larger wheel. That is the basic concept of a dynamic regional geography.

This is a part of the earth's surface, in this case in the Ruhr region. I am tracing the changes through which the region passed by studying regional cross-sections at certain moments; either when a kind of balance developed, such as existed in the virgin forest period; or when catastrophic stirrings led to fundamental shifts such as the Roman invasion,

---

[19] *A. Hettner, Die Einheit der Geographie in Wissenschaft und Unterricht (The Unity of Geography in Research and Teaching).* Geographische Abhandlungen, Vol. I, Berlin 1919.

the Thirty Years War, the Napoleonic disorders, or the World War. These cross-sections should be drafted in such a way as to present the landscape synchronously in order to make clear the value of each individual force. By superimposing such cross-sections I can survey the regional past of the Ruhr region.

While proceeding I asked myself again whether I should not describe all the facts first. However, I was again convinced: whoever describes only, is bound to omit many things which would have claimed his attention had he done research. It is impossible to divorce description and research as being opposite poles. Many facts are only revealed in the course of research, but vice versa, a mere description also stimulates and supplements research. Both work together. Therefore I presented descriptions and stories from the past on appropriate places in the presentation of the results of research.

. . . A special difficulty arose in fixing the temporal starting point for the cross-section. When I started I was sure only of the significance of the years 1857 and 1873; I had no notion of the rest. . . . Therefore, it is obvious that only towards the end could I dictate the broad surveys which are found at the close of the chapters, after that the summaries in small print in front of them, and finally the form of the headings.

From this procedure it is obvious that we did not work simply with a new outline in place of the old one, by which we can immediately pigeonhole morphological observations in this column, economic ones in that, as in the drawers of a chest. In beginning the research of a landscape we are unable to survey the order of the material. And by this very search for an outline we are forced — healthily — to adhere to reality and the hard facts. . . .

It would be completely erroneous to preface the pre-Roman epoch with individual chapters on geology, morphology, climate, and flora, especially with the justification that the soil, water, and plants were there before. That would be a serious methodical fallacy. In a presentation which aims at pointing out the development of a landscape and its present appearance one must present only the temporary appearance of the region at any moment. Such an appearance is, in the past, as today, an association of several "dynames" (forces),[20] among them one or two predominant ones, such as the forest, the steppe, or ice. It did not consist in the beginning of peneplains and terrace surfaces, as morphology teaches, nor of effects of temperature, precipitation and wind, as climatology presents it. . . .

. . . It is impossible in regional geography to look exclusively in one direction, at only the importance of minerals, the forms of relief, or at any of the formative forces of man; it is necessary to look in all directions.. . . Thus an association of coal and iron with favorable road connections and access to the sea still does not create a Ruhr region; other large groups of factors have to be considered. Only in a critical survey is it possible to master the regional material and the forces which shape it. . . .

. . . On principle I refrained from giving preference to either the natural sciences, or to those which are called unfortunately the cultural sciences; rather both are always considered equally. I did not confine myself to the problem of to what extent the face of some landscape can be explained by the action of natural forces, in the way that Richthofen introduced the problem in the eighties — a way that is still the basis for many regional geographies. This attitude was a great step forward half a century ago; now it should be replaced by another which appreciates how human action changes the face of a region. Not only does nature influence man with its products, but vice versa — man also by his actions or neglect, even in his highest development as a personality quite definitely influences nature and the products of a landscape. Only by considering both these points of view is it possible to explain a landscape and its life.

I must also say that in the last sections, following the cross-sections of 1857, I treated several things in more detail than is necessary in a regional geographical frame, especially the ups and downs of booms and crises. However, they are extremely noticeable in their effect upon the landscape, because basically they condition the transformation of large areas,

[20] Spethmann uses only the Greek word.

either by expanding coal fields or by reducing forested areas or by encouraging exploitation of field and pasture. At that moment when the economic trend upward comes to a halt, they cease, too. Booms and crises are the temporal measure of the transformation.

. . . (The 3rd volume) will summarize those forces which are active in the Ruhr region. Among them financial and legal ones and also technical ones will be discussed. Without the laborious and artful work of technical science wide stretches of the surface of the earth would look quite different — in our area this differentiation started as far back as the Roman period. Special attention will be devoted to the human personal motivations which the materialism of the last decades has suppressed almost completely, the human instinct, the earthly feeling and the influence of fate. Extremely important are the racial qualities. . . . We shall also discuss the influence of the landscape upon the soul and vice versa; the emotional attitude of man toward the landscape, when it appears, for example, in attempts at conservation. . . . Finally, the permanent factor in the midst of change will appear, the lasting in the midst of the transient, the staying power in the continuously changing landscape. . . .

These problems will be treated because they are by no means peculiar to the Ruhr region, but rather can always be found on the whole earth's surface, and because to date they have not evoked the consideration they deserve. The same phenomenon is to be found in the Ruhr region when the forest is cleared and the stakes are driven, as when virgin forests in any climate are cleared. Trees everywhere are cut according to legal institutions, financial capacity, and technical knowledge, and not according to the insight of one individual into the larger, economic relationships.

I consider the chief merit (of my book) to lie in the fact that materialism, which has almost completely dominated our geography, has been mastered. Looking at the main line of development, regional geography was rescued from metaphysical growth approximately in the middle of the last century; this tendency should never be allowed to return in the same way. However, another metaphysical trend ought to arise in the future, which does not see the ultimate salvation in mechanistic causal thinking, and which, especially, does not move within the limits of a materialistic concept as do the methods of Alfred Hettner, methods which largely have taken the lead in our time. . . .

Also regional geography can contribute much to overcoming materialistic tendencies. I hope it shall become clear from my study that the economic action of man on the face of the Ruhr region and generally on the whole globe is not a ruthless struggle of interests from day to day. Many regard it as such — among them scholars on the basis of a materialistic philosophy, whose consequences, perhaps they do not fully realize: it is ,on the contrary, an highly artistic organism with deep roots. For many decades the entire structure of regional geography was influenced considerably and excessively by the overtreatment of morphology which made mechanical causality the uppermost principle. Now, again, a wide field of new knowledge is opening. One can enter it only if one is aware that the landscape, which surrounds us and in which we are living is not composed of a number of facts standing side by side and connected statistically, but that it is continuously in dynamic motion. It is the living landscape in which the creative is the essence.

WALTER CHRISTALLER (1893-)

Christaller has made contributions to theoretical, spatial thinking which must rank him among the most influential modern geographers. He is included among the German "Dissenters" for there can be no question that his work is a departure from classical Germany geography. But more important than this "dissenting" is the fact that his work is transitional. In the selection included here it can easily be seen that he is writing about *place* but he has also treated the central places of Southern Germany abstractly (i.e., *spatially*). His primary interest is settlement geography, but his work is more inclusive; he "attempted to study an entire economic system, spatially-oriented and -coordinated, and located. He incorporated political, social, economic, and geographic factors into his investigations." [21]

The Central Places in Southern Germany [22]

Are there laws which determine the number, size, and distribution of towns?

In recent literature on geographical settlements, following the example of Gradmann,[23] rural and urban settlements are sharply distinguished. Gradmann speaks very correctly of "two things as different at the root as the village and the town." The root from which the village has its existence, is distinct; it consists quite prevalently of agricultural and other land uses. The connection between the number of people living in villages and on farms, and the size of land area, is given in this manner: There are as many people in a given area as can live from the cultivation of the land with given agricultural technology and organization. Whether these people live in large settlements, i.e., large closed villages, or in smaller villages, hamlets, or on individual farms, is not clear a priori. Yet, these questions are explained by the investigations of Gradmann and others: A definite type of settlement is usually predominant within a certain region.

The situation with towns is somewhat different. In the same region, we see large and small towns in all categories, one besides the other. Sometimes they agglomerate in certain regions, in an improbable and apparently senseless manner. Sometimes there are wide regions in which no single place deserves the designation as a town, or even as a market. The connection between the town and the professional activity of its inhabitants, it is always emphasized, is not an accidental one but is based upon the nature of both. But why are there then large and small towns, and why are they distributed so irregularly?

---

[21] C. W. Baskin, *A Critique and Translation of Walter Christaller's Die Zentralen Orte In Suddeutschland*, University of Virginia, (Ph.D. Dissertation), Charlottesville, Virginia, 1957, p. iv.

[22] *A Critique and Translation of Walter Christaller's Die Zentralen Orte in Suddeutschland*, C. W. Baskin, University of Virginia (Ph.D. Dissertation), 1957, p. iv.

We seek an answer to this question. We seek the causes for a town being large or small, because we believe that there is still some ordering principle governing the distribution, which up to now, we have not recognized.

These questions are not only dealt with by the geographers, but also by the historians, the sociologists, the economists, and the statisticians. But only once was there a significant attempt to find the real laws determining the distribution and size of towns. Almost 100 years ago, it was made by Kohl. . . .

* * *

But how can we find a general explanation for the size, number and distribution of towns? How can we discover the laws?

Can pure geographical inquiry produce them? It proceeds, as a rule, from topographical and geographical conditions and then explains simply, that here a town "had to originate," and, if the location is favorable, that here especially, a town "had to" develop favorably. One does not observe, thereby, that there are innumerable locations equally as favorable, or still more favorable, as all others, where no town is found; and on the contrary may be found in very unfavorable spots and, circumstances permitting, may be even fairly large. Neither the number, nor the distribution, nor the size of a town can be explained by its location in respect to the geographical conditions of nature. Hettner demonstrated in 1902 how important is an investigation into the number of settlements and the average distance from one another are settlements of equal economic character. Since that time such facts are seldom missing in a monograph on geographical settlements. Yet, up to now, no one has obtained clear, generally-valid laws in this manner.

Could, perhaps, an historical investigation bring a general answer? If the development of all towns from the first beginnings up to the present state were investigated in detail, one could obtain laws in this material by picking out those facts which, regionally and periodically, have a certain precision. One can find a certain order in diversity, but the principle of order itself can never be found through historical investigations alone. This was also recognized by the historical school of economics. It could bring to light exceedingly abundant factual material, but it could never obtain valid economic laws with its historical method.

Finally, can the statistical method help us? One computes the town-density of a region and average distances between two towns; one establishes size-classes and records the number of towns belonging to each class; and one finds, in this manner, frequencies and averages, and perhaps certain regularities, and frequently existing combinations of phenomena in particular. However, the logical proof that these are genuine laws, can never be furnished by statistics alone.

If the "geography of settlements" were a discipline of the natural sciences, or at least predominantly such a discipline, as it almost appears to be with some authors, then there is naturally no question but that the laws of natural science must govern here; for every natural phenomenon rests upon such principles. But we have the view that the geography of settlements is a discipline of the social sciences. It is quite obvious that for the creation, development and decline of towns, the fact that a demand must exist for the things which the town as such can offer is decisive. This means that economic facts are decisive for the existence of towns; for the existence of rural settlements, the houses of which are all, simultaneously, places of production, economic reasons are self-evidently decisive. Therefore, the geography of settlements is a part of economic geography. As in economic geography, it must draw upon economic theory if the character of towns is to be explained. If there are now laws in economic theory, then there must be also laws in the geography of settlements, and that means economic laws of a special character which could be spoken of as special economic-geographic laws. The question whether there are really economic laws cannot practically be dealt with here; the author answers this question decisively in the affirmative and agrees therein with the large majority of economists. These laws, to be sure, are of a different type from the natural laws, but no less "valid" on that account. They are, perhaps, not to be designated as laws, but more conveniently as "tendencies," since they do not, with equal inexorability and inevitability, work themselves out as natural laws. But the terminology is not so important where one is not dealing with an abstract theoretical research. It is sufficient for us to keep the fact in mind that there are economic laws which determine the life of the economy, and also that there are, consequently, special economic-geographic laws, such as laws which determine the size, distribution and number of towns. Therefore, it does not seem senseless to search for such laws.

* * *

Centralization as a principle of order. The crystallization of mass around a nucleus, a center, is, in inorganic as well as organic nature, an elementary form of order of things which belong together: a centralistic order. This order is not only a human mode of thinking, existing only in the human world of imagination and developed because people demand order, but it really exists through the inherent pattern of the material.

The same centralistic principle is found also in certain forms of human community life, prevailing in the organization of certain sociological structures and expressed in the visible materialization of these forms of life. We therefore think somewhat of single buildings: the church, the city hall, the forum, the school; these are the outward signs of a centralistic order in the various types of communities. These buildings, by their locations in the center of scattered individual residences (the usual form of expression for non-centralistic family organizations), by their special type of construction, their towers, porches, and above all, by their size and height, take a special rank among the buildings of the settlement. The stronger and purer the centralistic character of such community buildings is expressed in location, form and size, the greater is the esthetic pleasure felt by us, because we acknowledge the congruence of purpose and sense with the outer form and recognize the order as logically correct and therefore as beautiful.

* * *

It is for us in this book to consider, not the form of expression of the centralistic order as it appears, for our way of looking at it is that the town with a medieval nucleus is wholly on the same level with a modern town or any settlement which appears as a village, so far as the one or the other is the central organ of a centralistic order. We look not at the appearance of a town, but at its function in human community life.

Central places. We do not look at the entire appearance of a "town" but only at the definite characteristic of a town which is decidedly important for the meaning of town and the geography of settlements; it is that which Gradmann has called the "chief profession" of a town, namely, "to be center of its rural surroundings and mediator of local commerce with the outside world."

As one might think, this "chief profession" affects the small country towns which are really exceptions and nothing more than the centers of their rural surroundings. But it also affects, in the same way, the larger towns — not only in respect to their immediate vicinity but in respect to a system of many smaller regions. They all have their "closer" centers, yet they find their center of a "higher" order in that larger town where such demands of the country and of the smaller towns become satisfied which the little towns are not able to satisfy. Then, we can broaden and generalize the above statement of Gradmann in this way: The chief profession — or chief characteristic — of a town is to be the center of a region.

As this chief characteristic applies not only to those settlements which we usually call "town" — it applies also, for example, to the greater number of market spots — and as there are, on the other hand, towns which do not, or only in a very small measure, show this characteristic, we should call those settlements which are prevalently centers of regions, central settlements. Central is relative in meaning. It refers to regions. More correctly, it refers to the settlements dispersed over a region.

In contrast to these central places are the dispersed places, i.e., all those places which are not centers. . . .

* * *

Henceforth, when we speak of central settlements we shall have to avoid the introduction of a new meaning for "town", for we will only cause considerable confusion. We should go even further and substitute for the term "settlement" another term in order to have greater precision of expression. The word settlement has many meanings, but especially it calls to mind a detailed picture of streets, housing, towers and so on, which could veil the individual meaning of the facts important to us. For we do not mean the multifold meaning of "settlement," but only the location of the function of being the center of the geometrical place of the settlement. We should, therefore, speak of "central places." The expression "place" is also more correct, in a concrete sense, because in our consideration we deal neither with the settlement units, nor with the political community, nor with an economic unit. This "place" reaches as far into the surrounding settlements as the inhabitants of those settlements exercise urban, or as we should now say, central, professions. The "place" may be larger or smaller than the settlement unit or community.

The places the central function of which extends over a larger region, in which other central places of less importance exist, should be called "central places of a higher order." Those which have only local central importance for the immediate vicinity should be called correspondingly "central places of a lower," and "of the lowest order." Smaller places which usually have no central importance and besides, exercise fewer central functions, should be called "auxiliary central places."

EWALD BANSE (1883-1953)

The main representative of an organic geography in Germany, Banse, regards the landscape not only as an organism, but sees in the living organism something mystical. Though the idea of the state — not the landscape — as organism had many adherents in Germany and abroad from the time of Ratzel, it was as an organism which is capable of scientific, biological research. For Banse, on the other hand, the intellectual approach remained secondary to a mystical comprehension by the soul and to an esthetic appreciation. During his long career as a geographer, Banse succeeded in antagonizing most German geographers both by his theories and by his assertive character. As a young geographer, in his book on Turkey, he produced a vivid, descriptive, and still well founded regional geography. Later, however, his ideas on folk, nation, and the collective soul brought him into close proximity with Nazi ideas. However, his self-confident assertiveness kept him apart and his insistence on the necessity to prove German superiority by world conquest in his book *Geographie und Wehrwille* (Breslau 1934) evoked alarm in England and aroused Hitler's ire as premature indiscretion. In his last years Banse led a lonely life, shunned by Nazis and anti-Nazis alike.

Historical Development and Task of Geography[24]

He[25] noticed that none of the scientific regional geographies took cognizance of the landscape aspect of a region. Whatever you could learn from them, one thing was never mentioned: how does the area look? An integration of all the elements into one picture was missing. Analytical observation can lead to mechanical addition, which is ultimately not much better than a compilation, but it does not rise to the level of an organic integration. Even those among the geographers who discussed in a regional geography an area in which they had traveled and which they had seen, suppressed their visual and emotional impressions of the country and the people lest they appear unscientific. It remained, therefore, intrinsically the same whether they had been there or not. They had not fully experienced the country, but had rationally investigated it. They considered it unscientific and subjective to offer more than external concepts. Thus, the description of the landscape was left to travelogues and remained in the state of a poor Cinderella.

In 1906, when Banse went to the "Orient" for the first time he was most impressed by the significance and power of the landscape which dominated everything. By this experience his

---

[24] *Entwicklung und Aufgabe der Geographie*, Ewald Banse, Humboldt Verlag, Stuttgart-Wien 1953. p. 69-70, 172-176.

[25] In this short history of geography he shows that the development reached its climax in his own work. Banse speaks of himself in the third person and devotes a whole chapter to his personal development and ideas. The following pages contain the main body of this chapter, called "Gestaltende Geographie" (Creative Geography).

previous suspicion was deepened to a clear insight of the fact that geography had failed. When in 1907 and 1908 he went from North Africa to Southwestern Asia, his inner experience of the oriental landscape widened to a recognition of the unity of these two regions. Customarily these two regions had been assigned one to Asia, the other to Africa. He questioned the justification of forcibly separating North Africa and Southwest Asia, although the same conditions prevailed on both sides of the Red Sea. This led him to the recognition of the Orient as a geographical concept. . . .

In the succeeding years he enlarged the concept of the Orient to a new concept of continents. He did not know then the well-meant, but inadequate — because one-sided and rationalistic — attempts by A. J. Herbertson in 1905 [26] and by A. Hettner to achieve a natural division of the surface of the earth. In 1912, Banse undertook such a break-down according to principles of a unified geography.

He distinguished fourteen organic continents in place of the traditional, schematic five continents. At the same time he tried to develop a concept of geography different from the customary one. Thus started a forty-year-long work of developing a new geographical doctrine. It has its basis not only in the rational faculty but in inner experience; it strives to free itself from analysis and approach synthesis; and he named it *Gestaltende Geographie* (Creative Geography). It is necessary to follow this development because it presents a renewal of the basic principles of geography; it completes the undertakings of Ritter and Richthofen and Marthe. And further it is necessary if one is to follow the gradual development of the series of new ideas.

The first publication was the essay "Geographie" in *Petermann's Mitteilungen*, 1912. It states: Geography is a monistic, not a dualistic science; it has no content of its own, but a particular point of view; starting therefrom it investigates the material things in relation to their local conditions and their mutual relationships. The local moment prevails over the content; for this reason regional geography alone is true geog-

---

[26] See Herbertson in this book.

raphy, while general geography should be abandoned because it tries to salvage a separate content. General geography has to be rejected for the additional reason that it is illogical in itself, considering primarily the material content within the inorganic nature, but investigating in the organic world not matter, but merely its distribution and its living conditions. Also general geography is unable to replace knowledge of the auxiliary sciences for the student; it is, therefore, also without value as preparation. The author states: "Geography is the philosophy of the earth's crust (geosophy); it reviews the spatial content of the earth's surface by a uniform method from the point of view of localisation, mutual relationship, and its causes. Geography inquires: where? in what content? why? and what follows from that?"

Then the author introduced two new concepts into geography: landscape [27] and *milieu* (environment, background). He defines as *milieu* the sum total of all vital features of a region, comprising not only all visible and tangible qualities and peculiarities, but also the spiritual ones. The *milieu* comprises the typical landscape which is the concentrated essence of a uniform region, and the scenery, the appearance of some accidental location in the region, which is not necessarily typical for the entire region, and, therefore, of no particular geographical interest. The use of the word landscape for a region is rejected. The author regards the perception of landscape and *milieu* as the apex of geographical work.

He also uses the *milieu* as the basis for his division of the earth's surface into natural continents. A certain milieu, such as the oriental one, loses "density" all around a core where it can be recognized with greatest clarity. It ends where characteristics of another milieu, in this example of the European, the Indian, and the Negro-African become dominant. There the Orient ends and other continents begin. In the *Illustrierte Länderkunde*, published in 1914, the author produced a general geography based upon this novel division. . . .

The second publication of Banse was his pamphlet "Expressionismus und Geographie" published in 1920. Its main trend

[27] New only in Banse's definition.

of thought is: up to now geography has failed both in description and investigation, because it deals one-sidedly with the material aspect and is unable to give a practical presentation of a country. Geography can be saved from this stagnation if it adopts concepts and methods of art. Thereby it could also accomplish a higher standing in cultural life. The exaggeration of analytical research of cause and effect has diverted attention from the principal goal, the comprehension of the individuality of countries. It has focused attention on the material elements for their own sake and atrophied the view of the essence (*Wesensschau*). The main interest has been shifted from the method to the content and has given to the auxiliary sciences an importance which they do not deserve.

The introduction of artistic contemplation into geography stresses both the exterior of things and their internal being, their genuine essence, and recognizes the soul of a country. This synthesizing process strives for the rebirth of experience in the soul; it begins where analytical research finds it impossible to proceed further. Therefore the goal of geography is the artistic moulding of individual pictures into comprehensive compositions. Individual pictures are developed through scientific observation and research, as well as by spiritual, emotional experience, while the visible landscape and the intangible milieu are the center of the comprehensive composition.

The third publication was an essay, "*Künstlerische Geography*" (Esthetic Geography) which introduced a periodical "*Die Neue Geographie*" (The New Geography) in 1922. This brief article repeats the call for complementing scientific methods with artistic ones, not excluding the former, but having each supplement the other. Only by such integration will it be possible to attain full recognition of all experienced factors in colors and sounds and to capture the spiritual impression of the picture upon the observer. . . .

In 1924 in the little booklet "*Die Seele der Geographie*" (*The Soul of Geography*) Banse further elaborated upon his idea. He stressed that the perception and moulding of the scientifically obtained raw material ought to be esthetically penetrated. This process must be preceded by the spiritual experience of a country. In contemplating a landscape it is not the external beauty which is essential, as F. Younghusband suggested in 1922, but rather the power of expression of its special character. The three basic concepts of geographical work, accordingly, are landscape, race, civilization. Landscape is the interaction of all external factors of terrain, climate, vegetation and fauna, as they become visible. Race is the emergence of man from natural conditions within a certain region through gradual evolution. Civilization is the sum total of the common result of the cooperation of race and landscape as it appears as human products. By introducing the concept of race as the organic link between nature and humanity the author took the decisive step in erasing the gap, which existed in all geography books until then; and which analytical geography had proved incapable of bridging.

In 1928, in his book *Landschaft und Seele* (*Landscape and Soul*), Banse interpreted the task of geography. This science has to give as emphatic an impression as possible and as vivid a picture as possible of the surface of the globe and its parts. It is only capable of this task if it combines research and creative faculty. Creative faculty is born from intimate experience of a country, which penetrates through the external appearance into its innermost essence and into its true and ultimate substance. Only that substance, not the appearance, distinguishes objects from each other. Moulding aims at unification and oneness. It is not only illustrative, but also interpretative. It gives not only an impression, but the very import of the object. It demands the faculty of sympathetic feeling and of expressing description beyond mere recognition. Geography must penetrate from the individual, material elements, through the landscape — the appearance of the integrated individual objects — to the soul of a country, the indefinable something which hovers invisibly between and above the individual objects and ultimately and truly keeps them together.

In a book published in 1932, *Die Geographie und ihre Probleme* (*Geography and its Problems*), Banse summarized all his ideas on a renewal of geography, assigned them to their appropriate places in the development of geography, and tried to prove that æsthetic, creative geography is the final result of all attempts to narrative, descriptive, or examining methods. Geography strives for perception of relationships of all terrestrial phenomena, of all intellectual and real phenomena of the earth's surface and its individual regions; thereby a condensed and comprehensible likeness develops. The geographical method selects from the infinite amount of material, which is the real field of its auxiliary sciences, and transforms the selected material into geographically usable matter through analytical research and synthetic creation. Investigation selects the usable from nature and humanity and explores its origin, result, and appearance to discover its mutual relation in space. Creation goes farther in order to grasp sense and a picture of space in true experience. For this purpose creative activity arranges matter around the concepts of landscape and nation (*Volkstum*), these being the two foci into which the essential elements of nature and mankind coalesce. It would be wrong — as has occurred so far — to treat the subject according to individual topics one after another, because this would result only in a second, diluted version. You can arrive at this final goal of geography, that of endowing space with sense and form, only if you acquire the material around the two concepts of landscape and nation and fuse them. The visual perception of the factors and appearances in the landscape has to be supplemented and enriched by the empathic [28] experience into the innermost relationship and awareness of the national soul. The final tool is the word, which describes and explains, imitates, condenses and interprets in order to warrant as impressive and vivid a presentation as possible.[29]

The last publication of the author is his *Lehrbuch der Organischen Geographie* (*Textbook of Organic Geography*) published in 1937. This book treats what is customarily called general geography as a preparation and introduction. In this book the method and manner of work in geography is briefly explained to supplement the previous concepts. Composition

---

[28] Banse's expression was retained in the English translation because such expressions are characteristic for his style. Webster defines empathy as "sympathetic understanding of other human beings." gs

[29] Banse, though not condemning the use of maps, does not think too highly of the concentration on them.

in the final result of geographic activity. All topics unite therein in holistic harmony. The material concepts of nature and humanity have to be condensed to landscape and nation. The first two have no connection; and because of this unbridgeable gulf, their treatment necessarily remains unreconciled. The other two concepts merge organically in the concept of race, because race, merely biologically, is part of nature, while race embodied in a nation is the basis of all cultural achievement of man. Figures 1 and 2 exemplify this idea in a few lines.

Mechanically analytical investigating geography

nature **population**

FIGURE 1.

Following this, the concept of "configuration of ideas" is introduced. Nature and man are revealed to the observant

Organic-synthetic creative geography

landscape **race** **nation**

FIGURE 2.

eye, to the perceiving, feeling brain, and to the organic experience. In this concept the numerous elements coalesce into impressive pictures and stirring ideas. The synthetic-organic-creative method recognizes and isolates ideologically the configuration of ideas of the individual regions, selecting from the choatic multiplicity of their material content. Finally it integrates everything in the dominant configuration of ideas of the globe's surface. Thus geography becomes the science of the configuration of ideas of the surface of the globe through organic thinking and experience and the synthetic-creative method. It tries to recognize the pictures which are visible in all terrestrial phenomena and the ideas which dominate all human relations. Geography attempts to isolate them and to mould them in their universal combination.

CHAPTER 8

THE FRENCH REGIONAL & HISTORICAL SCHOOLS OF GEOGRAPHY

There was a continual interest shown in geography in France during the 19th century, but until almost the end of the century no work of general interest or importance was produced. Then a distinct French school developed under the influence of Ratzel and, more directly, of Ritter, and with the leadership of Paul Vidal de la Blache. Lucid writing as rated in French classical writing and introduced into geographical writing by Brun is apparently a general French heritage and is quite different from the turgid style of many German scientists. The skillful treatment of the region is characteristic of much of French geography, as is a predominating interest in the historical ties of geography, rather than the physical facts.

ELISÉE RECLUS (1830-1905)

Reclus was the leading French geographer of the late 19th century. He had been a student of Ritter in Berlin and accomplished that task which Ritter had attempted in vain — to write by himself a detailed and uniform geography of the world. The nineteen volume *Novelle Geographie Universelle* appeared in regular weekly installments through almost twenty years — in both French and English translation. All later similar world geographies are either on a much smaller scale, lacking such detailed discussions, or were written by several collaborating authors. Like Ritter, Reclus had a tremendous knowledge of literature and the same accurate and critical approach in using it; but he traveled more widely than Ritter, having seen much of Europe and North and South America, and was influenced by Humboldt in his brilliantly executed attempts to give esthetically satisfying pictorial descriptions. He regarded the world as a kind of organism, using the term in the same restricted sense as Ritter. In describing foreign countries he successfully avoided any higher or lower evaluation: his work is singularly free from national or racial prejudice. This attitude is probably closely connected with his championship of a philosophical anarchism.

The Earth and Its Inhabitants [1]

Introductory Remarks

Our earth is but an atom in space, a star among stars. Yet, to us who inhabit it, it is without bounds, as it was in the time of our barbarian ancestors. Nor can we foresee the period when the whole of its surface will be known to us. . .hitherto no explorer has succeeded in reaching the extremities of our earth, and no one can tell whether land or sea extends beyond those icy barriers which have frustrated our most determined efforts. . .

And the polar regions which present so many natural obstacles to our explorers, are not the only portions of the earth not yet known to men of science. It may be humiliating to our pride, but we feel constrained to admit that among the countries not yet known to us there are some, accessible enough as far as natural obstacles are concerned, but closed against us by our fellow-men! There are people in this world, dwelling in towns, obeying laws, and having customs comparatively polished, but who choose to live in seclusion, and are as little known to us as if they were inhabitants of some other planet. . .

As regards most countries which have been visited by travellers, and figure more or less correctly upon our maps, a great amount of further research is required, before our knowledge of their geography can be called complete. . .A prodigious amount of labor must be performed before their climate, their hydrography, their plants and animals, can be thoroughly known by us. Minute and systematic researches

---

[1] Edited and translated from *Nouvelle Géographie Universelle*, 19 volumes, 1875 - 1896, by E. G. Ravenstein, D. Appleton and Company, New York. Without date. Pp. 1 - 5.

have to be conducted to elucidate the slow changes in the aspects and physical phenomena of many countries. The greatest caution will have to be exercised in distinguishing between changes due to the spontaneous action of natural causes and those brought about by the hand of man. And all this knowledge we must acquire before we can boast that we know the earth and all about it.

Nor is this all. By a natural bent of our mind, all studies are carried on with reference to Man as the center of all things. A knowledge of our planet is, therefore, imperfect as long as it is not joined to a knowledge of the various races of man which inhabit it. . .

We are thus not in a position at present to furnish a complete account of the earth and it inhabitants. . . .For the present an individual author must rest content with giving a succinct account of the Earth, in which the space occupied by each country shall be proportionate to its importance, and to the knowledge we possess with respect to it.

It is natural, perhaps, that each nation should imagine that in such a description it ought to be accorded the foremost place. Every barbarous tribe, however small, imagines itself to occupy the very center of the earth, and to be the most perfect representative of the human race. . .

If in our description of the Earth we accord the first place to civilized Europe, it is not because of prejudice similar to that of the Chinese. No! This place belongs to Europe as a matter of right. Europe as yet is the only continent the whole of whose surface has been scientifically explored. It possesses a map approximately correct, and its material resources are almost fully known to us. Its population is not as dense as that of India or of China, but it nevertheless contains about one-fourth of the total population of the globe; and its inhabitants, whatever their failings and vices, or their state of barbarism in some respects, still impel the rest of mankind as regards material and mental progress. Europe, for twenty-five centuries, has been the focus whence radiated Arts, Sciences, and thought: Nor have these hardy colonists, who carried their European languages and customs beyond the sea, succeeded hitherto in giving the New World an importance equal to that of "little" Europe, in spite of the virgin soil and vast area which gave them scope for unlimited expansion.

Our American rivals. . .have scarcely been able hitherto to ascertain the material resources of the country in which they have made their home. "Old Europe," where every clod of earth has its history, where every man is the heir of a hundred successive generations, therefore still maintains the first place, and a comparative study of nations justifies us in the belief that its moral ascendancy and industrial preponderance will remain with it for many years to come. At the same time, we must not shut our eyes to the fact that equality will obtain in the end, not only between America and Europe, but also between these two and the other quarters of the world. . . . civilization will have "its centre everywhere, its periphery nowhere."

The central geographical position of Europe has undoubtedly exercised a most favorable influence upon the progress of the nations inhabiting it. The superiority of the Europeans is certainly not due to the inherent virtues of the races from which they sprang, as it is vainly imagined by some, for in other parts of the ancient world these same races have exhibited far less creative genius. To the happy conditions of soil, climate, configuration, and geographical position the inhabitants of Europe owe the honor of having been the first to obtain a knowledge of the earth in its entirety, and to have remained for so long a period at the head of mankind. Historical geographers are, therefore, right when they insist upon the influence which the configuration of a country exercises upon the nations which inhabit it. The extent of table-lands, the heights of mountain ranges, the direction and volume of rivers, the vicinity of the ocean, the indentation of the coastline, the temperature of the air, the abundance or rarity of rain, and the correlations between soil, air, and water — all these are pregnant with effects, and explain much of the character and mode of life of primitive nations. They account for most of the contrasts existing between nations subject to different conditions, and point out the different highways of the globe which nations are constrained to follow in their migrations or warlike expeditions.

At the same time we must bear in mind that the influence exercised upon the history of mankind by the general configuration of land and sea or any special features of the former, is subject to change, and depends essentially upon the stage of culture at which nations have arrived. Geography, strictly speaking, confines itself to a description of the earth's surface, and exhibits the various nations in a passive attitude as it were, while historical geography and statistics show man engaged in the struggle for existence, and striving to obtain mastery over his surroundings. A river, which to an uncultured tribe would constitute an insurmountable barrier, becomes a commercial high-road to a tribe further advanced in culture, and in process of time it may be converted into a mere canal of irrigation, the course of which is regulated by man. A mountain range frequented by shepherds and huntsmen, and forming a barrier between nations, may attract, in a more civilized epoch, the miner and the manufacturer, and in course of time will even cease to be an obstacle, as roads will traverse it in all directions. Many a creek of the sea, which afforded shelter of yore to the small vessels of our ancestors, is deserted now, whilst the open bays, which vessels dreaded formerly, have been protected by enormous breakwaters, and have become the resort of our largest ships.

Innumerable changes such as these have been affected by man in all parts of the world, and they have revolutionized the correlations existing between man and the land he lives in. The configuration and height of mountains and tablelands, the indentations of the coasts, the disposition of islands and archipelagoes, and the extent of the ocean — these all lose their relative influence upon the history of nations in proportion as the latter emancipate themselves and become free agents. Though subject to the condition of his dwelling-place, man may modify it to suit his own purposes; he may overcome nature as it were, and convert the energies of the earth into domesticated forces. As an instance we may point to the tablelands of Central Asia, which now separate the countries and peninsulas surrounding them, but which, when they shall become the seats of human industry, will convert Asia into a real geographical unit, which at present it is only in appearance. . . The advantages, on the other hand, which Europe derives from its backbone of mountains, its radiating rivers, the contours of its coasts, and its generally well balanced outline are not as great now as they were when man was dependent exclusively upon the resources furnished by nature.

This gradual change in the historical importance of the configuration of the land is a fact of capital importance which must be borne in mind if we would understand the general geography of Europe. In studying SPACE we must take account of another element of equal value — TIME.

EMMANUEL DE MARTONNE (1873-1955)

The founder of physical geography and geomorphology in France was de Martonne. Although he could build upon the preceding work of Davis and Richthofen, and of geologists such as the Austrian Suess and the French Emmanuel de Margerie, he reached many independent conclusions and his approach was quite original. For him, as for his predecessor Vidal de la Blache, the highest accomplishment of geography was the production of well-balanced, well-documented, well-rounded and well-written regional monographs. But he was first to lead French geographers to use geomorphology as the unifying bond. In his studies, he also successfully integrated systematic studies with the regional approach. His definition of climatic zones and climatic regions was important, though less widely used, outside of France, than that of Köppen. Despite his stress on and accomplishments in physical geography, he endeavored to organize the first French institute of geography in the social science faculty in close collaboration with history. Thus he followed and strengthened the French tradition — that historical events can be understood only in their geographical setting. Some of his work in human geography, generally in the spirit of Ratzel, became a guide for later French work. Except for Vidal de la Blache, Martonne was the most important French geographer in Europe.

The Teaching of Topography [2]

It is apparently self-evident and sounds rather trite to state that the knowledge of topography is necessary for a geographer, and that it ought to be his introduction into the study of surface forms. However, this truism is one of those which has to be reiterated at times. As a matter of fact, it seems that many geographers do not estimate too highly the teaching of topography, neither are the services which it can render both to teaching and scientific research sufficiently appreciated.

An inquisitive mind cannot occupy itself with topographical matters without noticing that in its concepts a gradual evolution occurs which leads imperceptibly to a rational morphology. Such an evolution would parallel that of the French topographic school which has by now come to a climax in the splendid work of General de la Noë: *Les Formes du Terrain* (*The Landforms*). In retracing the principal stages one clarifies, one after another, the most important principles on which the modern science of landforms rests. To each one of these stages there corresponds, in the history of the science, a characteristic station where geographers have stopped, more or less according to their personal environments and the nature of their minds.

Since topography in the presentation of relief advanced from the crude scattered hillocks on the Cassini maps to hachures, arranged according to a definite system, one has to acknowledge a fact that must also occur to the topographer who starts out with our refined methods today. It is that the presentation of relief is not an exact rendering of reality, but rather an *interpretation* of nature based upon the knowledge of certain elementary forms of relief.

. . .However large the scale may be, you will see that it is impossible to render every shade of the relief. . . Even with modern methods and instruments one has to *interpret*. For a long time this interpretation remained without rival. Perhaps, one did understand nature better than the first topog-

[2] "Les Enseignements de la Topographie" by Emmanuel de Martonne, *Annales de Geographie*, Vol. 13, No. 72, 15 November 1904, pp. 385-399.

raphers of the General Staff, who gave us these admirable maps, though they used crude methods as compared with modern precision leveling.

A guide to this interpretation was the knowledge of certain basic forms, which are quickly recognized with only a small amount of observation. It is sufficient to name and to define them by the course of the countour lines.

The most common form is the *valley,* which is shown by a reentrant of the contour lines. . . The crest is shown by concentric, elongated contours which taper to pointed ends; the *peak,* by concentric curves which are closer together near the center. . . Plateau, basin, dome, etc., are other common forms.

The recognition of these basic forms was a great step forward on the way to rational topography. Among geographers an analogous development has taken place since the beginning of the 19th century. Ritter and Humboldt tried to give a definite meaning to the terms by which one describes landforms, to find principles by which these forms could be classified, and to compare them as accurately as possible. It was Humboldt who popularized the usage of profiles, which is so general today, and who made the first computations of mean elevation. Sonklar[3] enlarged and improved upon these methods and founded *orology,* or *orometry,* which was considered the true science of relief at that time.

. . . Even today . . . one notices that the discussions about some terrain features are made obscure by the lack of exact definitions. While the related natural sciences — botany, zoology, geology — have precise terms for each form and each organ, physical geography still cannot boast of having a really scientific nomenclature.

It is possible to find several reasons for this state of affairs. The first and most important is that the forms of the relief offer an infinite number of varieties, and that there exist almost always transitional forms, difficult to classify and to name, between the typical forms which one can immediately define morphologically and genetically. . . . The geographer cannot ignore the popular terms for landforms. Unfortu-

[3] Sonklar was the first geographer to become professor at the University of Vienna. He was strongly influenced by de Saussure.

nately, these terms are often lacking in accuracy, and it is difficult to establish synonyms in two different languages. In our opinion, the solution to this difficulty cannot be found in relinquishing the popular terms and creating a new language, — as has been tried occasionally — but, contrariwise, in a thorough search into the meaning of these terms, which are often more definite than one would believe.[4] The third and final reason is that we lack sufficient topographical knowledge. We have accurate maps only for a small part of the globe; and, therefore, many forms escape our analysis. . . .

The lexicographic trend has its counterpart in the morphometric trend. If it useful to make the meaning of landform terms precise, one can assume that the ideal would be to define these forms by numerical expressions, i.e., by mathematical formulae, derived from exact measurements. This tendency, especially noticeable in the German school, has given us the remarkable works of Finsterwalder,[5] Kurowski, Peucker.[6] The first volume of the *Morphologie der Erdoberfläche* (*Morphology of the Surface of the Earth)* by Penck contains the elements of this science. . . .

However, morphometry, useful as it may be, cannot be the last word in the science of relief. Measuring the forms can no more satisfy the geographer than can defining them. Like the other, older natural sciences, physical geography is not satisfied merely with describing: it wants to explain.

After having recognized the existence of the primary forms of relief, one soon will realize, after a little practice, that real nature rarely offers pure examples of these theoretical forms. Generally, the sculpture of the surface is the result of complex associations, in which the primary forms are modified by a kind of mutual influence.

. . .In order to be able to interpret the sculpture in conformity with reality, or to say it concisely, to understand the land-

---

[4] de Martonne quotes here the work of Penck in German.

[5] Sebastian and Richard Finsterwalder, father and son, were later pioneers in photogrammetry.

[6] Kurowski and Peucker worked out, among other things, light and color schemes of maps.

forms, we must regard them as the result of a development, the underlying laws of which we should try to discover.

Of all the primary forms the valley is repeated most often, so much so that there is hardly any association where it is not found. . . . If one observes that usually there is a water course in each valley and the more rapid its river, the deeper the valley; if one notes all the indications of erosion which are offered to the topographer along the *thalweg;* one cannot avoid concluding that the valleys were carved by rivers; and, as the valley is the predominant landform, one is bound to arrive at this fundamental concept:

The forms of the terrestrial relief, if studied in every detail, are primarily the result of subaerial erosion; and the pattern of the hydrographic net is a very important indicator of the type of relief—perhaps the most important[7]. . . .

. . .More and more one realizes that the arrangement of the valleys and water-courses offers the key for the explanation of relief, and holds a predominant place in all morphological studies.

It is interesting to note that the country where these ideas most easily took root and united all the people, where the study of the valley patterns became the object of the most penetrating research and enlivened all physical description, is also the country where the geologist and topographers collaborated most closely—the United States.[8] In Europe, especially in Germany and Austria, although the development of physical geography was singularly fertile, topography remained the special field of the military. For a long time geologists remained somewhat aloof or hostile to the ideas of the American school. In France it was the genius of a topographer [9] who saw early that these principles were spread with the force of original ideas.

---

[7] It should be noted that de Martonne later became the pioneer of glacial morphology in France.

[8] In the omitted paragraphs de Martonne quotes Gilbert, Powell, and W. M. Davis. Of the Germans he includes only Philippson, of the French de la Noë and Margerie.

[9] de la Noë.

Topographical experience has shown us two important facts; the genetic relationships of primary forms and the predominance of the valley formation. We are led from this point to the discovery of two basic principles of a rational morphology: the landforms are the result of a continuing evolution; the most important agent of this evolution is erosion. We can deduce still other useful ideas.

The pattern of the contour lines does not apply solely to the *thalwegs,* but also to the lines which indicate a break in the slope. . .

Therefore, the lines indicating a break of the slope are due either to the difference in the character of the rocks, or to dislocations in the strata of the earth's crust, or, finally, to different forms of erosional activity.

It is thus clear *that the rational study of relief is impossible without relying on the one hand upon an exact knowledge of the laws of erosion, and on the other hand upon that of stratigraphic and tectonic geology.*

These truisms have found their way into the geographical world since detailed geological surveys were initiated using topographical maps as base maps. One should not be surprised that the importance of the geological factor has been particularly stressed, because it was primarily the geologists who understood the importance of presenting careful explanation. One should not forget, however, that the geological background—character of rocks and tectonic dislocations—are only factors which modify the activity of erosion. First of all it is necessary to be thoroughly familiar with different methods of erosional action.

It is, therefore, obvious that a mind little given to thinking is led by the practice of topographical research to insights which become the germ of the most general principles of the rational study of relief. . .

Let us stop here with our analysis, which we could push much further. It is sufficient to show that intelligent topographic work leads from descriptive morphology to genetic morphology, and that together they constitute a natural introduction into the study of landforms.

It would be easy to demonstrate in every field of morphological research the advantages which accompany a familiarity with topographical methods. Is it not permitted to consider that occasionally our studies of landforms stray somewhat into description? Are we not sometimes the victim of what one could call the mirage of causation; and do we not forget to account accurately for the relief, itself, in our effort to discover the contrasts between different landforms? Frequently a regional analysis of forms can lead us quite far along the road to their rational interpretation. What better examples could we quote than the researches of Davis on the stream net, or of Richter [10]on the glacial forms of the Alps? To keep one's mind on this road, to lead it back to this fertile and truly original method of morphological research, would be a slight advantage for a strict morphological discipline. One should not fear this as a return through the backdoor to a merely descriptive morphology. Quite the opposite, we have demonstrated that a well-understood topography can inspire an inquisitive spirit and genetic explanation.

PAUL VIDAL DE LA BLACHE (1845-1918)

Vidal was the founder of modern French geography. Before the publication of Vidal's *Géographie Universelle* the encyclopedic, multi-volume description of the earth by Elisée Reclus had been the outstanding work of French geography. Vidal de la Blache, by his own work and by the suggestions and guidance which he gave to his numerous disciples, made French geography renowned for its well-rounded, well-written, and very thorough regional studies.

Indeed, Vidal de la Blache was influenced by German geography. Orginally an historian, he retained an interest in historical geography and the work of its two most prominent German representatives, Ritter and Ratzel. However, while other Ratzel followers, for example Ellen Semple, understood Ratzel as an environmental determinist and exaggerated the tendencies in Ratzel's work in this direction, Vidal developed concepts of possibilism from Ratzel's suggestions. He warned against neglecting or underestimating the environment, but

---

[10] Austrian geographer.

stressed that it makes possible — or impossible — certain developments; it does not force man into them.

Ways of Life in Human Geography

One knows that the physiognomy of a landscape is very susceptible to change according to the mode of life of its inhabitants. Such changes in Europe are less obvious to us because the conditions of existence here have been, so to speak, stereotyped and fixed for several centuries. Nevertheless, they do not escape a keen eye; and we can observe such things as the fact that growing urbanization has influenced the surrounding civilization, the groupings and physiognomy of the landscape, with by no means insensible modifications.

However, it suffices to consider the so-called new countries, the prairies of America, the pampas, and even the Puszta, the Russian steppes, and finally the Mitidja and other parts of Algeria, in order to appreciate the changes which the substitution of one way of life for another brings about. There we witness not only transformation brought about by the importation of new elements, but, that which upsets the previously existing equilibrium of living nature and causes a thorough revolution, which extends to inorganic nature. Vegetation changes around pastures to which our herds have been brought; trees appear where they had been excluded; certain unwanted plants appear by themselves under the impact of our civilization. And the opposite of this picture offers itself in too many landscapes where pastoral abuses, among others, are prevalent. Especially around the Mediterranean, and in Western Asia, there is no lack of examples of semi-deserts becoming the successors to semi-pastoral agriculture or to irrigation.

We face, for all purposes, a geographical factor which has not been fully appreciated, or at least, whose functioning has not been investigated, no doubt because of the lack of sufficient material for comparison. An established way of life implies

[11] "Les Genres de Vie Dans la Geographie Humaine," Paul Vidal de la Blache, *Annales de Geographic*, 20th Year, May 1911, pp. 193-195.

a methodical and continuing, though very strong, impact upon nature, or to use geographical terminology, upon the physiognomy of a landscape. Without a doubt, the impact of man upon his "environment" made itself felt from the moment that his arm was fitted with some tool; it is possible to say that, from the very beginning of civilization, this impact was far from negligible. However, an organized and systematized habit is entirely different, carving its grooves deeper and deeper, imposing itself upon the following generation with accumulated force, impressing its mark upon the mind, and forcing all powers of progress into a definite direction.

This impact is so strong that we are easily duped. The mental pictures which the pastoral stage, or the agricultural, or many other sociological classifications, bring to mind, are far from corresponding with the decisive contrasts in nature. These differences are so pronounced that herdsman and agriculturalist (to cite only these most highly developed types) have become two beings, very different socially because of habits and concepts adapted only to their particular way of life. There are irreconcilable concepts of property, family, race, or law, which each of these two social beings has formed. Law for one is essentially territorial, for the other, family law. However, these contrasting concepts are only very indirectly natural features. It would be an abuse of language to call them translations from the physical environment. Nature is much more diverse, more *malleable,* less absolute than these contrasts make it appear. It has many more different possibilities than one would believe from our abstract classifications. We will be able to judge more correctly to the same degree that our knowledge encompasses more countries which are at different stages of development. We see that, despite similarities of climate, there are great variations in ways of life. We see that people successively have dressed in different costumes. It is primarily modern colonization which has taught us to measure the extent of the power of modification of landscapes, which man controls; one has, therefore, to agree that if this power were restricted within rigid forms, this work of colonization, which evokes such legitimate interests, would have no role or make no sense.

I believe, in order to form a correct conception, one must first consider that both the action of man upon nature and that of nature upon man is exercised primarily through the media of fauna and flora, through something infinitely supple and tenacious which is called life. The influences of soil and climate, which dominate everything, affect us and this entire animated world on which our whole existence is based.

It is a world of great complexity, into which enter aspects of very different geological periods, some in retrogress, others in progress. There is a condition both of struggle and cooperation between animals which destroy each other, or plants which fight for space, or between plants and microbes and parasites which live at their expense. Side by side with plants which have succeeded in reaching the air, are others, suppressed, waiting for a propitious moment to sprout forth from the asylum in which they are imprisoned. From all this there results an unstable equilibrium where no place is definitely guaranteed. Into this struggle. . .human intervention has a good opportunity to modify the chances, to throw a decisive weight into the balance. That is what has happened; man has taken sides. However, while man deems it necessary to mobilize for himself part of the living forces in order to act as master, he thereby risks meeting very unequal chances on the battlefield.

If this living nature is poor, anemic because of restrictive features of climate, man himself is hindered or hampered in his means of life. An epizoon, which destroys a herd of reindeer, forces the Samoyede or Tchukch tribe to disperse. A canal, which ceases to function in Sind, changes a group of agriculturalists into a gang of marauders or brigands. The way of life in these regions is very precarious. . . .

* * *

Principles of Human Geography [12]

Critical Examination of the Concept of Human Geography. Human geography is a recent sprout from the venerable trunk of geographical science. If it were merely a question of terms nothing could be less novel, for the human element is an essential part of all geography. Man is interested in his own kind more than in anything else. As soon as the age of travel and distant voyages opened, it was the discovery of social as well as environmental differences which chiefly excited his interest. What Ulysses retained from his travels was "the knowledge of cities and customs of many races." To most of the early authors who wrote about geography the notion of country was inseparable from that of their inhabitants—the food supply and the appearance of the population were no less curiously foreign and unaccustomed than the mountains, deserts and rivers which made up their environment.

Human geography, therefore, is not to be contrasted with a geography from which human interests are excluded. Indeed such has never existed except in the minds of specialists. But our science offers a new concept of the interrelationships between earth and man—a concept resulting from a more synthetic knowledge of the physical laws governing our earth and of the relations among the living beings which inhabit it.

Human geography is the expression of a growth of ideas rather than the immediate, one might almost say material, result of discovery and the extension of geographical knowledge.

It would seem as if the new light shed upon the entire surface of the earth during the sixteenth century might have given rise to human geography in the real sense of the word. But such was not the case. However, manners and customs, to be sure, do play a large part in the narrations and compilations which that age has bequeathed to us. But emphasis

---

[12] Principles de Geographic humaine, Paul Vidal de la Blache, Ed. by Emmanuel de Martonne, 1921, translated by Millicent Todd Brigham, Henry Holt & Company, N. Y. 1926. Some slight changes of the original English translation have been made. *Introduction. Meaning and Aim of Human Geography*, pp. 3-29.

was laid upon the extraordinary and bizarre, if not upon mere anecdote. There was no principle of geographical classification underlying the various types of societies described. Those who try to reconstruct pictures or "mirrors" of the world by using data of such a nature are no more dependable than Strabo. In regard to human phenomena necessarily included in descriptions of countries, Bernhard Varenius — whose *Geographia Generalis,* written in 1650, was the most remarkable work up to the time of Ritter — uses phrases showing an almost contemptuous condescension on his part. And so, though knowledge about the most varied types of peoples had been increasing throughout two centuries of discovery, nothing resulted which was either clear-cut or satisfying from the point of view of scientific classification.

Nevertheless, scientific thought had long been attracted by the influences of the physical world upon human society. It would be unjust to a line of scholars reaching from the first Greek philosophers to Thucydides, Aristotle, Hippocrates and Erastosthenes, to forget the ingenious and often profound ideas which are often expressed in their writings. How could the varied and ever-widening spectacle of the external world fail, after reasonable reflection upon the progress of human societies, to awaken an echo in the philosophical schools that sprang up along the Ionian shores. There were certain sages who, like Heraclitus, true predecessor of Bacon that he was, thought that man, rather than confine the search for truth to the contemplation of "his own microcosm," would do very well to widen his horizon and seek truth from the "great world" of which he is a part. [13]

These wise men began by investigating the physical environment for the explanation of whatever was particularly striking in the character of the inhabitants. Then, as with the passage of time, observations of the march of events and of societies accumulated and broadened in scope, it became more and more evident just how much importance should be attached to geographical causes. The reflections of Thucydides upon archaic Greece, and of Strabo upon the location of Italy, are

[13] Francis Bacon, *De Dignitate et Augmentis Scientiarum,* Book I, p. 43.

traceable to the same intellectual traits as certain chapters of the *Esprit des Lois* (by Montesquieu) or of Henry Thomas Buckle's *History of Civilization in England.*

Ritter is also inspired by similar ideas in his *Erdkunde* but he writes more as a geographer. Though he assigns a special role to each great continental country becauses of traces of historical bias, he nevertheless does regard the interpretation of nature as pivotal. For most historians and sociologists, on the other hand, geography exists only for purposes of consultation. One starts from man in order to come back by a detour to man once more. One pictures the earth as "the stage upon which man's activities take place" without reflecting that the stage itself is alive. The problem consists in enumerating the influences affecting man, in an attempt to discover in how far a certain amount of determinism is operative in the events of history. Important and interesting questions, surely, but answers to them require a knowledge of the world wider and more profound than any available until recently.

The Principle of Terrestrial Unity and the Concept of Environment.—The dominant idea in all geographical progress is that of terrestrial unity. The concept of the earth as a whole, whose parts are coordinated, where phenomena follow a definite sequence and obey general laws to which particular cases are related, had early entered the field of science by way of astronomy. In the words of Ptolemy, geography is "the sublime science which sees in the heavens the reflection of earth." But, the concept of terrestrial unity was long confined to the domain of mathematics. It did not become part of other branches of geography until our own day, and then largely through the knowledge of circulation of the atmosphere which governs climatic laws. More and more we have come to accept certain generalizations with reference to the world organism. Friedrich Ratzel very wisely insists on such a concept, making it the cornerstone of his *Anthropogeography.* [14] The phenomena of human geography are bound up

[14] *Anthropogeographie,* 2nd part, Die hologäische Ansicht (the wholistic concept), Stuttgart, 1891.

with terrestrial unity by means of which alone they can be explained. They are everywhere related to the environment, itself the creature of a combination of physical conditions.

Botanical geography has been largely responsible for throwing light upon the concept of environment, but the light reaches far beyond, embracing the geography of all living creatures. Alexander von Humboldt, with his usual foresight, pointed out how important is the appearance of vegetation in determining the character of a landscape, and when H. Berghaus, inspired by him, published in 1836 the first edition of his *Physikalischer Atlas*, the close relationship between climate and vegetation was clearly brought out. This fertile idea opened the way for a new series of researches. Classification of species became less important than a survey of the entire plant life of a region, made in such a way as to show how the influence of environmental conditions, such as soil, temperature and humidity, manifests itself. . . .

In conclusion, these researches result in an essentially geographic concept: that of environment as composite, capable of grouping and of holding together heterogeneous beings in mutual vital interrelationships. This idea seems to be the law governing the geography of living creatures. Every region is a domain, where many dissimilar beings, artificially brought together, have subsequently adapted themselves to a common existence. . . .

How far are these facts applicable to human geography?

Man and Environment.—But, before proceeding further, one point must be briefly considered. Botanical geography is based upon an imposing array of observations and researches: zoological geography, although far less advanced, has profited by much fruitful exploration. What facts are at the disposal of human geography? What is their source of origin? Are they numerous enough to warrant conclusions of which we have already had a glimpse?

In the study of relations between earth and man, the perspective has changed. We are looking at them from a greater distance.

Heretofore, only historic times have been under consideration, which include merely the last act of the human drama, a period exceedingly short in comparison with the life and activities of man on earth. Prehistoric research has shown that man has been established since time immemorial in widely diverse parts of the globe, equipped with fire and fashioning tools; and however rudimentary his industries, the modifications that the face of the earth has undergone because of them cannot be ignored. The palaeolithic hunter and earliest neolithic agriculturalists destroyed certain species of animals and plants and favored others. . . .

Another sign of progress is that we are better informed at present as to the distribution of our kind, we know more accurately how large the populations in different parts of the earth really are. . . .

Considering the instability of relations between living beings, the numbers and territorial distribution of each species has great scientific value. It throws light upon the evolution of occupation. Human population is a constantly changing phenomenon. This is most plainly in evidence when, in addition to statistics with reference to particular states, general distribution throughout the world is taken into account. There are regions so overpopulated that the inhabitants seem to have utilized all possible space. There are others where population has remained small and scattered, when neither soil nor climate seem to justify the anomaly. How can such differences be explained except as the result of immigration which originated in prehistoric times and of which only geography can discover a trace? And naturally these neglected areas are becoming a focus of attraction for present day migrations.

One of the most suggestive relationships is that between number of inhabitants and any given area, in other words, density of population. If detailed statistics of population are compared with equally detailed maps, such as are available in almost all the principal countries of the world today, it is possible by analysis, to find a connection between human groups and physical conditions. Here we touch upon one of the basic problems of human occupation. For the existence of a dense population, a large group of human beings living together in the smallest space consistent with certainty of a livelihood for the entire group—means, if one stops to think of it, a victory which can only be won under rare and unusual circumstances.

Today transportation facilities minimize the difficulties which our forebears encountered in forming compact groups where they happened to be. And yet, most existing groups were formed in ancient times; an analysis of them reveals their genesis. In reality the population of a region is composed, as Levasseur has well shown, of a certain number of scattered nuclei surrounded by concentric zones of decreasing intensity. It gathers about centres or lines of attraction. Population did not spread like a drop of oil; in the beginning it grew in clumps, like corals. Reefs of population collected at certain points by a sort of crystallization process. These populations, by their intelligence, increased the natural resources and the value of such places, so that other men, whether voluntarily or under compulsion, came to share the advantages of the inheritance, and successive layers accumulated on the chosen spot.

Now we have anthropological data in regard to some of the countries where human alluvium has been thus deposited. Central Europe, the Mediterranean basin and British Indies are for different reasons examples from which it is possible to gain some idea of the composition of peoples. In a general way, their complexity strikes us most. . . . Why some places should contain more heterogeneous elements than others is easily explained by their nature and location. But in the present stage of development of human occupation, regions which seem to have entirely escaped waves of invasion that have swept over the surface of the earth are very exceptional—only a few distant archipelagos and mountain fortresses. Even in the African jungle tall Negroes and lighter-skinned pygmies live side by side in mutual relationships. In spite of current usage which confuses the terms "people" and "race," the fundamental distinction between them can henceforth be considered established. Beneath similarities of language, religion and nationality, the specific differences implanted in us by an ancient descent never cease to be operative. Nevertheless, all such heterogeneous groups blend in a social organization which makes of the population of a country a unit when looked at in its entirety. It sometimes happens that each of the elements of this composite whole is well established in a certain mode of life; some as hunters, others agriculturalists, others shepherds; if such is the case, they cooperate with and supplement one another. It most often happens, except for certain most obstinately refactory units within our European societies, such as gypsies, gitanos, zingani, etc., that the sovereign influence of environment has forced all into similar occupation and customs. There is material evidence of this uniformity. Such is the coalescing power which blots out original differences and blends them in a common type of adaptation. Human societies, like those of the vegetable and animal world, are composed of different elements subject to the influence of environment. No one knows what minds brought them together, nor whence, nor when; but they are living side by side in a region which has gradually put its stamp upon them. Some societies have long been part of the environment, but others are in process of formation, continuing to recruit members and to be modified day by day. Environmental conditions leave their imprint upon such people, despite all they can do, and in Australia, at the Cape, or in America, these people are slowly becoming saturated with the influence of the regions where their destinies are to unfold. Are not the Boers one of the most remarkable examples of adaptation?

Man as a Geographical Factor—As a result of the particularism of the earlier geographical conditions, certain broad, general concepts regarding the relationships between earth and man begin to appear. Population distribution has been guided in its development by the proximity of land masses to one another. Ocean solitudes long divided inhabited countries (oekumenes) and kept them in ignorance of one another. Throughout the continents widely separated groups met with physical obstacles which only time could overcome; mountains, forests, marshes, waterless regions, etc.,—civilization recapitulates the struggles against such obstacles. The peoples which surmounted them were enabled to profit from the results of a collective experience gained in a variety of environments.

Other communities, because of prolonged isolation, lost the initiative which had inspired their early progress. Incapable of raising themselves above a certain level by their own efforts, they suggest certain animal communities which seem to have completed the utmost progress of which they are capable. Today all parts of the earth are interrelated. Isolation is an anomaly which seems like a challenge. Contacts are no longer mostly between contiguous or neighboring areas, as heretofore, but between widely separated regions.

Physical causes, whose value geographers have been proud of pointing out, are not without influence on this account; it is always necessary to note the effect of climate and relief, as well as of continental or similar position, on human societies. But, we should observe their effects on man and on the whole of the living world conjointly.

In this way we are in a position to appreciate better the role which should be assigned to man as a geographical factor. He is at once both active and passive. For, according to the well-known phrase, "natura non nisi parendo vincitur" (Nature is only conquered by new creation).

An eminent Russian geographer, Voeikoff, has noted that the objects over which man has control are chiefly what he calls "movable bodies."[15] On that part of the earth's crust which is modified by the mechanical action of surface agencies, such as running water, winds, frost, the roots of plants, the transference of particles by animals and the constant tread of their feet, lies a residue, the result of decomposition, constantly being renewed and prepared for use, capable of being modified and of taking on different forms. . . . Man utilizes not only inorganic agencies in his work of transformation. He is not content merely to make use of the products of decomposition in the soil by ploughing, nor to utilize the waterfalls, the force of gravity brought into play by inequalities of relief. He further collaborates with all living forces grouped together by environmental conditions. He joins in nature's game. . .and by his intervention can reinforce the positive

[15] A. Voeikoff, "De l'influence de l'homme sur la terre," *Annales de Geographie*, Vol. X, 1901, p. 98.

factor, establish, as it were, a permanent state upon a temporary one—permanent, at least, until a new order of things.

For example: Most of the plants assembled by agriculture are species which formerly were widely scattered. . .overpowered by competition with more numerous, vigorous species, and allowed to remain only in certain places. . . . Man by making them part of his own *clientele,* did them this service of allowing them more space. But, simultaneously he opened the way to a whole procession of uninvited plants and animals. New groups took the place of those which had occupied the space before his arrival.

In studying the influence of man upon the earth, and the scars which occupation, often of very long standing, has already made on its surface, human geography has a double aim. It not only has to take account of the destruction in which man may or may not have shared, one which has enormously reduced the number of great animal species since the period, but it must also find, by a more intimate knowledge of the relationships which make a single unit of the entire living world, a means of thoroughly investigating the transformations taking place at the present time as well as those which can be foreseen in the future. In this respect, present and future undertakings of man, henceforth master of distances, armed with all that science places at his disposal, will far exceed any influence that our remote ancestors could exert. Let us congratulate ourselves, because the task of colonization which constitutes the glory of our age would be only a sham if nature set definite, rigid boundaries instead of leaving a margin for the work of transformation or reparation which is within man's power to perform.

LUCIEN GALLOIS (1857-1941)

In 1918 after the sudden death of Paul Vidal de la Blache, who had conceived the cooperatively written *Géographie Universelle* and directed its early years, Lucien Gallois took over its direction. He wrote the preface when the first volume of that set appeared in 1927. Excerpts from that preface, which appear below, not only reflect the ideas of the author, but they are representative of the French school of geography at that time.

Gallois' own works are typical of the French school, and some are outstanding examples of regional presentation. He developed the regional concept so as to include the urban landscape and is considered one of the first urban geographers. In addition, his interest in historical geography led him into studies of the history of geography.

Geographie Universelle[16]

For a century, and especially for the last half century, geography has profited a good deal from the general progress of human knowledge. Finally, with the conquest of the poles, the discovery of the earth was completed. Consequently the natural sciences—meteorology, oceanography, geology, botany and zoology—claimed the entire width and breadth of the earth as their field. The results of all their observations have shown on maps, which have become progressively more accurate. Thereby, the mutual impact of all phenomena became evident. All these analytical researches were brought together into the great synthesis which is nature taken as a whole. The study of landforms was born out of the examination of relief in combination with the facts furnished by geography. For a long time one was satisfied to describe the present state of landforms without considering their origin. There exists today a general geography which borrows its results from the natural sciences, clarifying one by the other, deriving from their complexity not laws, which permit predictions (because, for the scholar, laws are only expressions of simple relationships, and nature is not always simple), but more or less general data which are repeated all over the globe and explain particular facts.

Through this more scientific and more intimate knowledge of the physical environment, advantage accrued to human geography, the study of the multiple activities of man on the surface of the earth. It has been said that this environmental influence, though very strong, almost tyrannical for primitive societies, is weakened as a civilization attains a higher level.

---

[16] *Preface to Géographie Universelle*, published under the direction of P. Vidal de la Blache and L. Gallois, Librarie Armand Colin, Paris, 1927, p. V-VIII.

It is true that by his intelligence man has extricated himself gradually from the tethers of environment. Man has forced into his service not only the animals, but the very natural forces themselves. The circle of his activities, nevertheless, has limits. Directly or indirectly, for his very livelihood he depends on the earth. He hardly can prevail against the climate. Study of history, and even of prehistory, if one considers events within the frame of their natural environment, very often reveals this dependence of man on natural conditions. It is not by accident that the great human agglomerations have formed where they have on the globe. It occurred because of the ease of life, provisioning, and communications, character of the country, and privileged location. It is true that these advantages may be relative, and that a new form of activity carries with it a change in respective values. The utilization of steam strongly favored those countries with many coal fields. The long-distance transmission of water power marks the beginning of an evolution the effects of which can already be measured. It is hardly necessary to state that the influence of environment does not explain all the facts of human activity. However, the existence of such an influence suffices to justify and to force its investigation. The means of information which are at our disposal today provide us with particular tools for this task: inquiries of all kinds, population censuses, statistical facts which are shown on maps. The localization of human facts on physical, geological, or climatological maps often constitutes a veritable revelation for the geographer. Among all the possibilities of inquiry into human activities, research on the influence of environment seems reserved especially for geography. Thereby it distinguishes itself from other sciences from which it has to borrow, and thereby it preserves its orginality and its field. It escapes the often raised criticism of being a kind of encyclopedia of all sciences, inaccurate because of its broad scope.

The frame which offers itself for a geographical treatment of various countries of the globe is the political frame. However, while it is obvious that a state cannot be studied physically, independent of the surrounding regions, is not the same true from an economic or human viewpoint? Vidal de la Blache said "A country does not live its own isolated life; it participates in a more general life which it communicates; and its general contacts must necessarily increase with civilization. Who could hope to escape the consequences of the great economic revolution, such as the discoveries in the 19th century in the means of communication?" "No nation," he said, too, "is the only creator of its own civilization. In order to rise to higher grade of development, it is necessary that each country's life be in contact with that of a larger area which enriches it from its substance, and which brings imperceptible new ferments." In the instructions which he addressed to his co-authors he insisted that they never lose sight of the whole. He reminded them that life of certain countries is intimately connected with the surrounding seas, sometimes even with distant seas. He compared the great traffic routes with the great currents which dominate climatic phenomena. In accordance with his ideas, the order for the following chapters was adopted. Thus we have grouped together the countries of Northwest Europe, taking into account their affinities which the countries on the coast of the North Sea shore. The same is true for Central Europe, which one must first study as a whole, before turning to the states which divide it between them, often without any reference to physical boundaries. The same is the case for Mediterranean Europe. France occupies a position between these three groups and participates in each of them. For the same reason we did not consider separating European Russia from Asiatic Russia, a division which no longer corresponds to the actual political situation. In Asia we first studied its western Mediterranean front, which is separated by large, mostly desert regions from Inner or High Asia, and Asia of the monsoons: India, Indo-China, Indonesia, China and Japan. The climatic rhythm establishes a veritable kinship among these countries. Africa, the colonial continent, has been broken up in such a way as to group together as much as possible the countries under French influence and those upon which England has left its mark. In America, Mexico was treated together with Central America, not only because it extends southward, but because it belonged to Spanish America throughout its whole colonial history. The study of the Polar regions was divided between the two hemispheres on which they depend.

If modern geography is more and more occupied with research into causation, it remains no less loyal to its old definition and objectives, that is, first of all, the description of the Earth. One has to be aware that words are often incapable of expressing the true aspects of nature, of making felt its beauty and greatness. One can only try to replace the direct experience with pictures. The editor has devoted all his care to the illustration of this work. It goes without question that the artistic value of the photographs was not the overriding concept in their selection. They have been included in order to complement the text; they are incorporated, as are the sketches and maps, to facilitate comprehension. In order to collect these photographs, we have borrowed from public and private collections. Many of these pictures were chosen following the suggestions of the authors, or by the authors themselves.

Our goal has been to put within reach of every educated person results which too often have remained reserved for scientific travellers, and to demonstrate the valuable help which a deepened knowledge of the physical world offers to the study of problems which are connected with human geography: distribution of population, types of groupings, way of life, habitat, and quite particularly economic problems, which take a growing place in the present life of nations and international relations. Without sacrificing scientific accuracy, it is possible to say everything if only it is clear. And it never was more urgent to study in their real setting the problems on which in part the peace of the world depends.

Confidently we present to the public a work of a school which often has been called the French school of geography, one which remains loyal to the teachings of the master from which it derives.

CAMILLE VALLAUX (1870-1945)

Vallaux defined geography as the study of relationships. Among the leading French geographers, he alone took a somewhat critical view of the study of regions as a suitable purpose of geography, but rather stressed the study of the interdependence of regions and of the components of regions. This view led him early in the century to draw attention to the growing interdependence of all nations of this world — before it had become a generally accepted notion.

Like Vidal de la Blache and others, he was impressed by the work of Ratzel, but he cannot be called a follower. Ratzel's ideas very often merely inspired him to approach problems in an original way. Characteristic of his independent approach was his early work on the human geography of the oceans, a thorough investigation of the subject, instigated by ideas which Ratzel proposed but never fully explored.

Vallaux shared with other French geographers a thorough grounding in history, and much of his work is in the border area between the two fields. In general his influence was overshadowed in France by that of Vidal and his regional school.

The Sciences of Geography[17]

No longer do we consider the surface of the earth an organism; but we have a certain feeling for the interdependence which unites all of its parts—those which appear as solid land, as liquid, or as air. We have learned to resist the urge for analysis to which the schematism of cartographic presentation led our predecessors; since the end of the descriptive period, with which it had to begin, we conceived geography as a science of forms and synthetic methods. Explanation was a failure: it came too late. Also description profits greatly from our acquired habit of envisioning things together, or at least of making an effort in this direction, because real things form a whole interruption of their continuity. They permit no other demarcations or divisions than those imaginary divisions which we make in order to alleviate our thinking a little and to prevent our losing ourselves in innumerable possibilities. No doubt, we are forced to arrange the features of the surface under general and somewhat rough categories before we start our research; these categories are forced upon

[17] (The plural is purposely used because Vallaux regards as separate sciences what are usually called branches..) Les Sciences Géographiques, Camille Vallaux. New edition, Paris, Felix Alcan, 1929. p 58-68.

us both by the schematic presentation of the maps and in order to bring some clarity into the investigation from the beginning. There are the facts of the surface relief, the features of the running waters, those of the stagnant waters, of the sea waters, those of the physical features of the atmosphere, of the plant and animal associations, and finally those of human life itself and those of human life in its association with the earth. But we know that these categories are not isolated or separated from each other. Quite to the contrary, we are convinced that it presents no difficulty if they infringe upon each other, whether we feel forced to delimit them or not—I would even say that we know that they are integrated partially and, *perhaps, in a rational manner,* in the same way as are the circles by which Euler presented the syllogisms. I stress that this integration occurs *perhaps* in a rational manner; but his rationality has not been proven; if it had, geography would be completed and uncontested, and we would not be here. At present, if we regard the surface features as inseparable, this point of view does not accomplish anything except to safeguard the scientific progress of description. It suffices to allow us to state that since geography entered the descriptive phase, geography appears as a science of masses, or still better a science of grouping. Those cautious spirits, who in imitating either history or the natural sciences, devote geography to research of multiple detail in infinite and repeated dissections and refinements of the real world, show only that they do not understand the object of modern geography and that they have not penetrated its meaning.

Of course, the reversal in geography of the logical process ordinarily followed by the observation sciences is well apt to surprise one at first. All the other observing sciences, whether they belong to the natural or social sciences—and we know that geography belongs to both—start out by dissecting reality in increasingly smaller fragments, either by direct observation or with the help of instruments, before putting it together again by syntheses which aim at a rational explanation; however, the first geographic synthesis does not aim at anything but a pure description. The zoologist who examines the body of an animal is correct to contend that he will never arrive at an understanding of the laws of this organism so long as he is content to study the features and their outward connections; he needs a microscope which allows him to reach the nerve fibres, the tissues of the muscles, the living cells in their varied combinations. In physics the search for the microscopic goes far beyond the point where the natural scientists stop: the latter at least see and touch with the help of very powerful instruments the cells which they study; the physicists are neither able to see nor to touch the atoms and electrons. They are almost metaphysical beings, not only beyond the grasp of the senses, but beyond that of the instruments, if one may use this expression. Nevertheless, modern science is based on this mysterious legion of infinitely small things. On another scale the social sciences, too, always start with research of what corresponds to the infinite minutiae of the physical science—that is with the most uncomplicated, or what they regard as such: the primitive man, primitive societies, tribes, villages, professional and social types of the least variety and complexity. In other words, all sciences which rely on observation consider it necessary to depart from the infinitely small or simple; indeed, they did not achieve great success before they recognized the necessity of this logical approach or before they had equipped themselves accordingly. The rapid growth of the natural sciences dates from the use of the microscope and would have been impossible without it.

One can easily understand the mistrust of the physicists, natural scientists, historians and sociologists, who are accustomed to the use of a real microscope or a kind of ideal microscope and convinced that the molecular sciences, except for mathematics, are the only ones capable of progress. Such mistrust is natural when they observe a new science such as geography attempting groupings from the outset of its research without the help of any new method of study, either based on instruments or on original logical procedures. For intellects conditioned to the ordinary development of sciences, it would probably appear that the method of geographical arrangement of things is nothing but a tentative, careless attempt to establish connections where there are none, or at best a flight of poetic or metaphysic imagination (which is the same, basically) to catch reality just in passing. In both cases, for men accustomed to proceed step by step in the sphere of solid facts, the attempt of geographical groupings can be nothing but futile and condemned to complete sterility.

This objection would be grave and, without doubt, indisputable, if all the materials of geographical observation were restricted to the terrestrial surface which geography views either by direct examination of the ground or by cartographic presentation. Luckily, that is not the case. In order to be valuable, the observation of groupings has to combine not only geographical materials but a vast amount of materials borrowed from other sciences—molecular sciences—which are capable of producing them, but incapable of utilizing them in our efforts to arrive at a comprehensive understanding of the surface of the earth. It is only geography which proves capable of using this knowledge to attain the latter goal.

If we consider a mountain massif, such as the Alps, we are well aware that a reasoned bird's-eye-view description, such as is the goal of modern geography, is impossible if we have not assembled beforehand a huge amount of data, which only the molecular sciences can give us. The inner structure of the surface rocks is always more or less reflected in their external decomposition, taking into account elevation, and is explained by the research of mineralogists with the help of the microscope and the polarized light of the laboratory. The superposition and co-existence of masses originating from ancient dislocations are determined by geology, sometimes with rigorous method, sometimes with a certain amount of constructive imagination. The mountain observatories furnish, or should furnish, numerical data not only on rain, wind, snow, variation in temperature and air pressure, but also on variation of insolation and effects of frost which affect the land forms; hydraulics contributes information about the dynamics of torrents and their erosive and depositional force; the plant associations, that of trees as well as of bushes and grasses, ordered according to elevation, contribute to the study of the firmness or mobility of the ground and thereby of the variability of its forms; the groupings of animals and man, especially the latter, testify to their effects on many points. There is a huge amount of observation worked out by many different sciences which, in their origins, have nothing specifically geographical; they do not become geographical until they characterize cogently the locality within a certain space. That is exactly what the geographer tries to determine with his grouped observation, adding the elements of the unity which the map or direct observation reveal to him. . . .

It is obvious, therefore, that in order to be valid everywhere and at every time, the observation of geographical grouping must be based on a substratum of numerous molecular observations, used by other sciences. That does not mean that geographical observation does not have its special sphere; it has it in the form of a necessary residue which cannot be easily defined in general terms, but which one will find easily enough in each specific case, as we have been in the given examples. It is nonetheless true that geography cannot succeed without a number of other sciences. This statement gives us the opportunity to explain a widespread, but often misunderstood, definition of geography. It has been called a cross-road of sciences. There is nothing more accurate concerning the procedure of observation, because within the immense totality of physical, natural and social sciences, there is perhaps none to which geography does not owe some series of observations and concepts. However, that does not justify one in treating geography too lightly as a mere parasitic science, because only in describing and for describing does geography borrow. It does not encroach upon the territory of any other science in its explanations. It has or should have its own, proper methods of explanation, which do not owe anything to others; and, as we do not cease to repeat, true science consists of explanation or in striving for explanation. As to facts, they are available to all; and geography does not intrude by using whatever facts are pertinent.

Procedures of borrowing and grouping distinguish it as a distinct science, since one cannot find them to a similar degree in any other order of research. Perhaps one could maintain that, at least in respect to preliminary borrowing, there is one other science which uses analogous procedures, though it uses them much less critically. This other science is physical astronomy. Like geography, it considers from the very beginning large masses and establishes their inter-connections; the huge dimensions with which it deals seem to exclude any possibility of analyses similar to those of the molecular sciences. However, in their points of view there is only a superficial analogy between geography and astronomy, whatever may be the bonds which unite them in other respects, bonds to which we shall return. As a matter of fact, the distances — which are not incommensurable, but rather unimaginable — which are found between the masses, are the objects of astronomy; in our point of view they all change into veritable celestial molecules, which we study as such across the enormous spaces, just as we study the crystals of the minerals or the cells of organic being. The procedures of the spectral analysis allow us to dissect, somehow, these distant bodies, the same as the chemist in his laboratory analyzes the bodies given to him. In the celestial bodies everything incidental disappears, obliterated by the distance, and nothing weakens or hinders a rational grouping of the facts under scrutiny. It is, therefore, its relative simplicity which makes astronomy appear in our eyes as a more solid edifice, more harmonious and more complete than geography; but this simplicity disappears the moment we start to study those stars closer to us in which at least some peculiarities appear. It is then that the procedures of grouping in astronomy become more comparable to those of physical geography and thereby as open to criticism and sometimes as weak. Every day new problems arise concerning the general heat budget of the sun. The sun astronomers know today is no longer the same sun P. Secchi knew; it has complicated and diversified, and Delandres calls it a variable star. The moon is still closer to us, and consequently crowded with perceptive distinctive features. One knows how much these peculiarities of the surface have hindered the astronomers in evolving explanations, despite the apparent simplicity of the structure of this celestial body. As a matter of fact, with our powerful telescopes we almost are able to apply to the moon the general principles of research which we have declared as valid in geography, not only the grouping in great masses, but the grouping within one's horizon; it is in the study of the moon that astronomy and physical geography meet and interpenetrate. . . .

Are the regional frames the same for physical and human geography? In other words, are the natural regions at the same time, necessarily and inevitably, also human reactions? Is there a rational connection without exception — Leibnitz would have said a predetermined harmony [18] — between the groups of determining physical agents and a predetermined human society — without otherwise prejudicing the faculty of this society to react?

If it were possible to answer in the affirmative, not only the unity of geography would have been firmly established, but a decisive orientation would have been given to the human spirit in one of the most important matters which has ever occupied it. The existence of prepared and adapted frames for the life of societies, accompanied by recognized human reactions upon the physical pattern of these frames, would be the most powerful argument in favor of the theories of final causes and Divine providence. Such a concept would render geography a tool of deterministic metaphysicians; geography, which is at the same time a natural and social science, would be led on a route totally opposite to that which the sciences of these two groups have followed with so much success for a century.

In any case, without prejudicing the question of determinism in geography, we must immediately say that as far as the regional groupings are concerned, to the degree that our researches approach the true facts the clearer becomes the discrepancy between natural regions as physical geography defines these and regions as human geography establishes them. The framework of region is not capable of unifying the two compartments of science. It rather separates them.

---

[18] The German philosopher and mathematician G. F. Leibnitz (1646-1716) assumed such a harmony, preordained from creation, in order to explain why body and soul, though following different laws, act harmoniously.

It makes us conceive two branches of evolution, instead of the large relationships we seek. They may have been intertwined in a distant past, but have since followed diverging routes and seem to diverge more and more every day.

We cannot recognize the real relations between natural regions and the groupings which have common features and can be traced on the globe and which one can call human regions, except under one condition. Natural regions should be based on a few cardinal facts and coincidences which we have specified before, each one comprising an important slice of the surface of the globe where the action of some very general force makes itself felt in a definite manner, essentially, latitude, elevation, distance or closeness to the sea. Of the influences of these great regional frames upon human life, the main, relevant effects are factors of limitation and inhibition, capable of restricting the vital activity of our species rather than stimulating favorable reactions. Man finds the stimulants within himself, rather than in the environment. Therefore, the natural regions which coincide more or less with human regions are first of all the main terrestrial zones, which are derived from our position in the universe and the general zones of contact between the hydrosphere and the lithosphere. These zones, between the equator and the poles, present strange alternations of environment which both limit and undeniably further man in the development of his character: limitation in the equatorial forest, where human life somehow is annihilated by the exuberant vegetation; flowering in the humid tropical environment with its teeming centers of humanity in India and China; limitation in the desert zone, where human life is restricted by lack of water; free flowering recently developed in the Mediterranean and temperate zone; finally, limitation in the polar zone, where all forms of life vanish and man can be only a transient guest. One may add to these main zones the principal mountain areas, where the limitations of human life exist in altitudinal zones; the great continental masses, remote from the sea; and the archipelagoes and peninsulas, where sea and land interpenetrate intimately: you have almost all the geographical forms which enforce limitations upon human ways of life and necessitate adjustments. One should add that, as definitive geographic features, these zones do not cover the whole surface of the earth although they are considered zones. There exist natural areas which, from the point of view of man, do not suffer at all from the main effects which constitute the physical region.

Social Geography, The Earth and the State[19]

Though the present volume treats briefly the same subject as the *Politische Geographie* of Fredrick Ratzel, it differs entirely in its method and spirit. The political geography of Ratzel is neither objective enough, nor far enough removed from considerations of the present. Those excellent thoughts which it does contain, it has taken over from previous works of the author, his *Anthropogeographie* and his *Die Erde und das Leben.* We have tried, we do not say to do better, but to do differently, in order to separate political geography from journalism, and within the orbit of our power, to render it a true science.

We have attempted in the preceding pages to lay the essential foundations of the geography of the state. For this purpose we had to start by remembering that there exists a political science, and that geography, seen as the science of the relations between physical forms and human activities, is something different than a collection of notions deprived of any bonds of coordination or causality. Physical geography on the one hand, the State on the other, are two true objectives of seasoned knowledge which can be joined legitimately in a synthetic study, because the state is a social organism based on the earth.

However, it is difficult to discover bonds of causality and interpenetration between the earth and the state which would provide that characteristic necessity without which no science can exist. Any theory of strict physical determination stating that political societies are directed by one or several natural factors must be rejected; even that relative physical determination has to be rejected which sees in the natural char-

---

[19] *Géographie Sociale, Le Sol et L'Etat,* **Camille Vallaux Vol. 5 Bibliothéque de Sociologie, ed. by Gaston Richard, Paris, Octave Doin et Fils, 1911. Preface. Conclusion.**

acteristics groups of causes which act independently and separately upon the evolution of states. Neither the first nor the second kind of determinism can be justified. The very often seductive and brilliant analogies which have been cited cannot stand up under a rigorous critical examination.

From the beginning it seems impossible to recognize other than incidental connections between that which moves and that which does not yield, between that which changes continually and that which has suffered only slight modification throughout the ages of human existence. The political and social movement never stops; it is so dynamic that we are hardly able to analyze and count its infinitely changing forms; it is so general that no genuine state can be conceived without the existence of adjoining states. The relations created by contiguity, pressure, and interpenetration between states are infinitely complex; no political body resembles itself at two different moments of its history, even if they are close together, though the natural frame hardly changes.

Nevertheless, political bodies sink their roots deeply into the soil, though they are occasionally uprooted and displayed to all in an undeniable way. There exist, therefore, connections between the state and the earth which are more general and at the same time more real than the single influence of natural factors, separated or combined.

Ratzel thought that he had found a double abbreviated formula of these relations in the concept of space and the concept of position. However, the mere space concept does not contribute materially to political geography. It is static and ineffective. In relation to states the concept of space is based on that of time, because pure space, considered independently from nature, forms, and qualities of the earth, is nothing other than distance.

The concept of position is much better founded. Still it is not complete. It is spoiled by a kind of passive determinism by nature which does not allow the states any faculty for active adaptation. It is, therefore, necessary to enlarge and adapt this concept.

This can be done through the general method of differentiation, which is synthesizing to the highest degree. Essentially it consists of the idea that the most favorable conditions for the formation of states are concentrated in those parts of the globe where there are found superimposed close together most of the physical and human characteristics which in their entirety give us the impression of teeming life, and which are grouped in contrasts or diversities, according to whether they contradict each other violently or form graduated series. In these zones of contrasts and diversities states germinate, emerge, evolve, and die; their natural progress of growth carries them beyond their zones of origin toward the undifferentiated zones.

However, the centers of differentiation are not immovable. They have a constant tendency to spread out because of the progress and the continuous acceleration of human circulation which removes the barriers behind which the main groups of bodies politic formerly lived secluded and separated from each other. The modern, very complex states grow and expand to the very limits of the habitable world—either they themselves, or through their colonies, or through their ancient, now independent, colonies.

Their general occupation and their expansion of the forms of the state and its activities over the whole world give additional value to the land. At the same time, while occupation becomes general and the number of men increases, the inequality of their distribution grows. For reasons which pertain equally to political, economic and social geography, men crowd together in the big cities. These two phenomena—increasing ground values and urban congestion—render the study of cities and of boundaries especially interesting.

To summarize, what is the central concept of the geography of states? It is the concept of an uninterruptedly increasing differentiation which does not deny the dependency upon the earth of the body politic, but which side by side with passive adaptation and natural determinism recognizes the legitimate role of active adaption and social determination.

ALLBERT DEMANGEON (1872-1940)

Demangeon first achieved prominence as a young man in 1904 when he wrote a regional geography of a part of northern France, the Picardie. As the first well-rounded regional geography it became a prototype for regional monographs and is still considered one of the very best. Progressing from small regions to whole countries, Demangeon created what is probably his masterpiece in his volumes in the *Géographie Universelle* on the Low Countries and the British Isles. The volume on the British Isles has been translated and, for a long while, had no rival in English. Finally, following in the footsteps of Ratzel and his own teacher, Vidal de la Blache, he became a leader in human geography. His lucid essay, translated on the following pages, was printed posthumously as the introductory chapter to *Problémes de Géographie Humaine* (Problems of Human Geography).

Problems of Human Geography [20]

Since antiquity, many authors of inquisitive mind and observant inclination have pointed out the differences in the customs of men on the surface of the earth. Many travellers since Herodotus have described them; many historians and moralists since Thucydides have taken them as the starting point for their philosophic deliberations. But the idea of making them the object of a science, looking for their explanations, appeared quite late, certainly not before the end of the 18th century. Until then the study of the facts which we group under the name of Human Geography, the way of life of man on the surface of the globe and the types of his groupings, was nothing but a simple description, regarded mainly as a useful and practical bit of knowledge or as a picturesque delineation of the habits and different customs of peoples. There were collections of instructions for the guidance of travellers; tales, often romantic, of marvelous adventures, written primarily to please the imagination. There were enumerations of places and distances interwoven with historical reminiscences; there were archaeological and geneological considerations; information on statistics and administration. These works seem to have satisfied the curiosity of all, even the lowliest, with what they said about foreign peoples

[20] Problémes de Géographie Humaine, Albert Demangeon. Librarie Armand Colin, Paris 1943 (2nd. ed.), pp. 25-34.

and exotic landscapes. But, as a matter of fact, all these collections of notions were only disarranged chaos, without a constructive effort, without explanatory enlightenment, and thus, without scientific character.

The progress of human geography as a science is related to knowledge of the globe, as brought about primarily by the series of voyages of discovery and colonization in the 18th century. These voyages were made mainly by scientists or explorers, motivated by scientific curiosity. They were able to gather for comparison elements of human societies across the globe which have arrived at different degrees of civilization; in other words, the spirit of comparison stirs the scientific mind because it creates a feeling for the generality of facts.

Vidal de la Blache, the initiator of human geography in France, has shown that the scientific spirit of this geography derives from two German geographers: Alexander von Humboldt (1769-1859) and Karl Ritter (1779- 1859). Both have shown that certain relations of cause and effect exist between physical phenomena and the phenomena of life, but each of them has contributed his own conception of this relation. The author of *The Cosmos,* Humboldt, primarily a naturalist, has tried to study natural phenomena and show among other things the influence of altitude, temperature, humidity, and dryness upon the forms of vegetation. The author of the *Allgemeine, Vergleichende Geographie,* Ritter, a man with a strong historical background, shows that in human geography nature is not the only causative power and that man himself is active in transforming life on the surface of the earth. Thus nature and man—or in the words of Ritter, nature and history—are "the two continuously associated factors" between which geographical thought must continuously gravitate.

Human geography has pursued this path, led by two outstanding personalities—Ratzel in Germany and Vidal de la Blache in France. Their doctrines and their teachings have pervaded geographical thought in almost all countries, inspiring works which have contributed toward popularising the new science, have encouraged learning outside scholarly circles, and with their principles have reached the well-educated in general. One can mention in France, J. Brunhes; in

Germany, A Philippson; in Great Britain, Mackinder and Herbertson; in the United States, Miss Semple; in Italy, Marinelli; in Yugoslavia, Cvijic; in Russia, Woeikoff.

I. **Definition and object of human geography.** If we try to define the spirit which dominates the works on human geography and to find the common principles they follow, we can reach by successive approximations a definition of this science.

On the lowest level human geography appears as *the study of the contacts of man with the physical environment.* This idea first originated in the work of Humboldt and Berghaus in the field of botanical geography. It particularly derived from the branch of botany called ecology, the study of the degree to which factors of climate and soil determine the life of plants. In the same way one is able to a large degree to describe the life of man. One of the first tasks of geography is to put human facts into a relationship with the series of natural causes which can explain them, and once again put them in their proper place in the chain of causality. Knowledge of these causes clarifies for us the way of life and the material habits of man. This influence of the physical surrounding, the environment as some Americans call it, becomes obvious in all human activities; and geography, in quest of examples, is only embarrassed by the multiplicity of choice. For example, the three partners of an association which links closely a plant, a domestic animal, and a way of life, such as the lichen, the reindeer, and the Lapp, are in a state of causal dependency. The sovereign influence of the environment led the natives of Central Africa to be hunters and collectors, those of the Asian steppes to be nomads and herdsmen. In arid countries there is a close association between wells and the location of villages; in high mountains, between those rare plots of good land with favorable exposure and the human habitat. Is there not from the point of view of development a profound difference between Europe, located in the centre of the continental hemisphere, and Australia, in the middle of immense oceans? Have not islands and peninsulas contributed to the formation of human individualities and states? Cannot the separation of Portugal from Spain be explained by its oceanic orientation in the west and by the rugged terrain and wild gorges in the east, which isolate it from Spain?

However, if one pursues this definition of human geography to its logical conclusion, one would recognize that it does not comprise the study of all human contacts with the environment. The definition soon appears too all-encompassing, for many contacts certainly are beyond the realm of human geography and belong to well-established sciences. L. Febvre in his book on *La Terre et l'Evolution Humaine* has defined quite well these intermediate zones: for example, some human groups seem connected with a well-limited geographic region; it is not for human geography to explain the differences between races concerning the reaction of the color of their skin in relation to their reaction to the climate. Let others investigate the physiological elements of human nature. Let us not forget that man has anatomy, physiology, pathology, which look into hereditary traits, the study of which constitutes anthropology and medicine. Let us try to clarify our first definition.

One can give this second refined definition: human geography is the study of human groupings in their contacts with their environment. Let us stop to consider individual man. By the study of an individual, anthropology and medicine, but not human geography, can arrive at a scientific result. Human geography studies man as collectives and groups, the actions of man in societies. Our researches must start from groups, not from the individual. From the most remote time we are able to observe the actions of groups, not of isolated individuals. As far as one can delve into the past, he finds as an inherent trait of human nature the tendency to live in societies with people of similar ways of life. These groupings are sometimes as small as the numerous neolithic villages of which evidences have been found. Sometimes they are as immense as the societies of the palaeolithic period, which shared worldwide a similar inventory of tools. It is, therefore, through these groupings that man enters into contact with his environment. At the beginning of civilization and the conquest of material nature we find efforts of cooperation and cohesion. Efforts such as the constructions of dolmens, organization of irrigation in Mesopotamia and Egypt, and the domestication of animals can only have been cooperative undertakings. However, even this definition does not suffice to cover the whole concept of human geography; and there is a last correction which definitely brings us close to reality.

Human geography is the study of human groupings in their contact with the geographical environment. The term "geographical environment" is more comprehensive than physical environment. It not only includes the physical influences, but also the influence of man himself, an influence which contributes to the formation of the geographical environment, the environment as a whole. In the very beginning man certainly was the slave of and wholly dependent upon nature. But this man, *nudus et inermis* (naked and without arms), did not hesitate to become himself, thanks to his intelligence and his initiative, which exert a powerful influence upon his environment. He therefore became a natural factor, transforming nature in a basic way, creating new associations of plants and animals, oases for irrigated cultivation, vegetation formations such as the thicket and the heath at the expense of the forest. And these transformations extended over vast regions because there are migrations, borrowings, imitations, from human group to group. And these effects of human societies upon nature have become the more manifold and stronger because of man's initiative, which enabled him to extend his radius of action. There are gifts of nature which man has deeply disturbed by his action. In antiquity, the British Isles were at the extreme part of the known world in an eccentric position; in modern times, since the discoveries and the peopling of the New World, they occupy a central position. In our days the action of man upon nature has been amplified by the weapons which science has furnished, and by his mastery over distances which transportation has given him. Thus human works in every period of human history have constituted themselves a factor in transforming the geographical environment, which in its turn shapes the life of peoples. Therefore, we can adopt as the definition of human geography the study of contacts of human groupings with the geographical environment.

This definition of human geography allows us to conceive,

in a definitive manner, its object and to determine its limits. It comprises four great groups of problems which result exactly from the contacts of human societies with the geographical environment.

First is the utilization (*mise en valeur*)[21] by human societies of the resources which nature offers or which are taken from it; the ways of life (*modes de vie*),[22] as the great natural zones form them: human life in the cold zones; human life in the temperate zones, its complement of domesticated plants and animals; human life in mountains; and human life on the coasts.

Second, is the progressive elaboration by societies throughout time and space of different procedures by which they have drawn for their subsistence natural resources from the most elementary to the most complicated; whether it concerns hunting and fishing, agriculture and husbandry, or industry, commerce, exchange and transport. It deals, altogether, with the evolution of the types of civilization.

Third, is the distribution of man, itself a reaction to natural conditions and the resources which have been developed by his exploitation; the spread of mankind, his efficiency and density, movements and migrations.

These four groups of problems comprise, it seems, the content of human geography. It is within this wide framework that the whole research, and the whole work, is done.

II. **The Method of Human Geography.**—It is not enough to conceive the idea and limit the content of human geography. It is necessary to have methodological principles—to follow them and not to deviate from them. Here are the essential principles of this method.

First Principle: One ought not to believe in human geography as a kind of brute determinism, an unavoidable fate dictated by non-human factors. The causality in human geography is very complex. Man, with his free will and his initiative, is himself a cause which brings disturbance into the apparent natural order; for example, an island is not

---

[21] The French expression *mise en valeur* has become a peculiar term of human geography, which is not used in common language .

[22] Another term peculiar to French human geography.

necessarily given to maritime life. The birth of maritime life often precedes cultural contacts. Thus the English became mariners only through the contacts with Scandinavians and Hanseatic merchants. In the same way, agriculture is not merely a function of the qualities of the soil. There are fertile countries which are uncultivated; there are poor countries which are cultivated. Often all depends upon the cultural stage of the agricultural population. Man is sometimes master of the fertility of the soil, as when he practices irrigation.

The previous extension of the vine in Western Europe—to Belgium, England and Northern France—occurred in contrast to the natural needs for its cultivation; if it were able to expand so far into these cool and not too sunny countries, it was because it was needed for the celebration of mass. And because cheap transportation was lacking, it was impossible to receive wine from the more southern countries. However, to the same degree that transport became less onerous, the cultivation of the vineyards receded southward into less hazardous locales, better adapted to the needs of this plant. The same country can completely change its value for human occupation to coincide with the stage of civilization of the inhabitants. Before the arrival of the Europeans, Australia was in the stage of savagery; there was no big game, except the rare kangaroo, and the poor game of marsupialia, snakes and insects; there were no animals for domestication, few wild-growing edible plants; the famished indigenes wandered about in search of inadequate food. The moment the Europeans arrived with their cultivated plants and domesticated animals, and later with their powerful means for work and circulation, they made this continent, which so long had remained backward, a country of great cultivation and intensive husbandry, a country of progressive culture and human comfort. Therefore, there is no absolute determinism, but only the potentialities activated by human initiative; no fatalism, but human will.

Second Principle: Human geography has to apply its work to some territorial basis. Every place where man lives, his way of existence implies a necessary relationship between him and the land. It is precisely the regard for this territorial bond which distinguishes geography from sociology. Sociologists have a tendency to take cognizance of the psychological aspects of human groupings, ignoring the relations of man with the land, and to treat man as if he could be studied independent of the earth's surfaces. One should not forget that there are social elements other than the earth, especially those which are based on psychological nature—such as parenthood and religion—and that their study belongs not to the geographer, but to the sociologist.

However, human geography takes as its own the fact that man cannot be studied without studying the ground on which he lives, and that the ground is the foundation of every society. One can even say that the larger and richer this basis, the more intrinsic are the bonds between it and its inhabitants. The density of population increases, the exploration of the soil is more intensive, and the bonds become closer.

It is also possible to state, as has Sanderson, that even among hunting tribes the utilization of the same territory creates a certain social solidarity, independent of blood bonds, and stronger than them. Among the Algonquins, a North-American hunting people, the territory of each tribe was divided among the families from time immemorial. These family groups formed the genuine social unit; the cement of this unity was not common ancestry, but common dominion over the same territory or sector. These sectors were an average of 200 to 400 square miles in the centre of the tribal territory and two to four times as much as the frontiers of the territory for each family. On this territory the family hunted, and the hunt was thus regulated so only the natural increment of the animals was used. Care was taken to leave enough animals to assure the provisions for the next year; it was known that a thoughtless slaughter would expose the family to starvation. In all the hunting regions of pre-Columbian America (caribou, bison, guanaco) the same organization existed. Among the inferior peoples of Australia, the tribe shared the same rights of gathering and hunting in a precisely delimited area; within the tribal territory, each family had similar rights. Among agricultural peoples the territorial base imposes itself even more as a socially binding element upon the psychological nature. All agricultural communities have a structure, determined by the bonds which tie them to the soil: the grouping of habitations in villages is due to the necessity of defense and, primarily, to the necessary common work. The strict organization of the utilization of the cultivated fields is based on the rotation of cultivation from one sector to the other and on the permanent character of the borders. In certain countries the localization of irrigation works forces the territorial distribution of the cultivated land. "The village community" says Sanderson, was the means to give mankind a government based on the territorial principle much more than on that of ancestry." By replacing a tribal by a territorial organization, most civilizations since antiquity have given a geographical basis to rural groupings. These places where men gather or work are very unequal in size, varying from the elementary locality to the large territory. They form the cadres from which geographical factors spread out, and by their very character they impress orginality upon those men who gather there. To understand and describe these regional units is one of the basic functions of geography, because each of them often constitutes a kind of personality which one has to bring to life. This regional geography constitutes one of the essential starting points for the general geographer because very often it is impossible to come to an understanding of the large units without an analysis of the small areas (*pays*) which constitute them. In order to comprehend the general facts, it is well to begin with the particular, the bond to a certain locality, or the parochial, to observe the particular things of a region, its plants, its residents, and to define what kind of living being results from the union of a piece of land with a group of mankind. One is thus forcibly led to the starting point of our knowledge of the earth, to the immediate substratum of our material existence. Often, by the analysis of the characteristics drawn from the physiognomy of a region, one is best able to grasp the bonds which unite man and his environment.

Third Principle: If it wants to be comprehensive and explanatory, human geography cannot confine itself to the actual state of things. It has to look at the evolution of things and go back into the past, to appeal to history. Many things, which appear fortuitous if regarded as functions of present conditions, become explicable if they are considered as functions of the past. History opens wide vistas of the past, which has seen the succession of so many experiences. This concept of time and evolution is indispensable. Without it the reason behind present things would often escape us. How, for instance, could urban geography neglect history? How could one explain Rome, London or Paris without their past? How could one understand the peopling of an old country such as France if we did not know its history of clearing, deforestation, division of land, drainage and construction of dykes? The whole study of this conquest of the land is at the base of history. That is the reason why studies in human geography always include much historical research and why geographers often meet historians in the archives. The geographer, in order to explain observed facts, cannot be satisfied to place them sensibly into space; he must also project them into the past. He must, in addition, know how to use historical documents and where to find them. To take only the example of France, there exist great archives. . . . One could also quote the great mass of unpublished economic documents of the French Revolution, which comprise more than a hundred volumes and which give such a vivid picture of so many facts of human geography: the cultivation of heaths, community land, right of passage and free pasture, rural handicraft and cottage industries; metal works and forests; the beginnings of machinery, of the route network and waterways; movement of population, development of agriculture, and agricultural regimes. Indeed, the study of the past is necessary if one is to explain the facts of human geography. Mankind evolves within time. For understanding this evolution, the testimony of history is as necessary as the knowledge of the physical laws.

JEAN BRUNHES (1869-1930)

Brunhes became famous through his work on human geography. Though he proclaimed himself always a faithful follower of Vidal de la Blache, he went beyond the master's emphasis on regional presentation to generalization in his special fields. He recognized that human energy is so intricately interwoven with natural factors in creating the human landscape that it cannot be separated in geography. Careful observation, a peculiar method of analysis, and artistic presentation are combined in his work. Some of his most fertile years he spent at the French-language University in Fribourg, Switzerland.

Human Geography[23]

There is a double zone that constitutes the proper sphere of geographical study—the lower stratum of the atmospheric envelope that surrounds the earth and the solid crust of the earth itself. At all points where these two concentric zones are in contact with each other three groups of primary phenomena are produced.

(a) The heat of the sun is the great source of all activity and all life on our earth, and its principal effects are accumulated where the atmosphere and the crust of the earth are in contact. The "heating surface" of our atmosphere is the surface of our own earth.

(b) It is also at the point of contact of the atmosphere and the earth's crust that such atmospheric occurrences as change of temperature, wind, and rain, and particularly those geographical phenomena to which they give rise, such as streams and glaciers, are incessantly at work to break down the heights and fill up the depths.

(c) Lastly, it is on the surface of our globe and in the lower stratum of the atmosphere that all forms of vegetable, animal, and human life are concentrated.

. . .This "place" in which all these essential phenomena are mingled or superimposed one upon another marks off the geographer's sphere of observation, and is the primary domain of geography. Most of these phenomena are entirely exempt from all human influence. . . .

---

[23] Human Geography, Jean Brunhes. Abridged edition by Mme. M. Jean-Brunhes Delamarre and Pierre Deffontaines, translated by Ernest F. Row from the French edition of 1947, Rand McNally & Company, New York, Chicago, San Francisco, 1952 (Copyright by George G. Harrap & Co. Ltd.) p. 19-48, 213-229.

But a general glance over the earth reveals an entirely new and very abundant set of surface phenomena: there are towns and railways, cultivated fields and quarries, canals and irrigation tanks and salt-pans; and here and there, in particular, there are masses or groups, of varying density, of human beings. These human beings are themselves surface phenomena, and therefore geographical. They live on the earth; they are subjected to atmospheric and terrestrial conditions; they belong to certain climates, certain altitudes, and certain zones. Moreover, they live on the earth in another sense also, for it is by submission to natural phenomena that they obtain sustenance for their bodies and provide for the development and expansion of their faculties. . . .

. . .The idea of interrelation should dominate every complete study of geographical facts. We must not be content with observing one fact by itself, or an isolated series of facts. After this preliminary observation our task is to place the series in its natural setting—that is to say, in the complex group of facts within which it has been produced and has developed. We must find out how it is connected with other phenomena around it, to what extent they are determined by it, and how far it has been influenced by them. In meteorology, in zoology, and in botany it is possible to isolate certain facts and to study them entirely by themselves, but in geography we cannot be content with this method.

. . .We should never confine our attention to one order of phenomena. Even the smallest geographical study, if it aims at completeness, cannot be limited to the observation of isolated facts. There are no watertight compartments on the earth's crust; there may be partitions, but there are no walls. A mountain is not a single, self-contained entity; a town is not an independent unit, but depends on the soil that bears it, the climate that it enjoys, and the environment on which it subsists. . ."No part of the earth," says Vidal de la Blache, "can be explained by itself alone. Not only that, but the full working of local conditions can be clearly discovered only to the extent that observation reaches beyond them and can include analogous cases that lead naturally to terrestrial laws of general application". . . .

And so we arrive at the highest concept of all, that of the "terrestrial whole" or to the unity of the entire globe. Different forces do not act upon one another only in determined conditions; it is not only in a few defined cases that they act reciprocally. In fact, it can still be maintained that in a more or less distant manner, and in more or less visible form, each of these forces is bound up with all the rest, because of the countless interactions of the conditions brought about by them.

. . .The term "terrestrial organism" no doubt sounds too bold, but we may nonetheless borrow Claude Bernard's expression and say that there is an "organic or social solidarity" between all the phenomena of the "terrestrial machine."

We have just passed in review all the principal forms of human activity on the earth; the geography of the prime necessities of life and of the exploitation of the earth, economic and social geography, political geography, and the geography of history. We can see now for what manifold reasons and in what very general conditions man's actions are enveloped, combined, and sometimes even hemmed in, by the physical universe. That introduction to human geography is, as it were, its necessary preface. . . .

Wherever there are men we find also other surface phenomena of a concrete kind, and the more numerous the men the more numerous are these phenomena. They can be reduced to six essential types, as follows:

First comes one of the most obvious—a kind of superficial excrescence—the house, shelter, habitation, or human construction. Under the general term "house" we include all those innumerable and varied objects strewn over the earth's crust like thousands of tiny spots. . .

Structures are accompanied almost always and almost everywhere by a second feature, the road or highway, devoted—one might almost say "sacrificed"— to movement or circulation. . . .

Houses and highways, then are in close connection with each other on the inhabited earth, and are the two essential human things which can be said to occupy legitimately the soil unproductively, in a strictly literal sense, and with no deprecatory significance at all. . .

There are still other patches appearing on the earth's surface, and the denser the population the more numerous they are. These patches have fairly regular and definite outlines, and their colors vary with the seasons. . . .They are those parts of the surface where the soil is scratched or turned over or altered in some way, and the general term for them, which expresses what we actually see, is fields or gardens. They are indeed the geographical and material expression of "cultivation"—the subordination of the plant world to the human will. . .

There is a fourth phenomenon that occurs sometimes in association with "field" and "garden" and sometimes—often to an important extent and in a highly developed form—where the cultivated patches are few and far between. In both cases, however, they are dependent always on the presence of man,. . . an animal population plainly subjected to the will of man, and described by the two general and concrete terms—the herd and the beast of burden. . . .

It remains to notice from our point of vantage two other kinds of phenomena, both representing, though in different degrees. . .the "destructive economy" or, in the forcible German phrase, "robber economy" (*Raubwirtschaft*). . . .

The quarry and the mine, which exhaust the wealth of the earth without replenishing it, are found in particular as geographical companions and neighbors of the two things that mark the "unproductive occupation of the soil"—i.e., houses and roads. But the sixth and last kind of surface phenomenon, also a destructive one, belongs rather to the sphere of "plant and animal conquest," with which it is frequently intermingled. It includes actions that are often brutal and violent, almost always ephemeral, and always definite and decisive. In the vegetable realm it takes the material form of wild fruits plucked and eaten, trees cut down, and forests burned, and in the animal world of wild beasts hunted and killed and fishes caught.

. . .*Primary and fundamental human geography* or *human geography,* in the proper sense, should be first the *geography of the material achievements of man,* thus preparing the way for *the geography of groups and races of men,* particularly as these groups and races translate their specific and different forms of activity into material achievements, or reveal their existence and their presence by these achievements themselves.

. . .What chiefly interests the geographer is the predominant feature, which is merely the most representative type in a given region. Anything exceptional has less value for the student of human geography than anything typical.

What is the geographical spirit? The true geographer knows how to open his eyes and see things, but he does not see by merely wishing to. In physical geography as in human geography a training in seeing clearly the realities of the earth's surface will be the first step, and it is not the easiest one. Consequently the geographical method in all spheres where it can be adopted is a method that accords the first place to the exact, precise study of what exists at the present time, and that is its main interest.

Geographers should strive always to find out exactly where the phenomenon they are studying takes place. This concern with locality will have to be translated into maps and diagrams showing two kinds of facts; (1) the actual places or zones where the phenomenon appears at its best or greatest, and (2) the boundaries of the area over which it extends.

. . .Not only the economic and demographic sciences, but all the philological, ethnical, and historical ones also, are becoming permeated more and more by the geographical spirit . . .Linguistic and ethnical geography are becoming increasingly essential to students of the problems of languages and races from the purely scientific standpoint. . .

By following up all traces of mankind on the earth, step by step, various questions have been reopened and elucidated which were or would have been incapable of solution by the sole method of economic or political history. . .

Between facts of a physical character there are sometimes causal relations, but between facts of human geography there are hardly any relations except those of coexistence. To strain, as it were, the bond that unites phenomena to one another is unscientific. . . .Hence there arises a complication which sometimes makes it hard to determine the actual bond between man and nature. This connecting bond is, in fact, variable because it depends on man's wants—both his spontaneous and his considered desires—and these psychological elements, being by nature extremely variable, necessarily cause the relations even between earth and man to vary. Thus we reach a new kind of complication resulting from different phenomena following each other in the course of time in the same place. The geographical setting remains the same, but the men who dwell in it have wants that are constantly growing, changing, and becoming more complex.

Relations between the constant natural factor and the variable human one are continually changing, and it may even happen that in course of time the relation becomes almost exactly opposite what it was at first.

Many geographers, after speaking, not without reason, of the action and reaction of natural and human forces, ask themselves too strictly and in too abstract a manner up to what point the influence of natural forces is exerted on human activity and to what extent man reacts to these forces. . . . The man who takes refuge by night in a natural cave profits by a natural circumstance, and the part he plays in relation to physical Nature is reduced to a minimum. Nevertheless, it is not the cave alone that is a fact of human geography, but the cave as a place of human refuge. Even when man in no way creates or modifies the fact that he makes use of it. . . the cave presents a complex phenomenon in which the man, it is true, submits to what nature suggests, but in which he also shares, if only by a kind of very obscure instinct.

Surely, it is at least partly an illusion to think that by increasing his power of dominating and conquering the earth man throws off its tyranny and increases his own independence. . . .Is it not also an illusion to imagine that the concentration of human beings, and therefore of human forces, at one point in space must show a greater mastery over the earth? That is the illusion of number and multitude. Surely a city like Paris is more firmly riveted to the site on which it stands than is the ancient Lutetia [24] or those tempo-

---

[24] The Celtic name for Paris in pre-Roman time.

rary villages of dried mud in the Nile valley that we described earlier? So strongly is Paris enslaved by the need for food and economic life in general that the slightest interruption of her normal communications would lead to catastrophe.

. . .The human individual is active and mobile with an intensity and a might that have increased more than a hundredfold during the past hundred years. But this very case of movement on the part of individuals should not blind us to the relative but real degree of fixity with which human groups and masses are rooted in the soil. . . . The dwellers in an Alpine valley, if driven from their homes by an avalanche, a landslide, a fire, or economic ruin, can up to a certain point, leave those homes and emigrate, whereas on the morrow of a catastrophe a city like San Francisco, Tokyo, or Messina remains bound to the same site, or its immediate neighborhood. Though each of the individuals who live in London or Berlin is free to take a train each day and go away, it is equally certain that the entire population of these cities, if it wants to remain fed and housed, is as a body inexorably compelled to stay where it is.

It should not be thought, therefore, that as human forces grow and become more concentrated man's dependence on natural conditions has been done away with; all that has happened is that the dependence is of a kind. And geographical facts are more and more becoming man's supreme masters. The facts that tend increasingly to influence the destinies of human groups—the tyrannical factors of human geography—are *space, distance,* and *difference of level. . .*

Space, distance, and *difference of level* become, in fact, geographical values because, to satisfy his need, man enslaves and tames them. Now, this domination by man can show itself, over and over again, only by the construction of factories and fortresses, roads, canals, and railway stations, the creation and upkeep of fields and gardens, transport animals and flocks and herds, and the exploitation of the earth's natural covering of vegetation and its mineral wealth. *Space, distance* and *difference of level* are conditions and factors of human work and settlement, but they must never be confused with the actual forms of that work or physical evidences of that settlement. They are means, more or less favorable or unfavorable to life, wealth, or power, but they are not the direct ends pursued by individuals, tribes, or nations. In themselves they belong to pure natural geography, and it is only if they are "animated", as it were, by the spirit of man and mingled with our life that they influence and take their place in the geography of man. And this simply means that they must find expression in some of the six types already described. Thus we reach, over and over again, the same important conclusion that physical phenomena, like human ones, have right of access to human geography only to the extent that they are connected with positive surface phenomena belonging to one of the three groups of facts—*unproductive occupation of the soil, conquest of the vegetable and animal worlds, and destructive occupation.*

HENRI BAULIG (1877-1962)

Baulig was one of the most important geomorphologists in France. During a long stay in the United States he was in contact with W. M. Davis and became a life-long friend of Douglas Johnson. He demonstrated that eustatic movements as well as tectonic movements must be studied as causes of geomorphic processes. Like most French geographers he was also interested in man. As the author of the volume on North America in the *Géographie Universelle*, he displayed the mastery of the French school of regional geographical presentation. For that book he received the Daly Medal of the American Geographical Society. Terminology was a peculiar interest of his, and he contributed many new terms to French as well as international terminology. In advanced age he began to reflect on the methodological basis of geography, as shown in the following article.

Is Geography a Science?[25]

Whether geography is a science is a problem that is not new, but still formidable. First it is necessary to define what

[25] *"La géographie est-elle une science?"* *Annales de Géorgraphie*, vol. LVII, no. 305, Jan.-March 1948.

one means by "science". Definitions abound, ranging from most restrictive ones to very loose. . . .

Let us, therefore, rather start by looking at what geography is, what it has been, what it has become, and what it can hope to be. We shall then ask to what degree, or rather in what sense, it can claim the flattering title of "science".

Man made use of geography for a long time, largely without knowing it. He knew about geography, as far as we can ascertain, from the dawn of Greek science; it was in the first half of the sixth century (B. C.) that Anaximander of Miletus constructed the first "world" map. But since its beginning, geography has been divided into two opposing, or rather complementary, tendencies. On the one side are geometers and astronomers. They apply their science to defining the size and shape of the Earth. . . .But besides geometers there are travelers, curious, sensitive to the various aspects of nature, products, peoples, and their customs; and there are historians, politically-minded, who ponder the relations between countries and human societies. . . .Later, the 19th and even the 20th century has seen a rich flowering of geographical sciences which one could classify in a logical sequence approximately as follows: mathematical geography; geodesy, which occupies itself with the true figure of the Earth, because the surface of equilibrium of the oceans is not a perfect ellipsoid, but a geoid which varies slightly from the ellipsoid. The deviations refer to variations in gravity, therefore to the distribution of the masses in the depth. Geodesy leads to geophysics, which is constituted of an agglomeration of fairly divergent sciences, mainly concerned with gravity, terrestrial magnetism, the polar auroras, ionized layers, cosmic rays, even with meteorology; but its proper domain is the study of the internal structure of the globe by different methods, of which the most fruitful is seismology. Meteorology is the science of the atmosphere, of which climatology is the most geographical branch. Oceanography is supplemented by the hydrography of fresh waters.

Geology, a relatively old science, has manifold branches: crystallography is nothing else but a branch of molecular physics; mineralogy and its sister science, petrography, study only isolated minerals, the other complexes which form rocks in their structure and genesis; stratigraphy, by examining sedimentary formations and fossils which may be enclosed, reconstructs the physical history of the earth and establishes its chronology; tectonics studies the deformations of the terrain; palaeontology, which undertakes to investigate the succession and affiliation of living beings, belongs in principle to biology, but is for practical reasons attached to stratigraphy; geomorphology, the last-born of the geological sciences, remained closely attached to geology in the United States, while in Europe geologists left it to geographers. Biogeography is divided naturally into plant geography and zoogeography.

Let us stop here. These different sciences merit the designation of geographical sciences, not just because, as a rule, they are practiced by geographers, for they are cultivated by mathematicians, by physicists, and chemists, by natural scientists who use their particular methods, which are not geographical by themselves. But they are geographical sciences, not only because they occupy themselves with this particular object, the Earth, but because they study the distribution on the surface of the earth of forces, objects, beings, phenomena and their variations of frequency and intensity: and, almost invariably, that is presented on a map. The map is an accurate, faithful, objective tool of presentation, but it is also an instrument of research! The trends of isophleths, especially their irregularities, betray a disturbance, or a secondary factor. Even more intrinsically, the earth sciences are geographical because inevitably they find themselves confronted with elements, forces or phenomena which they are not prepared to isolate and which present themselves as complexes, the elements of which condition and limit each other mutually, briefly, as changeable balances. Let us take an example. In latitudes 30° to 35°, on the east side of the oceans, exist regions of permanent high pressure, the source regions of the trade winds. The location of these high pressure areas is due, partly, to the low temperatures of the ocean at its surface; but the low temperature is a result of the rising of the subsurface waters which itself is caused by the impact of the trade winds. You see: the effect becomes cause and the circle is closed. To explain the phenomenon means to grasp all the factors, not separately, but in their mutual dependency.

No doubt, analysis could try to isolate the factors in order to measure them. But in this type of material the classical tools of the laboratory, experiment and calculation, can not be disposed of. Calculation can furnish the order of size and the direction of changes, but nothing more, because the given data are too uncertain and, most important, because the relations of the forces which are involved are too little known. For several reasons experiments yield few certain results which can not be obtained otherwise: for example, the scale of natural happenings which can not be reduced considerably without falsification of the results, because it is generally impossible to reduce all the parameters in a convenient proportion. Time is one of these parameters; many natural phenomena which unfold at an infinitesimally slow pace can not be reproduced nor even imitated, adequately, at an accelerated rate. The interpretation of phenomena of this kind requires large extrapolations, based on the legitimate and necessary postulate of the permanence of nature's laws. What are the laws of nature except what experience teaches short-lived beings? And do not exceptional phenomena which surpass all observed ones in intensity, include the occurrences which are directly outside the norm, such as the glaciations (quarternary and more ancient) which happened at very long intervals and lasted for a relatively short time, for which up to now we are unable to ascertain the cause? For us, they are purely perfectly mysterious accidents.

You will notice that all the sciences present a double aspect: the analytic, abstract and general which characterize such sciences as physics or biology; and the synthetic, concrete and specific which are geographical. Let's take as an example phytogeography, which one may consider as the most perfect of the physical geographies. At first, botanists find themselves face to face with groupings or natural complexes, which some of them analyze while others endeavor to consider them as wholes. The former look at the plant in isolation as a type, describe it, draw it, classify it, and finally ask questions of family and derivation, and look for the secrets of heredity and the laws of evolution; thus they arrive at systematic general conclusions. Anatomists, for their part, recognize in different plants either similarities or differences of corresponding organs, and regard as equivalent the function which they fulfill: they recognize that, though the form may be manifold, the underlying reality is the same. Likewise, the physiologist recognizes a common fundamental basis of elementary processes, nutrition, growth, reproduction, which are susceptible to general formulation and even to quantitative expressions.

But the botanist can also take a geographical approach. He will study first the distribution of species, genera, families, etc., over the earth and will draw a map. He will notice that the limit of such a form or such a group of forms is determined, in a general way, by the climate—one could speak of a climate of the vine, of the olive, of the date palm—specifically by the location, soil, exposition, shelter, groundwater, etc.; that is geography. However, irregularities pose problems, especially non-contiguous area. If the relationship is well established between forms, separated by great distances or insuperable obstacles, one is led to postulate landbridges—on this point the geologists have something to say—climatic changes, or deep-seated changes in the maritime circulation, etc. In short, the problem is to reconstruct a vanished state of things in a coherent manner: a perfectly satisfactory reconstruction would constitute a genuine retrospective geography, a palaeogeography.

However, plant geography may be presented in another aspect. It examines the natural aspects of the vegetation, the 'associations": the forest—high or low, dense or open, of resinous or broadleaf trees; the grassland—luxuriant or poor, high or low, of grasses or of plants with big flowers, etc. Such formations deserve to be described and studied, first because they exist, and second because such a study may lead to completely new results. Actually, it is easily recognized that a certain formation with its dominant and subordinated plants responds to a given climate, to such and such a habitat. Ecology is an eminently geographical science.

However, there is more to it; the plants which constitute such a formation are separate and yet joined, competitors for space, light, air, and water. They are also associated: the trees protect each other from the wind and too great evaporation; the higher plants give shade to the smaller ones; and those which have a shorter life span sustain the humus cover and renew it with their debris on which bacteria work. We encounter, therefore, a living association, a biocoenosis (which also embraces animals), an association which creates its own climate and its peculiar soil, briefly, a particular environment which one has to know if one wants to explain the existence of a forest, and just this forest, or a grassland, and just this particular grassland.

Let us go a step farther. Such an environment is not immediately established. On a bare spot, e.g. on the place of a forest fire, first, lowly plants appear which demand little and which disappear or decrease in numbers as soon as they have played their role as pioneers. Then appear sun-loving trees which are tolerant of isolation. Finally, in their shade come other species which in the end may supplant them. Therefore, one sees different associations in succession, series which develop at the same time as the environment which they produce and modify by infinitely repeated contacts: a mobile equilibrium strives toward a stable equilibrium, an apogee, a climax which realizes the fullness which the vegetation is capable of obtaining under the given conditions. On the contrary, repeated conflagrations, an unfavorable change of climate, will introduce a degradation and regressive successions. The soil itself, with all the microbic and macrobic life which it includes, is intimately joined to this evolution through the substances which the vegetation loans to it and those which it returns by the groundwater, which fulfills the demands of the plants. Ultimately, as time goes by, the soil will put itself into equilibrium with the climate and vegetation, a complex which itself indicates the interaction of other complexes and which reacts on them.

Since man appeared—and by man one has to understand not the individual man, but the group—the concept of environment has become peculiarly complicated. Man does not accept the environment passively. He reacts, just as the plant or the animal, or even some inanimate force does when its equilibrium is threatened. Only his reaction can be deliberate and thought out. He can apply different solutions to each problem: the ethnographical museums bear witness to this inexhaustible inventiveness. It is possible to state that, until human freedom intervenes, nature frequently prohibits, permits, favors or discourages, but it never, or almost never, imposes one solution rather than another. In this sphere one has to give up looking for that determinism which was imagined by certain political theoreticians such as the Greeks, Bodin, Montesquieu, the geographers Ritter and Ratzel, or Taine and his followers. Human freedom baffles all predictions.

That does not say that human freedom is unlimited. At each stage of civilization it is limited by what is possible and what is desirable, or better what the group thinks to be possible and desirable. That implies that in human geography the concept of environment includes elements which are strictly human, the group's physical and mental capacities, inherited or acquired, and its cultural heritage; techniques, of course, but also collective mentality and its stratification, its enlightened zones and its obscure depths, which are almost unconscious. Therefrom stems the connection between human geography and social history which, to speak the truth, is the whole useful history.

It is often said that with the stupendous progress of technical knowledge today, man liberates himself more and more from the rule of nature. Especially the present evolution in the means of communication and transport makes the world contract, become more and more penetrable, and strive toward uniformity—the physicists would say, entropy. That is not true except in a certain manner. If the techniques of transportation performed miracles and did not cease to perform them before our eyes, distances would not be abolished thereby by as much. The true and practical distance is not measured in kilometers, but in time, length of the trip, frequency of departures; in the net cost, which especially depends on the volume of traffic; and in security. The air route via the Azores, though geometrically longer, may be preferable during the bad weather season to that via Newfoundland because it is safer, therefore more frequented and perhaps even more economical. It is preferable at all seasons to that across the Pole, except in time of war. Practical problems always carry several data with them; they require a choice between advantages and inconveniences. Or, with the progress of knowledge, the elements of the problems—at least the material ones, are better and better known and can be evaluated and put into numerical values. The better man knows his habitat and the better he is equipped by science and technology, the greater the value, often the determining value, taken on by two factors; the factor time, and the factor cost, which itself at least partially depends on time.

For the European peasant of the past century time hardly counted at all; to calculate the cost of time would have appeared to him to be an insoluble, if not an absurd, problem; however, he, or his father, or his grandfather would have noticed that this soil was warm and that cold, or that that corner suffered from freezing. He would have organized his crops accordingly; therefrom stems the often variegated, harmonious aspect of our landscape. The adaptation to the natural conditions occurred by trial and error at the scale of the ground. In scientific agriculture, as it has materialized in the United States under the regime of competition and is about to be realized in the U. S. S. R. in its socialized economy, the natural factors such as location, distances, soils, climate, etc. are no less taken into consideration. They are even evaluated with a precision previously unknown. Adaptations are made as in traditional agriculture, but now they are planned, thanks to the power of the means of transportation, for large zones, the corn belt, the spring wheat zone and the zone of winter wheat, on the scale of a large country, indeed, of an entire continent. Did not liberal theoreticians predict a time when, in a unified worldwide economy and thanks to ideally easy and cheap communications, the division of labor would be regulated at a planetary scale?

After all, what is geography? One could answer that it is first of all a method, or if one prefers, a means of considering things, beings, and phenomena in their relation to the earth: localization, extent, and local and regional variations of frequency and intensity. Further, the map is an indispensable tool, not only for presentation, but also for research. If, between two groups of well-defined facts which are well characterized, there is an accurate co-existence in space or parallel variations, one can conclude with assurance that there is a causal relation. This method is presently employed by all kinds of sciences, physical and human, from seismology to economics and linguistics. But the relation is not always direct. Mostly there is a concentration, the links of which can be physical or social, or sometimes one or the other, and set up all manner of sciences. Therefore, it is indispensable for a geographer, occupied in a certain type of research, to be fairly familiar with related sciences, not only in order to grasp their conclusions, but also to be able to appraise their value. This leads to pushing the research into multiple directions, on the local, regional or planetary level, in the hope of gradually reconstituting the links of the chain.

However, the geographer is not satisfied with decomposing the natural complexes, taking them apart, or unfolding them; he intends also to take hold of them, and to understand them in their complexity, and to describe them as such. These complexes offer themselves to him under the form of views of landscapes in the widest sense of the word: not only what the eye can see from a well-chosen observation point, such as an aerial view, but also what the spirit encompasses in the world view, local landscapes, regions—the *pays*— continental units, and finally planetary ones. It was said that geography ends with a reasoned, explanatory description of landscapes. But these landscapes are in part the work of man, which can quite well be the main part; of human groups, which without doubt are distinguished from others by physical and moral features, but which geographically are characterized by their way of life. This fruitful concept was suggested by Vidal de la Blache and was exploited primarily by French geography. One has to understand by it not only all the means by which a group assures its existence, but also its economic and social structure, and its collective mentality. All this together constitutes in truth the environment in which a group lives. In one sense, geography is the knowledge of the terrestrial environment.

Geographical description resorts largely to the visual picture, the map, the drawing, the photograph, and the film; one could imagine that it would turn to registering sounds, natural music, noises of city and factory. But its usual means of expression remains in the word. One will notice that, contrary to general geographies, regional geography has no technical vocabulary. It speaks the language of everybody, partly because it addresses everybody, but also because it invites the reader to active participation by arousing his memory and his imagination: the geographer suggests more then he describes. According to the degree of perfection, the beauty of the form does nothing but express the fullness and secret richness of the thought. Perfection is rarely attained except in the most beautiful pages of the *Tableau de la géographie de la France.*[26] At that stage the distinction between art and science, science and art, disappears, just as thought and form are indissolubly united in certain philosophical writings, and as in some masterworks of painting the purity of the line reminds one of mathematical harmonies.

Now we return to our initial question: is geography a science? Certainly not in the ordinary sense of the word; at most it is a bundle of rather different sciences, each one provided with its proper methods and, therefore, autonomous. But, in that case, what remains of geography as these so called geographical sciences depart from the common trunk? The answer has to be: a certain way to look at things, a way of thinking, perhaps a new intellectual category at which the western mind, and only it, happened to arrive. In the same way as history, also a latecomer, strives to think of past events in their time, each one in its period, which is by far the best way to place the present in its proper place and to be ready to understand it, geography tries to understand

[26]The main work of P. Vidal de la Blache, a regional geography of France.

things and terrestrial events as a function of the earth, conceived not as inactive support, but as a being endowed with an activity of its own which sometimes commands, and always conditions, the activities of the beings which live on it.

It seems to me that that is what Vidal de la Blache expressed in a little known, or at least rarely quoted passage from the preface of his *Atlas Général* (1894). "It is proposed," he said, "to put before the eyes the totality of features which characterize a region in order to permit the mind to make the connection. Indeed, the whole geographical explanation of a landscape consists of this connection. Considered separately, the features of which the physiognomy of a country is composed have the value of facts; but they do not obtain the value of a scientific concept unless one replaces them in the concatenation of which they are a part, which alone can invest them with their full significance. . . .One must go much farther and recognize that no part of the Earth carries its explanation in itself. The play of local conditions does not betray itself with any clarity before the observer unless he rises above and is in the position to recognize analogies which reestablish naturally the generality of the terrestrial laws."

MAXIMILIEN SORRE (1880-1962)

Sorre was a disciple of Vidal De la Blache and de Martonne and, like several French geographers of his generation, he crowned his life-long work with a "human geography". But he, more than most, stressed that the physical environment should be studied only as a framework. He introduced the term *oecumene* into international usage. His interest in man was given a peculiar twist through his thorough familiarity with sociology and medicine. He can be regarded as the founder of modern medical geography. A typical French geographer of the last half century, Sorre was a master of regional geography. He understood how to carry forward the ideas of his predecessors and to adapt them to modern developments. The article, excerpts of which are translated below, updates the definition of *genre de vie*, a central concept of French human geography.

The Concept of "Way of Life" and Its Value for the Present Time[27]

Thirty-seven years have passed since Vidal de la Blache in two articles in this review, admitted to the rights of citizenship this fundamental concept of *genre de vie* (way of life) of which Ratzel had shown an interest in Germany. It is remarkable that it has not been made the object of any critical elaboration since. Ethnographers, all over the globe, have accumulated materials for the knowledge of the way of life. Geographers, in regional monographs, have made valuable contributions to its description, especially in western Europe. There remains a kind of embarrassment: some feel that the concept has been defined insufficiently and prefer to say nothing about it, others are somewhat ashamed to introduce it into their systems, others, finally, think that while it may be appropriate for more or less archaic groupings, it has no place in the description of the modern world. Further, there is no systematic development in the *reliquiae* which Mr. Emm. de Martonne has published under the title *Principles de géographie humaine.* One should not imagine, however, that a definition of *genres de vie* would not have had a place in the final draft, so basic is this concept in all its discussions. There is nothing to prevent taking up again the thoughts of Vidal at the point where he left them at the end of his second article, making them the object of reflection in order to clarify them in the light of knowledge newly acquired by ethnography and sociology.

I. The Content of the Concept of Genre de Vie: We shall analyse the combination of customary activities which characterize a human group and are necessary for its continuing existence by adding some new examples to those given by Vidal.

The Elements of the Genre de Vie: The concept of way of life has an extremely rich content, because it embraces the majority, if not the totality, of all activities of the group and even of the individuals. Only at an advanced stage of civili-

[27] "La notion de Genre de vie et sa valeur actuelle," Maximilien Sorre, *Annales de Géographie,* 57th year, no. 306, April-June 1948, pp. 97-103, no. 307, July-Sept. 1948, pp. 190-204.

zation can one witness a kind of liberation from it. These material and spiritual elements, in the widest sense of the word, are the techniques and procedures, transmitted by tradition, with the help of which men secure a grip on the natural elements. Techniques of power, techniques of producing primitive things, of tools: it is always techniques which secure the duration of the group, together with institutions which assure its cohesion. Creations of the human genius! Indeed, the pressure of the environment stimulates, directs this genius, but one has always to remember its creative power. . . .

It is no misinterpretation to consider, at least for a start, the way of life as a combination of techniques. The practice of pastoral nomadism presupposes the knowledge of the returns of breeding; of raising domestic animals, including castration; of their use for food, milk and milk products; or for transportation, use of the saddle, chariot, and the different kinds of harnessing; of the production of clothing and of the tent. The procedures change with climate, the type of animals, the topography, the proximity of seasonal pastures and the distance of the displacements which it demands. To our mind, their effectiveness depends on knowledge won by experience about the properties of the living and inanimate environment. People have not considered the way of life in that manner for a long time. As familiar as it sounds to us today, the distinction between the natural and the supernatural was not recognized very long ago. Also, every material technique is duplicated by a religious or magic technique (we do not have to choose between these two words in this connection). The primitive knocks down his prey with the hunting spear or the arrow or the stone; of what help are his incantations, his presentations on stone in which we see the first stammering of art and which without doubt had a utilitarian objective? At another stage of civilization, all the rites of fertility, including water rites, belong to a description of the way of life as much as the digging stick, the hoe, or the plough. . . .Let's remember those rites, those processions, and those prayers, by which the Catholic peasant calls down the heavenly rain upon his thirsty fields. In the same manner these activities have their place in the way of life. Even if we define them, let us not mutilate them. By the side of the material factors, the spiritual elements have their place. And of course, the social elements: the establishment of a way of life can not be conceived outside an organized society.

Role of the Elements of the Ways of Life, Their Adjustment: The observation of complex ways of life suggests some distinctions which appear if one considers the most simple forms. Not all features have the same significance, either as to their role or to their age—this latter point is disregarded for the moment. Some are on the very fundament of the way of life, they are creators and organizers; the others have rather the function of conversing and fixing. It is possible also to describe those which have an antagonistic function, namely to limit the way of life. Finally one can find residual elements, the use of which is not immediately clear. These distinctions have to be taken with moderation. They explain the functioning of the way of life and do not have an absolute or sharply defined value.

The most ancient agricultural ways of life are available as examples of the definition of the features: creators and organizers. The choice of cultivated plants, the instruments, and the way in which the grains are planted can be regarded as the fundamental techniques around which the way of life is organized. Their association shows a remarkable stability through extended climatic regions: connection of the tubers and cereal of heavy grain, such as maize, with the planting stick in forested intertropical regions, association of small grains of the millet type with the hoe on the light soils of the Sudan and Deccan, flooding of the ground and transplanting of rice in the countries of the monsoon, and the triad of wheat, plow and oxen on the fields of temperate Eurasia. Other elements, such as the social structure and the organization of work, have rather a conserving function.

If we want to grasp the nature and action of these immobilizing elements, we should look at highly developed forms, such as the combination of cereal growing with the breeding of livestock in a social environment resting on a strong village structure with collective compulsion. It is certain that the way of housing, the agrarian structure, distribution and shapes of the fields, and the type of ownership and exploitation do inscribe upon the soil in tangible traits how the way of life functions. The distribution of the land contributes to immobilizing the agricultural group in its place. Can we not see to what degree the fragmentation and dispersion of lots impede the substitution of a modern cultivation method for an old one?

These latter features which played merely an arresting role in an ancient way of life survive today as antagonistic. One will find other examples in the description of the way of life based on animal husbandry. . . .Religion also serves as such a limiting factor.

Rites and practices which were connected with certain activities of a group may persist even after the forms of existence which served as their support have disappeared. Their meaning is lost. The Yakutes, who became reindeer herders, preserve a portion of the equipment which they used with horses, e.g. the saddle. The excavations of Russian archaeologists have revealed funeral rites which perpetuated the memory of the adoption of new domestic animals such as masks of reindeer laid upon the skulls of horses. In our rural areas, popular traditions remind of very ancient stages which were contemporary to our origins. All that collapses with the passing of our traditional rural civilization and the residual elements disappear.

An equilibrium between these elements of differing order is finally established, and this equilibrium assures the internal cohesion of the way of life, promise for perpetuity—which is one of its essential characteristics.

Ways of Life and Geographical Environments: We retain here only a few results of the general statements which Vidal de la Blache laid down. The ways of life, collections of techniques, are the active forms of adaptation of the human group to the geographical environment. On its particularity and its stability depend its (namely the way of life's) specialization and stability, its chances of permanence. Its local changes are expressed in variations.

The Imprint of the Way of Life Upon Man: The imprint made by the way of life upon the individual and upon the group is another factor in its preservation. It proves to be capable, to a large degree, of molding together their physical appearance and their mental structure. Vidal de la Blache has already stated the essential. "The ways of life have an autonomy which attaches itself to a human being and follows it. It is not only the bedouin and the fellah who think of each other as of different complexion, it is the Vallachian herdsman and the Bulgarian cultivator, it is the seaman and the peasant at our very shores. The soul of the one seems to consist of another metal than that of the other." These opposites clash if they find themselves in conflict over the occupation of space; the conflict of the sedentary cultivator and the nomadic herdsman is one of the commonplaces of history and geography.

It would be easy to continue the list of examples almost endlessly. What one has to keep in mind is the durability of the imprint. It is easy to understand if the two groups live in adjacent territories, but it is still more striking if they live side by side. In the highlands of East Africa, the Bakitara, Banyankole, and the Masai live in the middle of agricultural populations but preserve their way of life. They deliberately have rejected the economic possibilities which were offered to them, and shut themselves up in the breeding of cattle. Their existence shows to what point a traditional way of life can restrict the use of a potentially much richer territory. No less clear is the contrast of the Peuls and the surrounding agriculturists of the Sudan, into whose midst they have intruded like a wedge. The preservation of their ethnic type over vast areas is one of the most impressive facts of the human geography of Africa.

The influence of the way of life is exerted also upon the somatic type. If one objects that the physical differentiation of the Masais and Peuls is of distant origin, because they are intruders and we know some of their way-stations, one only pushes the solution of the problem back. There are in the way of life certain elements which are capable of influencing the outward appearance, such as the mode of nutrition, and the nature and quantity of work. We do not know how these factors express themselves in the hereditary patrimony and, from personal features, become ethnic characteristics.

But the formation of a psychological patrimony, due to language, traditions and rites, is an indisputable fact. The individual is a prisoner of his group, its prohibitions, antipathies, and hates. The most complex factor is the easiest to establish and to explain, in the light of the distinction made above between the roles of the different elements of the way of life.

Are the ways of life which have been defined this way capable of being classified? Usually they are grouped, taking as the starting point the prevailing activity. As today we have given up the doctrine of a succession of cultural stages, it would be incautious to risk a genetic classification. I think we must follow the current usage without too much care for precision.

II. The Evolution of the Ways of Life: A definition of the ways of life, as it shall be sketched presently gives only an incomplete and mutilated view. In order for this complex of customs to have a geographical interest and to be comprehensible, it must present a minimum of continuity and stability. However, continuity and stability do not mean immobility. The way of life has an origin, is transformed, and expands—and that is how it comes to that degree of maturity by which we characterize it. Therefore, the necessity to discuss a complementary aspect arises, one that is by no means contradictory, that of evolution. That is the opportunity to make progress in the knowledge of the ways of life. Vidal de la Blache has well demonstrated from what combinations they originate, under which circumstances they get organized and well-established. Without repeating what he has written and what can be regarded as well established, we can attempt another step forward in the analysis.

III. Circulation and Ways of Life: Though it is true that the establishment of a way of life requires a certain stability which is necessary for the adjustment of the constituent parts and their taking root in the environment, all changes, even if they follow an internal impulse, to a certain degree are bound to some activity of the circulation. It causes the human group to participate in a more general life and furnishes the germs of renewal which fertilize the old established modes of existence. It causes the birth of new modes, marked by its impress and organized for its own ends. There is no isolated region which is forever out of reach of its encroachment. . . .

Exchange, Agent of Destruction and of Differentiation: The effects of circulation are quite varied. They carry with them only useful, or even indispensable, elements of the ways of life: they open possibilities in every respect.

As the carrier of promises or illusions, circulation facilitates, in rural surroundings, the flight of those who dream of an easier or more brilliant life. The railroad was an active agent of the acceleration of the rural exodus; it did not cause it, but facilitated it. It disrupted the demographic equilibrium in the peasant environment and it contributes, thereby, to changing the functioning of our ways of life in an important way.

On the other hand, the easier transportation of products and their sale on an enlarged market stimulates production and can direct the economy of a country upon the road to specialization. Differentiated ways of life then can be observed, directed by the requirements of a particular type of production. Based on a diversified production, they replace the modes of existence which work essentially for the local market. . . .

So far we have had only a partial view of the creative force of circulation. In order to gauge it, let us look at the conditions of the existence of towns. Some were born along routes and on road crossings, all subsist only through active relationships and thanks to an abundant net of communications. The less important towns maintain regional relations, while the larger ones maintain more general contacts. These agglomerations do not draw anything from the cultivation of their soil, they do not even always renew themselves by their natural growth; from outside they receive their provisions, the necessary raw materials for their industry, and everything necessary to their human substance. Their expansion is not limited, rather it starts with the development of large industries. That is also the period when the means of communications multiply, when the means of transportation mobilize growing amounts of heavy materials and larger and larger masses of men. This way a close contact exists between cities and circulation.

IV. The Concept of Way of Life and the World of Today: With the description of the ways of life in cities we have come far from our point of departure: so far that we have to ask whether the same term can designate the behavior of a tribe of herdsmen and of citizens of a city of a million and more. At the least, the concept has been transformed and enlarged. The case would not be unique in those disciplines in which the language can not have the rigidity of algebra. Ours is a domain of moving things. The content of the terms of its vocabulary becomes richer with the times. A critical revision of its fundamental concepts is useful. In order to proceed, let us return to two articles of Vidal de la Blache and we can define still more precisely the classical concept of the way of life.

Original Extent and Comprehensiveness of the Concept of Way of Life: The expression belongs to the popularly used expressions, and as such it applies equally to the individual conduct of a person, as it is determined by his character, his social position, and his professional customs, and to the habits of a group. The moment geography seizes it, its use is restricted to matters concerning behavior of a group. There is no way of life other than the collective one. Whatever further changes are made in the meaning of the expression, it has to conform to this fundamental requirement, and also to the cohesion of those elements which we have pointed out as necessary from the beginning of this study. It is not without reason that Vidal, in order to qualify this complex of customs, uses the word *cemented*. The following are the permanent features by which we always recognize ways of life in geography.

It is obvious that the expression applies to the extensive categories of modes of existence, all of which rest on the direct exploitation of the environment, living by food gathering, fishing, hunting, breeding, and cultivation. Vidal de la Blache has mentioned all of them explicitly. . . .It is not too much to say that for the last four centuries they shared the largest part of the continental geographical space, and that they embraced the greatest part of mankind. . . .

As for the mixed ways of life, it is possible that in many cases they found all their raw materials, bones, wood, minerals, or textile fibres in their local environment. However, for a long time industries have been fed from the outside. Stability was closely tied to a harmony between the rhythm of agricultural and industrial occupations. If this were not the case, stability would be threatened by outside influences. The culture of the sugar beet in the Vimeu is dependent on all fluctuations of the market for sugar. The locksmith's trade undergoes the influence of all the consolidation within the metallurgical industries. The way of life is threatened in its internal cohesion. One does not want to say that it necessarily will dissolve, but it is threatened to the degree that it is dependent on the outside.

One sees from these examples, how even within a rural society the concept of way of life tends to change. We can summarize it briefly by saying that instead of being determined, as in the past, by the contact with the elements of the physical and living environment, it tends to be determined by the contact with an economic and social geographical complex.

The Concept of Way of Life Beyond the Rural World: Indeed, the concept of way of life in its classical form and with the modifications implied in the concept of the mixed ways of life still has a wide range of applicability in the modern world. We think of the great masses of peasants in Monsoon Asia, of the hundreds of millions of men who live on the culture of cereals, small grains, rice, or corn as basic resources. It has come so far, as e.g. in Australasia, that the farming of the indigenous populations has been altered by the plantation culture. One knows also that in the Tonkinese delta the small village industries help the rice-cultivating peasants. All this enters into the framework of our knowledge. Despite the great rural revolution, which breaks through the framework of our ancient rural societies, even in Europe districts are left where the concept of the way of life is applicable, sometimes with modifications. And the same is true in both Americas, although the new forms were born in the United States with the triumph of mechanization and motorization.

Nevertheless, we are less surprised by such persistent remnants than by the growing number of people who escape from the rule of the ways of life, based on the exploitation of the soil, in proportion to the expansion of Western European civilization. The most archaic types, fishing and hunting, are in full retreat, almost on the route of disappearance. Under our very eyes nomadism suffers the most palpable setbacks on the steppes of the Old World. Despite a production of greatly enlarged amounts of nutritive materials, the proportion of the peasant masses to the whole population decreases in all peoples of European descent. The absolute importance of these masses is declining while the population increases. The non-agricultural occupations absorb a growing part of human activity. There are even great countries where the work in the fields was the act of a small minority in 1939 as industrialization took its captives in all social strata of the nation. The change of occupation in general involves the relinquishment of the soil, formation of new groups and of new foci of attraction. The uprooted individual fuses therein. He acquires new habits. He participates in a new way of life, to say it directly and for lack of another term for characterizing this collection of well-organized habits. We sketched its formation, either for cities or for ways of life connected with circulation, and the use of this term seemed legitimate. The geographer has, therefore, to define a category of ways of life which is different from those which have won his attention before. New? Not exactly, because every flowering of a civilization for millenia has been translatable into a flowering of cities. However, today they are more developed and carry a greater weight for the destiny of mankind.

The Growth of Uniformity of the Ways of Life: We think we have shown that in order to adjust their meaning to the general evolution of our societies and for an explanatory description of the modern world, the geographer could expand the benefit of the concept in which Vidal de la Blache has shown his whole interest. Ways of life dissolve under our very eyes. Others get organized, expand, and impose themselves upon people. We need only to identify the ways of life. We hesitate nevertheless. Put in the middle of the stream, are we not incapable of recognizing the shores? Or better, does not the acceleration of the rate of change of all forms of life, due to the penetration of the scientific ideas into all the branches of activity, hinder the consolidation of complexes of customs and of ideas? Or at least both at the same time? But above all the contrasts which once were so marked and have been established between the human groupings by the practice of different ways of life are less pronounced.

At the time when Vidal de la Blache wrote, this mitigation had already been mentioned by European observers regarding trans-Atlantic life. E. Zimmerman, following the economic evolution from day to day, very often insisted on the progress of uniformity in the modern world. Our generation saw the progress in such an old country as France. Two series of factors are at work to reduce the differences, even though in different manners. First of all is the tendency for mechanization and motorization, which is apparent in all domains of creative activity. As the work of power passes to the machine, man become a supervisor. The habit of the profession becomes less visible in *habitus corporis* (deportment of the body) and even in mental activities. The phrase which we quoted before that "the soul of the one seems forged from another metal than that of the other" sounds less obvious. In the second place there is the leveling of the standard of living in which the prototype is the urban standard. At the moment of the start of big industry, when Robert Peel spoke of the new race of men forming in the cities, the comparison was not in their favor. Three quarters of a century later, things have changed. In the 20th century, the alimentary and clothing standards of peasants, those habits which indicate the standard of life, are aligned with those of the cities. And the totality of the elements of the way of life, with more or less delay, follows suit. Thus, as if it was regulated by some kind of a pendulum, the progress of life reduces the differences which it has created.

The world seems to lose its richness and its variety, and, at the present stage, perhaps man himself loses some of his profound richness. If one looks closely, one notices that the need for adaptation has been transferred from man to technique. Geography finds in the latter the variation of localized combinations which are the objects of its research. . . .In order to utilize the fruitful concept of way of life, one has at the same time to keep track of the gains and the losses.

THEODORE MONOD (1902-)

The geographical exploration of foreign countries always went hand-in-hand with the collection of scientific data, descriptive material, and occasionally with theoretical deliberation. But since about 1870 a separate branch of geography, colonial geography, has emerged, the goal of which is to study the non-European continents for their own sakes as well as for their dependence on European colonial powers. Colonial geography is an academic interest in the geographic areas themselves but not in their political status as colonies. It seems to have been mainly a French subscience, though it was followed very intensively for a short period in Italy and later in Germany. A few universities maintained chairs for colonial geography which were in the colonies themselves. Such men as E. Gautier and R. Capot-Rey, geographers of the first rank, worked out of Algiers. In Dakar, Senegal, Theodore Monod founded the *Institut Francais D' Afrique Noire* (French Institute of Black Africa). It became the nucleus of the present University of Dakar, and Monod is still the director of the unique museum there.

Monod, as this witty piece shows and as many others felt, saw a double task for colonial geography—the scientific exploration of the colonial countries and the enlightenment of the public at home concerning centuries-old misconceptions about the "dark continent". In this endeavor he and other true geographers distinguish themselves from the host of colonial writers who, under the disguise of spreading information, are agents of a racist imperialism. Monod is their enemy.

The Hippopotamus and the Philosopher[28]

Human beings, from indolence, are often not very inquisitive. How many people do you know who have travelled through Africa other than blindly or as inanimate objects? How many do you know who know how to walk with an alert and intelligent regard in a new environment, where so many new forms, so many new sounds, so many hues, so many unknown orders wait for them? For how many of us is the world without mysteries? Happy mortals! How I envy you! What security! Away with the scruples of the scholar! A cheer to the massive affirmations; to the many colors without transitions; the brute lights; to all the stupidities, if they are only enormous enough; to the most clumsy slogans, if only untiring repetition did transform them into "truths".

Leave these toys to the innocents. We are among our equals. You will understand me if I say that among the most marvellous picture books, the most outstanding is an atlas. The whole terraqueous globe, even with a little cosmography added, between the two covers of a single volume? And there you go to read the newspaper? Who would lift a finger against someone, who dares to say that he is bored with an atlas? Nobody? I doubt it. . . .

Where does Africa end? A funny question, is it not? "Whom do you think you are talking to? We have been to school. . . ." Indeed, that is exactly what I was afraid of, because elementary instruction, which has to be short, simple, crude, schematic, lapidary, microscopic can not—and believe me that that may be quite painful at times—can not at the same time be complex, expressing the finest shades, many-sided, critical, detailed, with one word—truthful.

With the signs of an announcement it is possible to hammer in a slogan, to impose a catchword, to order to make the customer believe that the alcohol *Untel* is a "*hygienic*" liquid or that Mr. Anonymous will deliver a general nostrum to you

---

[28] L'hippopotame et le philosophe, Théodore Monod, Renée Julliard, Paris, 1946. p. 111-112, 157-160.

for a modest price, but it is not possible to obtain the real thing or to tell the truth.

I am coming back to my original question: Where does Africa end? That is not, by far, as simple as it appears.

Unless you confuse Africa with its material form, simply geographically enclosing it by its beaches, hemmed with foam, like others who assume that they are talking of man but are describing nothing more than his mortal remains, the palpable and measurable support of an intangible reality.

And if there existed only one Africa, and as if the small map in the handbook could render a true picture! Agreed, there is a topographic Africa, fairly well delimited except in the Northeast, though even there the facts are fairly complicated; but beside it there are all the other Africas, the geological and its structure, the climatological and its zones, the botanical and its flora, the zoological and its fauna, the anthropological and its races, the ethnographical and its cultures, the linguistic and its languages: and how many others: the religious, the music-mad, the sculptural, the agricultural, and a dozen others. How many Africas! And how many maps! And so many, many which, unfortunately, are not coextensive. First the geographical Africa. Clearly to the north, the west, the south and to a great bit to the east, it is pretty simple. Still, one could ask where to draw the boundary in the Atlantic Ocean concerning the islands. No doubt about Fernando Po, Annobon, Principe, and San Thomé, or the Cape Verde Islands; not even the Canary Islands, at least for their eastern group, the ones which are obviously African? But are St. Helena or Ascension Island African?

That is a minor point. Let's proceed to the Isthmus of Suez. He would be a clever fellow who could say where Africa ends in this area. Although administratively the Sinai Peninsula is a part of Egypt, does this Egypt make an Asiatic power? After all, in which part of the world was the Decalogue proclaimed. I do not know; but in order to please you and respecting a venerable usage, I want to go as far as to concede that it is convenient to impose the Suez frontier on Africa, but without hiding the fact that it is a simple conventional usage, arbitrary and artificial. Do you believe truly and seriously that a traveller on his way from Mauretania to Iran when he passes over the Isthmus of Suez without a map, without knowing its width, would stop suddenly, hit his forehead and cry out: "Hey, I hit my big toe against a meridian. I have had the impression for a few moments that we are in another continent?" And what change would he see? People, bushes, lizards, wind blown sand?

The geological limits of the African continent have nothing to do with geographical. This great cake is only welded from several pieces, coarsely welded at that, for anybody who knows how to look at it. African Africa is a stable country, quiet, solid, rigid, what the geologists call a shield or a mass, something like the starched front of a shirt, the piece which refuses to be crumpled; too inflexible to follow the movements of the textures which surround it; it would break rather than fold. Against that base, which comprises ninety-five percent of the continent, are fastened—perhaps one should say crushed—the folded-Barbary in the North and the Cape system in the South, a bubble at each end, but as foreign to the dough as the ornament in a green creme to French pastry. Geologically neither Morocco, nor Algeria, nor Tunisia is in Africa. For compensation, a large part of Arabia, at least Yemen and the Hejaz, are basically as African as Nubia or Ethiopia on the opposite of the Red Sea. The Red Sea is nothing but a mediocre crack created by accident. I can see quite well the demiurge, sheepishly and awkwardly approaching the Creator: "Excuse, Lord, we just dropped your Africa to the ground; it is a bit split, apparently, but it should be possible to glue it again; don't be angry. Sign for an order for a tube of glue, the large type, and I shall mend it; by tomorrow nothing will be visible." And I can hear the Deity answer good-naturedly to the repenting archangel: "But no, but no, my boy, we will let it stand as it is; it is no more ugly, quite the opposite; because, I confess, it was made a little too compact; this way it will please the geologists and then, what a windwall for steamships!" And so it happened that a large bit of African granite appears in our atlases in Asia.

CHAPTER 9

BRITISH AND COMMONWEALTH GEOGRAPHERS

No nation sent out more explorers during the last 150 years than the United Kingdom. And it is interesting to note that much of the exploration was prompted by scientific curiosity. While in former centuries geographic exploration was usually a by-product of, or a means to, other purposes, geographic exploration for its own sake did not start before the 18th century. There has even been a long standing discussion about whether the explorations of David Livingstone, perhaps the greatest of all British explorers, were a means of accomplishing his missionary and humanitarian goals or whether they were just the outward justification for his unprofitable scientific curiosity. British civil servants all over the world have used their proximity to unknown regions to spend much of their off-duty time in exploration, often unconnected with their official duties. The *Geographical Journal* of the Royal Geographical Society in London contains more travel exploration reports than any other geographical journal in the world!

However, this preoccupation with exploration led to a relative lack of theoretical interest in the basic problems of geography. Only two papers have been selected to represent British geographers, emphasizing Britain's position in a history of geographic thought as opposed to that in a history of geography.

It is left to Griffith Taylor to represent the Commonwealth. . . .

SIR HALFORD J. MACKINDER (1861-1947)

Like many European geographers, Mackinder was originally a student of history. He became a pioneer in geography as a separate academic science in England and was the first person to be appointed Reader in Geography at Oxford University. Almost alone among British geographers, he wrote studies completely devoted to the theoretical aspects of geography. However, in the British tradition, he was active in exploration too, though in a minor way. His ideas on the "heartland" and the "rimlands" became world famous, especially when they were accepted in Germany by Haushofer, who repeatedly stressed the fact that he owed much to Mackinder, possibly as much as he owed Ratzel.

On the Scope and Methods of Geography[1]

What is geography?. . . .Another reason for now pressing this matter on your notice comes from within. For half a century several societies, and most of all our own, have been active in promoting the exploration of the world. The natural result is that we are now near the end of the roll of great discoveries. . . .It is needless to say that this paper would not be written were it my belief that the R. G. S. must shortly close its history—a corporate Alexander weeping because it has no more worlds to conquer.

The first inquiry to which we must turn our attention is this: Is geography one, or is it several subjects? More precisely, are physical and political[2] geography two stages of one investigation, or are they separate subjects to be studied by different methods, the one an appendix to geology, the other of history.

. . . .The function of political geography is to trace the interaction between man and his environment. . . .Physiology would answer to the definition of the science which traces the interaction of man and his environment. It is the function of physiology, of physics, and of chemistry to trace the action of forces irrespective for the most part of precise locality. . . .

---

[1] *On the Scope and Methods of Geography*, H. J. Mackinder, *Proceedings of the Royal Geographical Society*, Vol. 9, 1887.

[2]Used in the sense of human geography.

It is especially characteristic of geography that it traces the influence of locality, that is of environment varying locally. So far as it does not do this it is merely physiography, and the essential topographical element has been omitted. I propose therefore to define geography as the science whose main function is to trace the interaction of man in society and so much of his environment as varies locally.

Before the interaction can be considered, the elements which are to interact must be analysed. One of these elements is the varying environment, and the analysis of this is, I hold, the function of physical geography. Thus we are driven to a position in direct antagonism to current notions. We hold that no *rational* political geography can exist which is not built upon and subsequent to physical geography. At the present moment we are suffering under the effects of an irrational political geography, one, that is, whose main function is not to trace causal relations, and which must, therefore, remain a body of isolated data committed to memory. . . .

To sum up our position in a series of propositions:

(1) It is agreed that the function of political geography is to detect and demonstrate the relations subsisting between man in society and so much of his environment as varies locally.

(2) As a preliminary to this the two factors must be analysed.

(3) It is the function of physical geography to analyze one of these factors, the varying environment.

(4) Nothing else can adequately perform this function. Because, no other analysis can exhibit the facts in their causal relations and in their true perspective. . . .

The more we specialize the more room and the more necessity is there for students whose constant aim it shall be to bring out the relations of the special subjects. One of the greatest of all gaps lies between the natural sciences and the study of humanity. It is the duty of the geographer to build one bridge over an abyss which in the opinion of many is upsetting the equilibrium of our culture. Lop off either limb of geography and you maim it in its noblest part.

In speaking thus we are not blind to the necessity of specialism within geography itself. If you would do original work in the science you must specialize. But for this purpose either physical or political geography would be as unwieldy as the entire subject. Moreover, your special subject need not fall entirely within the realm of one or other branch; it may lie across the frontier. Geography is like a tree which early divides into two great branches, whose twigs may nonetheless be inextricably interwoven.

This question of possibility leads us naturally into an inquiry as to the relations of geography to its neighbor sciences . . . .First, then, as to the configuration of the earth's surface. We have here a bone of contention between the geographers and the geologists. The latter hold that the causes which have determined the form of the lithosphere are dealt with by their science, and that there is neither room nor necessity for the physical geographer. The geographer has in consequence damaged his science by refusing to include among his data any but the barest results of geology. . . . Two sciences may have data in part identical, yet there ought to be no bickering in consequence, for the data, though identical, are looked at from different points of view. They are grouped differently.

. . .True physical geography aims at giving us a causal description of the distribution of the features of the earth's surface. The data must be regrouped on a topographical basis. If I may venture to put the matter somewhat abruptly —Physiography asks of a given feature, "What is it?" Topography, "Where is it?" Physical geography, "Why is it there?" Political geography, "How does it act on man in society, and how does he react on it?" Geology asks, "What riddle of the past does it help to solve?" Physiography is common ground to the geologist and the geographer. The first four subjects are the realm of the geographer. The questions come in sequence. You may stop short of any one of them. But it is my contention that you cannot with advantage answer one unless you have answered those which precede it. Geology proper, in its strict sense, is unnecessary to the sequence of the argument.

The distinction between meteorology and geography must be a practical one. So much of meteorology, and it is much, as deals with weather-forecasting cannot be required by the geographer. Average or recurrent climatic conditions alone come within this ken. Even here he must be content very often to adopt the results of meteorology as data, just as meteorology itself accepts the results of physics. It is a mistake, especially of the Germans, that they include too much in geography. . . .Geography must be a continuous argument, and the test of whether a given point is to be included or not must be this: Is it pertinent to the main line of argument?

The truth of the matter is that the bounds of all the sciences must be compromises. Knowledge, as we have said before, is one. Its division into subject is a concession to human weakness. As a final example of this we will deal with the relations of geography to history. In their elementary stages they must obviously go hand in hand. In their higher stages they diverge. The historian finds full occupation in the critical and comparative study of documents. He has neither the time nor usually the turn of mind to scan science for himself with a view to selecting the facts and ideas which he requires. It is the function of the geographer to do this for him. On the other hand the geographer must go to history for the verification of the relations which he suggests. The body of laws governing those relations, which might in time evolve, would render possible the writings of much "prehistoric" history. John Richard Green's *Making of England* is largely a deduction from geographical conditions of what must have been the course of history.

A. J. HERBERTSON (1865-1915)

Herbertson was another of the very few British geographers who paid attention to the theoretical and methodological aspects of their subject. He never took part in the great explorations or even travelled widely outside the British Isles. Nonetheless, perhaps because he focused his attention on the whole globe, he was the first geographer writing in English to develop a system of natural regions. In some way Supan had preceded him, and also the work of the climatologist

Wladimir Köppen broke ground in the same direction. Herbertson's influence through his academic teaching was perhaps even more important than through his writings.

The Major Natural Regions: An Essay in Systematic Geography[1]

Those of us who teach geography at the Universities have constantly to answer the question, What is geography? and in preparing our work we have to be quite clear about its content and scope. In this country we are less tied by tradition than in some others, for there is practically no systematic geography to bind us. In Germany the Ritter and Humboldt tradition gave rise to two schools. To America the Ritter tradition was carried over by Guyot, but a new one developed by geologists has superseded it. For long in our country geographical progress meant exploration, mainly with a commercial or political basis, and descriptive and statistical geography was taught. It was only with the rise of an academic geography that the wider conception of geography as the science of distributions developed.

In studying distributions comparisons were inevitable between geography and orography, climate and vegetation, and so on, and we were led to think that there might exist definite natural divisions of our globe. This resulted in an attempt to replace the purely political divisions of the world by others based on configuration. At this stage both the teaching and textbooks gave a rational analysis of the main-feature lines as a guide to the general build of the continents, and this was supplemented by a general consideration of the climatic and biological elements also for the continents. In the detailed study of each continent, however, the descriptions were applied to the various political divisions. This is found to be unsatisfactory.

How are we to go about making more satisfactory subdivisions? At the outset two difficulties present themselves: (1) What characteristics should be selected to distinguish one region from another? Size is not a sufficient guide, although it must not be neglected; neither is structure, nor even con-

---

[3] *The Major Natural Regions*: An Essay in Systematic Geography, A. J. Herbertson, *Geographical Journal*, vol. XXV, 1905.

figuration, although this last suggests many important divisions of the Earth's surface, which must be taken into account in any rational classification. (2) How can we determine the different orders of natural regions? The British Isles, for instance, form part of a much larger natural area, that of North-Western Europe, while they themselves can be analyzed into a number of sub-regions.

The recognition of geographical forms has gradually been taking place. It has necessarily been late in the history of thought; first, because our knowledge of the surface of the globe was insufficient until the explorations of the nineteenth century had traced its fundamental features; and second, because the specialist interpretation of the accumulated data was a necessary preliminary to its utilization for systematic geography. . . .

In what way is the geographer to use this raw material in working out a systematic geography? This involves the question, what is the subject-matter of geography? This I take to be the study of phenomena from the point of view of their distribution on the surface of the Earth, in natural groups, and not as isolated phenomena.

Geography is not concerned with distribution of one element on the Earth's surface but with all. If geographers first regard the distribution of different phenomena separately, it is only in order to help them later to consider them together more effectively. That is not to say that all these different distributions are of equal importance, but that all must be taken into consideration before the problem of systematic geography is solved. Some may bulk more largely in the geographical consciousness than others, but all must be kept in view. Configuration is necessarily the framework, but we must not think of it as a more or less irregular surface; we must see it as part of a solid which comprises not merely the soil beneath, but the air above, with relations to other parts of the Earth, and also the influences coming from outside the Earth. This gives a movement, a life to the whole, and it seems to me useful and not altogether fanciful to speak of this geographically discerned complex as a macro-organism.

A reorganisation of more complex units than the individual has gradually taken place, and has grown more familiar in our country in recent years with the rise of such studies as those of plant associations, or in practical life with the development of self-government. One may not have the exact equivalent of the biological species and genera, but it is useful to remember the existence of these, which suggest different orders of geographical divisions.

The systematic botanist or geologist has no difficulty in defining the objects of his investigation, although he may have about their classification. The sytematic geographer has first to point out what he wishes to systematize. This I believe to be definite areas of the surface of the Earth considered as a whole, not the configuration alone, but the complex of land, water, air, plant, animal, and man, regarded in their special relationship as together constituting a definite characteristic portion of the Earth's surface. The question is, what are the characteristic and distinguishing elements of the areas which we may term natural regions?

The recognition of the possibility of dividing the lands into great natural regions I have found so useful both in investigating and in teaching that I venture to bring it before you, I think it should prove a stimulus to geography, similar to that derived from the development of a natural systematic botany or zoology. This paper does not profess to present a complete solution, which can not be arrived at in the existing state of our knowledge, but is intended to initiate a discussion on:

(a) the desirability of developing such a systematic geography

(b) the major units with which that systematic geography would deal. . . .

Configuration. Two facts have to be considered - first, extension horizontally and vertically; second, the surface form, which is determined by structure, the nature of the transforming processes, and the time during which they have been active.

It is hardly necessary to refer to the vertical distribution of lands.

The feature lines of both the high and low lands are varied and depend in the first place on the structure of the crust.

The accompanying morphological map is based mainly on Suess's classical work[4]. . . .

The study of these types - young folded mountains, tablelands, and platforms, denudation highlands and plains, and elevated and lower accumulation lands - suffice to give an idea of the main feature lines of lands of the globe. There is a very large number of variations, partly due to the relative importance of fracturing and folding in a given area, partly to the nature of the transforming agents at work—ice, running water, or dry air. To the distribution of these processes the rainfall map is a key, and for the secondary divisions of landforms, a superposition of the orographical, tectonic, and rainfall maps is necessary. The rainfall map is important in other connections, and this leads to the consideration of the distribution of climatic forms.

Climate. While the pressure and wind map is the key to many climatic peculiarities, for our present purpose the temperature and rainfall maps are of the greatest importance. . . .

. . . .The rainy season as well as the quantity of rain, must be taken into account. A new map showing seasonal rainfall, based on Supan's[5] seasonal rainfall maps, accompanies this paper. This permits the differentiation of regions which receive sufficient rainfall at none or one or more seasons, and the comparison between those regions where the rainfall is precipitated when temperature conditions are most and least favorable.

The first contrast is between the drier interior and the

---

[4] The book of the Austrian geologist Edward Suess (1831-1914), *Das Antlitz Der Erde* (*The Face of the Earth*), Wien and Leipzig, 1885-1909, has remained a standard work both for geologists and geographers in those countries where geomorphology was considered basic. It was translated into many languages, and reached perhaps an even wider public in the French edition (1897-1918), translated and enlarged by the leading French geologist and geomorphologist, Emmanuel de Margerie.

[5] Alexander Supan (1847-1920) was a well known Austrian geographer whose textbook was widely used. As a climatologist, he was working along the lines drawn by Humboldt, but his system was largely replaced by Köppen's system.

wetter coast; the second between the drier lowland and the wetter highland; the third between the east and west coast. . . .

In its main outlines the vegetation map follows the climate map, and only in its secondary characteristics does it show the effects of the soil and drainage. If the existing plant-covering of the Earth is mapped, then the influence of man is a third factor, which in most botanic maps is eliminated. The vegetation map may be looked upon as a commentary on and a summary of the climatic ones.

The mapping of human conditions has less significance in indicating the natural geographic regions, for the fact of human development has to be taken into account as well as the possibilities of the natural environment. The density of population map is the most direct expression of the actual economic utilization of the natural region. One has only to cite the central plains of North America before and after the introduction of railroads and the exploration of minerals to measure the importance of the human factor in determining this density. Each geographical region has its potentialities as well as its actualities, and a study of these is one of the most complex and fascinating the geographer can tackle. The necessary preliminary, however, is a just appreciation of the natural physical condition of relief and climate.

Hitherto it has been customary to study the geography of the world according to political divisions. These, expressing the most complex and unstable of human conditions, must be eliminated from any consideration of natural regions.

In the determination of natural regions, climate and configuration must both be considered. Climate, because it not merely affects the physical features, but also because it best minimizes the various influences acting on the surface. Climate even more than configuration, for the great barriers of the land are climatic—wastes of arid desert or ice mountains—for it is the climate more than the configuration which renders lofty mountains effective barriers. Only when minor forms are taken into consideration does configuration become the all-important factor. . . .

A natural region should have a certain unity of configuration, climate, and vegetation. The ideal boundaries are the dissociating ocean, the severing mass of mountains, or the inhospitable deserts. As a rule, save in the case of the shore, the boundary is not at all well marked, but the characteristics of one region melt gradually into those of another. . . .

The importance of regarding the Earth in this way can hardly be overestimated. Take, for instance, the application to education. Knowing each of the chief types, it is a simple matter to learn the peculiarities of each variety, and a great saving of time is effected, while the intellectual discipline of distinguishing the species and comparing the varieties is great. The application to economic and political affairs is even more obvious. Speaking generally, the permanent elements of each region are similar and the history of the exploitation of the variety of any type of region where human development is most advanced should be of great profit to those interested in the exploitation or administration of the relatively undeveloped varieties of the same type. The recognition of natural regions gives the historian a geographical foundation for his investigations into the development of human society, such as he has not hitherto consciously possessed. By comparing the histories of the same race in two different regions, or of a succession of races in the same region, it should be possible to arrive at some knowledge of the invariable effect of a type of environment on its inhabitants, and permit estimation of the non-environmental factors in human development. It should be difficult to exaggerate the importance of this investigation, which seems to me a fundamental one for all who have to deal with the study of man, or with his economic exploitation or his proper government.

GRIFFITH TAYLOR (1880-1963)

Taylor is Australian by birth but has for long been a citizen of the world. He has been a member of the faculties of educational institutions in England, Australia, the United States and Canada. But wherever he has been in residence he has been a stimulating and controversial figure, willing to tackle any new geographic field with vigor and imagination.

In GEOGRAPHY IN THE TWENTIETH CENTURY, which Taylor edited, he wrote the introduction to the volume, from which the excerpt which follows was taken, as well as chapters on "Exploration of Antarctica", "Racial Geography", "Urban Geography", and "Geopolitics and Geopacifics". There is not a dull word in the lot!

Taylor is grouped with British geographers as a matter of convenience. Actually, he is in a class by himself.

Fundamentals of Geography[6]

In every branch of science we find specific differences developing as organisms spread into different environments. This is true in regard to the outlooks of exponents of geography in different parts of the world. Thus geographers in France, Germany, and England were dealing with areas for the most part fairly completely occupied by man. They were blessed with adequate detailed maps long before this was the case in such lands as the United States, Australia, or Canada. As a consequence there developed about the turn of the century a somewhat different feeling as to the main purposes of geographic reesarch in the two contrasted areas, the Old Lands and the New Lands.

Vidal de la Blache taught in Paris from 1877 to 1918, and he developed the concept that the environment contains a number of *possibilities,* and their utilization is dependent almost entirely on human selection. This concept gave rise to the school of *Possibilists.* He realized the necessity for detailed synthetic studies in geography; and through his inspiration a number of regional monographs were published in the last decade of the last century. It is very important to understand that la Blache was dealing with the land of France —which some geographers are willing to accept as the best environment for all-round human development to be found on earth. What was the natural result of this environment, and of the plentitude of detailed maps of all parts of the country? Surely enthusiasm for the detailed study in the minutest particulars of all aspects of the human habitat, and the growth of a firm belief that man played the chief part in the development of the region.

---

[6]*Geography in the Twentieth Century,* Griffith Taylor, New York, pp. 7-12, 14-16.

Another somewhat psychological factor comes into play here too. Although the emphasis on regional studies was soon stressed in Germany, yet the latter had been the birthplace of Ratzel's determinism. It is probable that there was a slight tendency of French geographers to swing to the other extreme and support very strongly the new 'regionalism'. To sum up we may say that a somewhat determinist approach fostered by the great advances made in the knowledge of evolution, was the characteristic of the later part of the nineteenth century; but that in Europe in the next half-century the popular point of view, following Vidal de la Blache, Brunhes (and in Germany Hettner and Passarge) was the regional and possibilist outlook on geography.

What was the state of affairs in the first of the New Lands to develop a geographic outlook? Here in U. S. A. the population in 1900 was just half of what it is today, and the law of diminishing returns had hardly begun to operate. The greatest names in fields allied to those of geography were geologists such as Gilbert, Powell, Agassiz, and later William Morris Davis. It has been pointed out that early publications of the American geographers around 1900 consisted largely of morphological research, and regional studies were almost unknown. In those happy days the geographer discussed the structure and climate of a country, and then proceeded to show how man had spread through the land in response to these major environmental factors. Ratzel was honored and Ellen Semple was his prophetess.

However, a younger generation of geographers was soon occupying the chairs of the main teaching institutions. As ever, as new ideas appealed to many of them, and accurate maps accumulated and detailed research was possible, the disciples of the possibilist and regional school became more and more numerous. The concept of the 'cultural landscape' rapidly spread throughout the United States. Some leaders went so far as to state that 'an *uninhabited* region can only be considered geographically in regard to its potential value to man'. They stated that the landscape as a whole is greater than its parts, and in this landscape the emphasis is to be laid on the changes due to man rather than on the original environment. Thus the regional complex must include both the natural and the cultural landscape; though to the writer the emphasis should be laid on the former.

Most geographers accept regional geography as the core of our discipline, and this aspect is discussed in later chapters. Sauer in his *Morphology of Landscape* (Berkeley, 1925) discussed the relations of systematic and regional geography much as in the following summary by L. S. Wilson.

> The Agent (culture) working on the Medium (natural landscape) through Time yields the Forms (habitation by type and group, population, land use and workshop, communication, population, density and mobility) of the cultural Landscape. The cultural landscape is moulded from the natural landscape by the cultural group. The group is the active force, the natural area the medium in which the group works, and the cultural landscape is the final result.*

In the same article Wilson makes a plea for a closer liaison between geography and allied sciences such as physics, geology, and botany. This aspect of geographic philosophy is pursued further in a final chapter in this volume dealing with Geopacifics. It seems to the editor that far more geographers have written voluminously about the *need* for liaison than have written texts to *illustrate* the virtues of such a pooling of results! May I venture to refer them to my tetralogy on Race, Nation, City, and Civilization. These volumes definitely attempt such interrelations.

The writer has no objection to most of what is implied in the preceding paragraphs emphasizing the landscape. He agrees that a vast amount of useful research has been done by the 'landscape gardeners' of geography, especially in those memoirs which emphasize the changing cultural pattern. Here Whittlesey has introduced the useful phrase 'sequent occupation' as an important feature of the cultural landscape. But I am of the opinion that we shall see a swing away from this 'micro-geography' to a broader point of view in the next decade or so. After all geography is the science of the *world;*

---

* L. S. Wilson, "Geographic Training for the Postwar World," in *Geographical Review*, Oct. 1948.

and it is the understanding of the whole world that concerns us mainly. Those micro-geographers who oppose the older environmentalism are doing useful work in the unusually endowed regions where most of them work; in France, Germany, and the eastern United States. Let them however leave the less attractive portions of the world to the 'macro-geographer', who believes that the old controls of structure and climate are all-important in our efforts to make the most of our varied habitats.

I find that some geographers use the term *environment* to include *every cultural* factor which affects man. To use an extreme example, they would call the tobacco and chocolate —donated to us by kindly manufacturers in the Antarctic expedition with which I was connected—part of the explorers' environment. The American pioneer moving to the far west carried with him—as pointed out in a private letter recently —a hundred technological inventions due to man's intelligence in the last million years. These minor cultural accretions have little relevance, in my opinion, in a discussion of the importance of environmental control. Their field of study is *sociological* rather than geographical.

Geocratic versus 'We-ocratic'

Let us examine this idea of the difference between the habitats of the micro-geographers (who to some extent are possibilists) and macro-geographers (who are nearer environmentalists) somewhat more closely. One of the best studies of the broad capabilities of the world is the well-known memoir by O. E. Baker (*Geographical Review*, 1923) dealing with the arable lands of the earth. He assumed there were about 52 million square miles of land surface, for at that time the extent of Antarctica (some 5 1/2 million square miles) was not known. He estimated that only 10 million square miles are arable, leaving 47 million square miles as not likely to be of great importance for man's close settlement.

The writer has had extensive experience in three large areas of the world. Some of his earliest geographical publications dealt with the 5 1/2 million square miles of Antarctica. Is this to be completely ignored by the geographer, because in the phrase quoted above, its potential value to man is at present zero? Quite otherwise. It is an outstanding example of the fact that a very small knowledge of structure and climate is enough to demonstrate that the environment is all-powerful here, and that man has practically no say in the development of this huge region.

Let us turn to Australia—a land of 3 million square miles. For twenty years the writer was vilifed because he stoutly maintained that the environment precluded any important settlement in 55 per cent of the continent. What is the use of talking of 'possibilism' in a region such as the arid centre of Australia? I quote from the writings of one of the leading American Geographers—'Deserts may be transformed into garden spots by irrigation.' Such remarks, made without qualification, to my mind do far more harm than good. Applying them to Australia we find there that there is an area 1 1/2 million square miles which needs more water. The total amount irrigated is less than 1,500 square miles, and I am unable to see how more than 3,000 square miles can ever be irrigated. We may conclude that irrigation may make a garden-spot of *one part in 500* of the desert, but this statement does not seem to support the opponent of environmental control very satisfactorily.

Finally let us glance at the Dominion of Canada for a moment. Here is an area 3 1/2 million square miles, which the writer has divided into two divisions; firstly 800,000 square miles with a population of more than about one to the square mile; and secondly the remainder, some 2,700,000 square miles, which is practically empty. It is to be remembered that the whole of Canada was sufficiently known for us to estimate its major possibilities fifty years ago. Is the macro-geographer to cease to try to discover the best way to develop empty Canada—which in his opinion is along the lines of structure, climate, and soil—i.e. environmental control? In fine he is unwilling to agree that the possibilist approach is superior in the 80 per cent of the lands of the world of poor quality, for they are better understood by the older (in part) determinist approach.

I have been accustomed to refer to the ideas of the possibilists as the 'We-ocratic' approach, as opposed to the geocratic and theocratic systems mentioned earlier. I often wonder why there is so much opposition by many geographers to the concept of environmental control. One would think little of a doctor who spent ten years studying medicine, and threw his learning overboard, and practised according to the tenets of Mary Baker Eddy! Or of a lawyer who summed up his studies in the words of Bumble the Beadle, and loudly proclaimed that the 'Law is an Ass'! It is our special duty to study geology, structure, climate, soils, etc. and their effects on man. It is not our special duty to study all the ramifications of *man's* interests. We share this duty with the sociologist, economist, historian, medico, parson, etc. Does not this suggest that it is the natural landscape—rather than the cultural landscape which is the prime factor! Far be it from me to belittle the cultural landscape, which has ever been one of the chief features of the writer's work; but he does hope that the present generation of young geographers will swing away from the 'we-ocratic' ideology towards the older 'geocratic' attitude; which is, in this writer's opinion, the one which most closely characterizes our discipline.

I have often used a familiar scene to illustrate the relation of nature to man in world geography. In any large city we see traffic moving along established routes, i.e. the main roads. The directions are completely established, but what is the function of the police officer at the crossing-places? He can block all traffic, he can accelerate the movement, or decelerate it at his wish, but he does not turn it out of the established routes. In nine-tenths of the world (and I am willing to agree the analogy is not so close in highly-endowed areas) man is like the traffic controller. Nature says, 'This land is too dry, or too cold, or too wet, or too rugged; there is very little choice as to what can be done with it.' Man can ignore the region, as in the case of Antarctica, or he can struggle along in a sparse pastoral occupation as in half of Australia, etc. He definitely has very little choice; and the extreme possibilists encourage those ignorant boosters, who are a menace to the scientific utilization of the almost empty—and very widespread—areas of the world. It is absurd to say that man can choose which he pleases among many possible directions. It is safer to adopt the concept which I have suggested above, which may be called 'Stop-and-Go Determinism'. . . .

While the writer believes that Nature in large measure determines the plan, it is of course obvious that man is the agent whereby civilization progresses. He is of great importance, and as his technology improves he develops a region farther along the lines of the obvious plan. Thus the concept of *stage* in the plan must be kept in mind. This may be illustrated by an example which I discuss in my recent book *Urban Geography* (1948).

Every geographer will admit that there is a close similarity between the environments in eastern Algeria, western Spain, and the southern littoral of Australia. In Fig. 2 I have charted the relation of population-density to rainfall in these three allied regions. To my mind they suggest to some degree different stages in man's development of Nature's 'plan' for an arid 'Mediterranean' environment. Let us confine our attention at first to Biskra and Coward Springs. The Algerian town is about 150 miles from the Mediterranean, while the South Australian settlement is 450 miles inland.

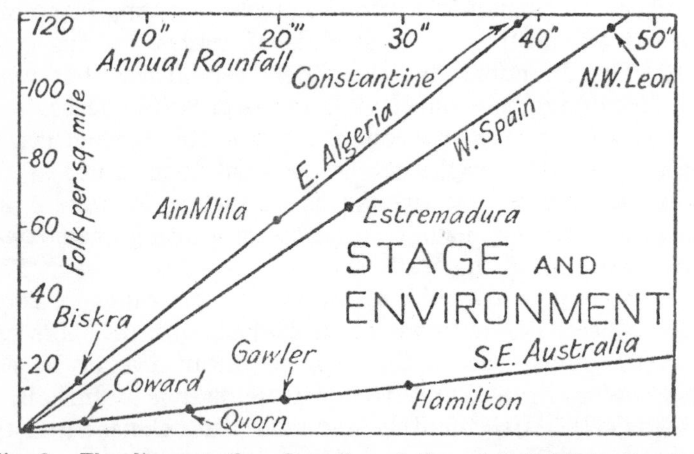

Fig. 2.—The diagram (based on the relation of Rainfall to Population) illustrates three stages in the logical development of the Mediterranean environment.

Both lie on the edge of the desert in artesian basins, and have a winter rainfall of four inches. The covering of sparse but regular vegetation in each case is similar in pattern, though not in genera. Both have railways which have been running for many years, in the case of Coward Springs in 1919 it was the chief settlement on the railway for fifty miles in either direction; yet there were only four houses, two of which were empty. (Given an excellent environment, such as at Chicago, a settlement might add a million to its population in the same period.)

Let us now see what has happened in the Sahara with a far lower standard of living and a far greater population-pressure. In spite of equally unfavorable environments, Biskra is an apparently flourishing town with about 10,000 inhabitants, of whom 2,000 are French. It is supported primarily by the date oases, but also by the French military station, and to a lesser degree it acts as a caravan terminus, and, in winter, as a tourist resort.

How does Biskra fit into our determinist-possibilist debate? When we think of the enormous length of the northern border of the desert, which extends about 2,500 miles from the Wadi Draa to Suez, it is clear that only a few districts are as favoured as Biskra. There is only *one* bygone 'Igharghar River" (i.e. that south of Biskra) with river gravels still carrying a little water; and probably no comparable artesian basin to that found at Biskra. Hence I should make use of our Biskra example as follows.

Given desert conditions such as obtained in the Sahara, there are only a very few sites where the ameliorating factors have justified modern enterprise as the French have developed at Biskra. Even the military site was strictly determined by the water and the traffic conditions. The possibilist, it seems to me, puts the cart before the horse. He would say, 'Ah! but the vital trade in dates owes much to the artesian bores and to the desert railway, and surely these are due to human energy.' The determinist replies, 'Man can put down bores and build railways anywhere in the Sahara; but in the vast majority of cases he takes very good care to do so only where Nature has provided the conditions to make such expenditure worthwhile. In such exploitation Nature determines the route of development, while man determines the rate and the stage.'

To return to the parallel with Coward Springs in Australia, I see no sign of man utilizing this southern region yet. But when population-pressure has increased to something like that present in Algeria, then we shall find man in Australia developing the environment along much the same lines as Nature led him to do in Biskra. In the graph (Fig. 2) the relation is expressed approximately by a straight line for each of these regions. Spain and Algeria exhibit very similar conditions; and to the writer this indicates that the population-pressure in Australia will increase considerably as time goes on. Later on, the graph line for Australia will climb to a position much closer to those for Spain and Algeria, and man will follow *along much the same plan* determined by the common environment. The difference is not really due to human choice, but to the immature character of Australian settlement. Nature's plan is the same, the stages are different.

A further example to make clear what I mean by scientific (or Stop-and-Go) determinism. Demangeon has stated as an argument against determinism, that Australia has been changed out of all recognition, as the result of British settlement there. I cannot follow his argument here. The scientist can determine pretty closely *today* what may happen, for instance, to the half million square miles or more of desert Australia. At present a few hundred miserable aborigines live there by precarious hunting. In the next stage of development Nature may allow ranchers to graze a few thousand stock there during specially good seasons. The third stage would be for an exceedingly wealthy rancher to dig waterholes ('tanks'), and so somewhat increase the usefulness of the area. (This has happened at Mutooroo.)

Nature's plan is obvious, and only the stage of development depends on man. Surely it is the character of the environment which should interest the geographer, so that he can best follow the plan 'determined' by Nature. Moreover, whatever man does in such a region, it will make little difference to the nation as a whole; since in better-endowed districts the stages of development will still keep far ahead of what he is doing in the 'deserts'. It is my firm belief that centuries hence the deserts of the world will still be deserts; and man will have shown that he has had the good sense to use the better areas, which Nature has determined shall be worth his attention. Much the same argument applies to the vast areas of semi-desert and precarious croplands of the world. Only as applied to such fortunate regions as Europe and Eastern U. S. A. (where most of my opponents live) are the arguments of the 'possibilist' at all convincing. These two paragraphs summarize what I mean by 'scientific determinism'.

Introduction to Chapter 10

Toward the end of the 19th century and into the early 20th schools of geography gradually developed in all European countries. The first leading geographers were often trained in German or German-language universities. A special role was played by the University of Vienna where the leading Serb geographer, Cvijic; the leading Hungarian, Teléki; and the leading Polish geographer, Romer, were students. In the 20th century French influences became strong in some countries, even remarkably enough, in German-language countries such as Switzerland and Austria. Some countries, such as Spain and Czechoslovakia, have yet to contribute to world geographical thought but have remained concerned only with the problems of domestic research and the application of methods worked out elsewhere. However, at least in the person of one or two outstanding geographers, most countries have contributed significantly to world geography. Foremost, especially in relation to their size, are the Scandinavian countries, including Finland.

CHAPTER 10

GEOGRAPHERS FROM OTHER EUROPEAN COUNTRIES

ROBERTO ALMAGIÁ (1884-1962)

Almagià was one of the leading Italian geographers of the 20th century.[1] Like other scholars in the smaller countries, he was familiar with the language and literature of several nations and absorbed ideas from abroad, especially from Germany and France. In the article quoted below he particularly acknowledges the stimulus he received from Hettner's writings; but the influence of Vidal de la Blache, Richthofen, and several others is unmistakable.

The ill-fated Italian colonization in North and East Africa offered Italian geographers a stimulating foreign field for systematic research. Accompanying the emergence of this vigorous geographical interest was a renewed interest in the explorations of Italians in past centuries and the stimulation of research in historical geography. Unfortunately, because the Italian language is not well-known outside its homeland, Italian geographical literature has not been widely read outside Italy.[1]

Almeagiá did field research in Africa and has written historical geography. The article which follows reflects the latter interest. His world-wide reputation is based on his work in historical geography.

Actual Problems and Trends of Geography[2]

One can speak of actual problems and trends of geography—like all truly dynamic sciences, geography is in continuous

---

[1]Olinto Marinelli is generally considered *the* leading Italian geographer, but among his numerous writings there is nothing which states his own philosophy of geography.

[2] "Problemi e Indirizzi attuali della Geografia," Roberto Almagiá *Atti della Societá Italiana per il Progresso delle Science*, 17 riunione Roma, Pavia, 1929.

development—and of problems, the solution of which wearied the students of yesterday. In addition, new ones, which will need to be solved by the scholars of tomorrow, present themselves; and —what is still more interesting—the very approach to certain problems changes, while the methods of observation and research become more perfect; these things also determine new tendencies and new courses of a science. The present problems and trends of geography, therefore, are not the same as those of the past, just as they will be different from those of tomorrow. One may add that geography—understood as the interest in knowing the world around us and, one may say, old as mankind—is actually very young as a science, younger than all the other earth-sciences, although it comes from their common trunk. In order to convince ourselves of this youth, it is enough to remember that the even roughly approximate knowledge of the relation between land and sea on the surface of our globe barely dates back to the end of the eighteenth century, after the travels of James Cook. And this knowledge of the distribution of land and water is an indispensable presupposition for the knowledge and explanation of a great number of those problems which geography happens to study—winds and ocean currents; distribution and types of climate; distribution of plants, animals, rain, communications, products; etc. Even 150 years ago all these problems were not available for a really scientific investigation. It is not by chance that only after the epoch of the great maritime explorations, which culminated in the travels of Cook, could the concepts of Humboldt and Karl Ritter develop. These two Germans are rightly considered the founders of modern geography. But even the geography of Humboldt and Ritter is something completely different from present geography; we have progressed enormously, and are separated by an abyss from what the Germans themselves call "classical geography"—from the geography of the first half of the nineteenth century.

This recent progress is also a consequence of the whole series of marvelous explorations of the last century. . . . In order to conquer the last unknown reaches, exploration today has new means at its disposal, primarily in the air. . . .

It is no longer possible to restrict ourselves—marvelous and attractive though it may be—to the story of the exploration of land, ocean, and the atmosphere; but one has to realize that geography must fix its attention upon the results of these explorations if it hopes to establish itself definitely as a true science, in its own right, with specific objects, tasks, and methods. Indeed, one can say that up to the beginning of the 19th century—the era of Humboldt and Ritter—geography always had the primary function of *ascertaining and registering facts*. But, if one speaks of a true and proper science only after it succeeds not only in ascertaining the facts, but also in classifying and explaining them (or giving an explanatory description), one has to recognize that geography assumed this aspect of a true science only after middle of the nineteenth century when the explorations began to come to completion.

One can conclusively state that only after the reconnaissance of the basic outlines of the terraqueous globe and its phenomena had been concluded or at least carried close to conclusion, it was possible to lay the foundations of the building of a scientific geography. Today the epoch, which one may call the heroic one, of explorations is closed; an epoch opens of explorations, much more circumscribed, but more profound, executed by ever more refined methods and processes. One can say that man, or better the scholar, after having reconnoitered the entire globe in its essential characteristics, retraces his steps over it again, step by step, investigating it intensively in all the particulars of its changeable and complex aspects. That is perhaps the most salient characteristic of present geographical science, which determines best, in my opinion, the trend of our days.

The part of geography which first established itself according to scientific principles and methods is that which studies the forms and aspects of the dry surface of the earth and which today is called terrestrial morphology.

* * *

At present there have developed in the scientific study of the forms and phenomena of the terrestrial surface two kinds of ideas which have had especially fruitful and profitable results during the last years. On the one side, the concept that the landforms are not permanent as was believed at one time, but that contrariwise they are in continuous transformation, and *that these transformations tend, through various transitions, towards final end-stages which are fixed and can be ascertained.*

* * *

These concepts of Davis are violently contested in Europe, even by some who were convinced followers at first: Penck,. . . Passarge. . . .At the present stage of our science, the ideas of Davis, if applied without exaggeration and with due circumspection, seem to offer the best rational method for describing landforms. I say *at the present stage,* because the application of these concepts cannot be regarded as more or less than a working hypothesis, which in the future with the progress of science may yield its position to a more perfect one, as has often happened elsewhere. . . .

The other group of ideas which lately has proved to be most fruitful, in my opinion, has been developed first of all by a French geographer, E. de Martonne. It tries to focus attention on the direct relations between landforms and climate, or better, to explain the differences of the result not only of present active forces, but also of some that were active in a not-too-distant geographical past, when the climate conditions may have been profoundly different.

* * *

Without entering into arguments which at the present hour are still vigorously fought over, one can meanwhile state that the object of human geography is to discover how man (it is superfluous to state that the word *man* is always used in a collective sense, as *man living in society,* thus as a synonym for human groups) is distributed over the earth's surface —that is to say, the way in which the *human cover* of the earth is changing.

* * *

Some modern geographers, Penck for example, . . .seem inclined to exclude economic and political geography from the circle of scientific geography in the strict sense. In my opinion, this is a mistake. If, indeed, geography investigates. . .the modifications which human activity brings about on the earth's surface (considering this activity from the same point of view as the other modifying forces, i.e., the physical ones) and the indications on the ground of such modifications, we definitely cannot exclude profound and durable modifications such as those which derive from the exploitation of the vegetable, animal, and mineral world, and those which derive more or less directly from the political divisions introduced by man over the globe.

In order to see clearly the borders (of geography), it is necessary always to keep in mind that the field of study of geography is always (and in every case) a more or less large part of the surface of the earth: landforms and water, climate and the vegetable cover, marks of the presence and the activity of man are studied by geography so far as they are constituent elements of the respective part of the earth's surface, elements which themselves can be represented on our maps. All these elements are in mutual relation insofar as they coexist in the same area, and work together in determining the special physiogonomy of this part of the earth's surface. German geographers have adopted the term *Landschaft* (landscape). . . .

* * *

The concept (of region) which to the present author seems most acceptable, can be best expressed by de Martonne's definition: "A region is (a segment of the earth's surface in which) the physical, economic, and social features are almost completely the same or at least in relation to the common features." In this case perhaps one can speak immediately of geographical regions, rather than of natural regions.

* * *

The dualism which formerly seemed to exist between physical and human geography has finally (through the study of landscape) disappeared; at a certain period—which nearly coincides with that of the first systematization of this branch of science—they seemed to be opposed by the diverstiy of their research methods, and also by the results of this research. Today, fortunately, this period has been overcome; there is monism in geography from the point of view of methods. . . .

One arrives at the statement that in the study of a certain country, the physical factors, which according to the German expression determine the "natural landscape," are important only so far as they provide the frame of the picture, which the human factors fill up. This is certainly exaggerated; but one has to realize that nowadays our attention concentrates first of all upon the human elements of the landscape, which the Germans call the cultural landscape.

* * *

Penck affirms flatly that "modern geography works from points of view purely of natural science;" others, like Kirchhoff and Wagner, have stated that it is "a natural science with integrated historical elements;" but Hettner, a geographer who has followed attentively the evolution of geography for forty years, observes subtly that this statement would be equally true if turned around, calling geography "a science of man with integrated elements of natural science." These turnabouts of words seem to me to prove that the discussion is rather moot. One can fix as a fundamental concept the fact that geography is and remains a science of observation, but certainly not only of facts of a natural order. Further, by the very fact that geography studies phenomena which exist or can be verified within the frame of a definite area or country, it can be colored if the phrase is permitted by the different ways in which scholars of different countries see things. And I, for myself, in my attempt to review the problems and trends of present-day geography was not able to free myself from the influence which consideration of the actual life of his country can exert upon an Italian scholar, nor those which its needs exert on the leading principles of its development. If some "pure geographer" should find that this is a fault of my paper, I shall not worry excessively. I have always considered geography as a science which draws value from these different applications to the highest degree.

PAUL MICHOTTE (1876-1940)

Michotte is easily the best known and most influential Belgian geographer. Though he was a great geographer in his own right, he also exemplifies the influence of the large neighboring countries on the development of ideas in a small country. Writing in French, Michotte reflects a greater influence of the French school than the German; but as individuals, Hettner and Brunhes are rivals in their influence. Beginning with local studies of his home country, Michotte advanced to systematic formulations which made his name widely known. His studies on Belgian human geography have won renown and have become the model for other such studies.

The New Trend in Geography[3]

I am addressing primarily my countrymen; that is my excuse if I insist on concepts which elsewhere would appear repetitious.

While most sciences based on observation have a definite subject and an exactly established method to such a degree that it never would occur to a physician or a botanist or a chemist or a zoologist to discuss the boundaries and the character of his science, the geographers, on the contrary, have no other subject which is discussed more.

Without doubt, the outsider is astonished by this peculiarity. It is due to the fact that geography, though a very ancient science, in its modern form is carried along by diverse and often contradictory currents. Its range is quite vast and very complex, and because of this very complexity, contains multiple and different points of view. . .

We just said that the range of geography was extremely complex. It was not so long ago that one considered geography a kind of general science of the earth, an "Erdkunde," a vast synthesis of astronomy, geodesy, meteorology, biology, social science, etc. . . a synthesis of which the marvellous "Cosmos" of Humboldt remains the perfect and unequalled example.

The development of the sciences in the last century, the more and more pronounced division of labor in science which led logically to a more and more distinct specialization, was destined to restrict fatally the subject of geography.

---

[3] Paul Michotte, "L'Orientation Nouvelle en Géographie," Bulletin de la Société Royale de Géographie, 45 éme année, 1921, Bruxelles.

It seemed doubtful that a single human brain was capable of embracing in one total view the world and its laws, except in a superficial way. Everything seems to point to the belief that future attempts of synthesis will rely rather on encyclopedias than on syntheses in the etymological and truly literal sense of the word.

The very famous inaugural address of Ferdinand von Richthofen marks the date, so to speak, of the beginning of the restricted concept of geography. Since then, it has been almost generally conceded that the field of geographical research is limited to *the phenomena of the surface of the earth*. . . .

. . . The preceding enumeration [4] does not pretend to be complete, far from that. We wanted only to place some markers, set far from each other in the immense field which the geographers claim as their property, in order to emphasize its immensity.

Leaving aside, for the moment, the "innovators" and those striving for originality, let us review the numerous definitions of geography to which we alluded before; [5] or, still better, let us go through the writings of the great masters of geography, preferring to judge rather by their work than by their programs; and let us on the other side neglect the incidental qualities, the details of form and expression. Thereby, we will see emerging clearly two dominant ideas which are continually repeated by the pens and through the mouths of the geographers themselves, and which are therefore the condensed expression of their thoughts and of their method: the first states that geography is a distinct science, because it studies the *interdependence of the surface phenomena* of the globe, and the second, that it studies distribution over the surface of the earth.

. . . The "principle of connection" penetrates, so to speak, the whole of modern geography; "the fertile concept of connection" writes J. Brunhes very clearly [6] "must dominate every complete study of geographical facts; one should not be satisfied

---

[4] Omitted here

[5] Omitted as indicated above.

[6] Jean Brunhes, La Géographie Humaine, Paris, 1910, p. 18.

with the observation of a fact itself or an isolated series of facts; after such an initial observation, one must put this series back into its natural whole, into the complex whole of facts in whose midst it has been produced and where it develops; one has to investigate how it fits into the series of adjoining phenomena, how it determines them, and to what degree it has been influenced by them. . . . It is possible to isolate certain features in meteorology, geology, or botany, and to study them only for themselves. In geography one cannot stop there,. . .one has the aim of studying those features in their natural and real connection, which aim of analytical study is also the aim of the specialized sciences. . . ." [7]

If that should be the aim of geography, is it really a distinct science: we do not believe it. Let us say truly:

First. The principle of connection is in no way specifically geographic, as the geographers pretend. It is not true that the special sciences consider the fact isolated; the study of the relations between the phenomena and the environment in which they occur is an integral part of the sciences based on observation . . .

Second. It is impossible to define the domain of geography just on the basis of the principle of connection alone. . . .

Is the second principle to which the geographers refer better justified? What distinguishes the geographical point of view is that in geography the apportionment or distribution of the phenomena over the surface of the earth is studied rather than—again this phrase—facing the islolated phenomena themselves. That is the "principle of extension" of the geographers. . . .

. . .Neither the botanist, who determines the expanse of the extension of a plant; nor the geologist, who fixes the exact location of volcanoes; nor the statistician, who takes into account the distribution of the population, are concerned with geography, but still are working in their field of botany, geology, or statistics, because the "principle of extension," is

---

[7] Michotte quotes from Vidal de la Blache, Hettner, de Martonne, and W. M. Davis. However, Brunhes is the geographer who is most frequently quoted throughout this article, primarily as the best authority in Michotte's opinion. Most quotations have been omitted.

no more specifically geographic than the "principle of connection" . . .

What conclusion should be drawn from the above? We arrived at the conclusion that the two principles, that of connection and that of extension, are not "specifically geographic" and leave "the borders of its subject still indefinite,"—though they are considered necessary and sufficient by a majority of geographers in order to define geography and to give it a scientific personality. These principles leave the borders of the subject indefinite. Then, are those right who do not recognize geography as a distinct entity, who state that it is nothing more than a collection of heterogeneous notions, borrowed from the most diverse sciences? We do not think so; . . .

We have, therefore, to investigate in full frankness and with full impartiality, the "actual," the limits of the individual sciences and the limit of the self assigned aims. We will ask ourselves, afterwards, whether we have left out anything we might have done for geography . . . .

. . .The plants, which are studied by botany and are arranged into distinct families in a logical order, are arranged in the natural environment in a quite different order; united in "different form and floristic associations," they dot the surface of the globe with spots of different aspect and different color; they constitute "plant spaces."

To *describe these spaces,* to *explain their character* through general principles of the botanical science, to overstep thereby the limits of botany by this complement which terminates our knowledge of the world of plants, that is the aim of *plant geography;* to compare the diverse spatial units one with another, to establish a hierarchy, to combine them in more and extended spaces, that is what one could call provisionally, due to the lack of a better term, *comparative plant geography;* or in other words and in a more concise manner, *plant geography is the scientific description of different plant areas,* or *of different botanical landscapes of the earth*. . . .

The sciences which are based on observation are, according to the usual classification, in three categories: [8]

---

[8] A. Hettner, *Das Wesen und Methode der Geographie,* pp. 550ff.

a) "the systematic sciences," are those which study "things," if it is permitted to express it this way, from points of view which can be very different; botany, for example, is a systematic science;

b) "the chronological sciences," are those which contemplate the succession of events in time, such as geology;

c) "the chorological sciences" are those which have their subject, space and its subdivisions with their distinctive characteristics, for example, geography.

Accordingly, the proper object of geography is chorologic; that is what distinguishes it from all neighbor sciences, both systematic and chronological.

From this it follows, if we return to our example, that the principle of classification is necessarily quite different in plant geography than in botany. In botany the principle is systematic and is based on affinities, degrees of parentage, family traits which unite different plants. In plant geography it is chorological, or spatial; it is no longer the species which is at the basis of the system, but the place, i.e., a locality of restricted extent which contains a complete and definite collection of conditions of existence and which is inhabited by a distinct association.

. . . Morphology is the child of geography . . . but during all the first half of the last century . . . morphological problems were studied by geologists. The recapture of morphology by geography dates from 1869. . . .

Nothing hinders us in asking the question whether this return of morphology to geography was legitimate: we do not believe so. Morphology is, in our opinion, for the same reason as botany, a science distinct from geography.

The "landforms", the same as plants, constitute a category of surface features. Morphology studies landforms from a systematic point of view. . . .

It seems difficult for us to see in morphology anything but a systematic science; the science of landforms.

The same principles apply to human geography, without much further elucidation.

Take for instance an evidence of human life on the surface of the earth, the house.

The aim of geography cannot be, as an application of the principle of connection, the relationship between the house and the environment, nor, according to the principle of extension, the establishment of the extent of distribution of this or that type of habitation; again, if geography would be restricted to this kind of work, it would not be different from that of other disciplines; but the proper object of geography has to consist in "delimiting" and "describing" the different "terrestrial spaces" characterized by some kind of settlement, or some kind of houses, etc. . . .and after this preliminary research has been completed, to search for the causes, the "why" of these regional differences.

Let us go a step farther. After what has been said, it is possible to approach a series of special geographies, based on this or that characteristic, some of them physical, others biological, others again human and dealing with the surface expanses of the globe. . . .

Landscapes also are of an immense variety; to *describe* them, and to *explain* them, is the object of *regional geography.* To classify them in spatial units of increasing size in such a way as to be able to determine the *main geographical regions of the world,* is the aim of *comparative regional geography,* or better called, in the proper sense of the term, *general geography.*

Geography is a chorographical science, and its object is the surface of the globe; that is what distinguishes it from other sciences which are based on observation and with which it has numerous points of contact.

The surface of the globe comprises a mosaic of patches, different in color, pattern, and physiognomy. One can understand them by a process of mental abstraction. . . .Delimiting these areas, describing the landscapes and explaining their character, finally classifying them in spaces of an hierarchical order of larger and larger extent, is the whole object of geography; it is, in the exact meaning of the term, a "geography," a scientific description of different spatial units, i. e., of different regions of the surface of the globe

ENGENIUSZ ROMER (1871-1954)

Romer is recognized as the leading Polish geographer. He represents the influence of both Penck and Ratzel in a rare combination. He has become famous for his cartographic work throughout Europe, as well as in Poland. Under the influence of Penck and the geologist Suess he made important contributions to glaciology. Ratzel's influence is more visible in the short piece reprinted below. When Romer started his career, for all practical purposes no Polish geography existed. At present most of the leading geographers are his pupils.

"Poland: The Land and the State"[9]

The foundation of the historical life of nations is laid down in the relatively unchanging features of the earth. Strong and organized human wills can temporarily deflect national life from the course favored by nature, but, sooner or later, life flows back into natural channels, and its return is almost invariably marked by some upheaval in customs, character or national life.

. . . Frontiers are, as it were, snap-shots of the life of nations. Being an expression of that life, they can only temporarily, or as a symptom of decay, follow the valleys of main rivers. Main rivers are arteries of national life which cannot, without exposure to fatal blows, be situated on the periphery of a living organism. Hence the vital expansion of a nation tends to proceed beyond the valleys toward the watersheds.

Rivers not only were decisive factors in determining the direction and extent of Poland's expansion as a whole, but also in determining her sub-divisions. For, in the lowland area that is Poland, the configuration of the land is in great part dependent on the drainage systems. . . .

These political subdivisions, based on the physiognomy of the country, again reflect the fundamental fact that the main waterways were always the axes, never the borderlines, of vital parts of the Polish organism. This is true even for Poland's first period of weakness, when she had fallen apart into numerous separate sections and the rulers of these petty

---

[9] Poland: The Land and the State, Engeniusz Romer, *Geographical Review,* Vol. IV, 1917, pp. 6-25.

states were fighting one another. Never even in this period did a great river become a border line, not the Vistula or the Warta, nor yet the Notec or the Pilitza.

Furthermore, just as the division and organization of the territory were based upon the character of the land, so did the nation itself draw its racial and spiritual characteristics from the soil. . . .

It seems all the more necessary to dwell upon the distinct physical difference between Poland and Russia, inasmuch as the conception of "Central Europe" has gained ground, especially in Germany.[10] From such a conception it might follow that whatever is not situated in Central Europe belongs, physically, to the great uniform area of Eastern Europe. To show the discrepancy between that idea and the facts is important.

It is not strange, therefore, that Poland, physiographically varied, should ultimately have attained the highest degree of culture. In control of all the natural highways of Lithuania and Ruthenia (Ukrainia), Poland was predestined to become the territorial link of three parts of a physical unit.

PAUL TELEKI (1879-1941)

Teleki is the foremost Hungarian geographer. A member of one of the oldest families of Hungary, (one of his forebears was Grand Duke of Transylvania) his family was prominent in scholarship for several generations. The Teleki volcano in East Africa was discovered by a member of this family. Despite Paul Teleki's intensive political activity—he was three times prime minister—he published a great number of geographical books and articles. His reputation was so great that he was sent as a member of a group of geographical experts by the League of Nations into the Mosul area, contested between Turkey and Iraq in 1924-5, a time when members of the Central Powers of the First World War were generally still shunned. His most important geographical work was done in economic and population geography, two branches generally neglected in Europe during this period. When his policy failed

[10] The reader should keep in mind that this piece was written during World War I.

to keep Hungary free from Nazi-German domination, he took his own life rather than compromise with the invaders.

The Economic Geography of America[10]

Geography is the science of the earth's surface phenomena and could actually be called a physiology of the earth-surface; thus, it embraces all phenomena, in all their complexity, which take place on the earth's surface everywhere and studies them as a unified life process. The more complex the natural, morphological or geological structure of an area and, on the other hand, the longer it is inhabited by man, the more involved will be the picture created by the sum total of these phenomena. If we therefore wish to study the life of the earth's surface, it is best to turn first to an area whose physiographic and morphological structure is simple and easy to comprehend and which affords enough contrast to emphasize characteristics of different parts. On the other hand, it is well to select as the first object of our studies an area of the world where (1) the activity and life of man can be observed, beginning with the earliest appearence of man in that area, and can thus be analyzed in every particular; and (2) where we do not have to study complex conditions, the reasons for which are partly quite remote, reaching far into the past, and as yet unexplained by history.

In geography, as everywhere else, there are two extreme views facing each other. According to one, man does not depend on nature, but commands it; according to the other, man is entirely dependent on nature. Extreme views are never true. Upon careful reflection we find that surface configurations exercise an impact on mass-phenomena, i. e., phenomena consisting of identical action of many and on great historical periods. The more we go into details, the more actions we discover; and when we get to the point of comparing the actions of two human beings, we only find human willpower as the motivating force.

---

[10]Amerika Gazdasági Földrajza, Paul Teleki, Budapest, 1922. p. 3. Translated by Geza Teleki.

The History of Geographic Thought [11]

The history of geographic thought is not the history of geography as a science; I believe geographic thought to be the permanent concept of the world outside and around us, that is of our surroundings. This thought then, represents the interrelation of thinking man with his habitat, the earth, and is not the prerogative of a single science but is human in general.

Geographic thought, even taken only as the thought of a geographically thinking man, is part of the great unifying philosophical thought which is but the evolution of human thinking searching for a *Weltanschauung* and, through its leading representatives, striving for metaphysical reality. Just as human thinking would become imperfect without geographic thinkers, these geographic thinkers can be fully understood only as a part of philosophical thought in its entirety; thus we cannot comprehend Eratosthenes without Herodotus, Thucydides and Aristotle; Toscanelli without Regimontanus, Savonarola and Dante; and, Humboldt without Goethe and Rousseau. . . .

True, the subject of crude observation forms part and parcel of science; but the essence,, the thread of scientific progress along which we build newer and newer values, is the thought which this observation produces in our minds. Thought is so to speak heterogeneous in comparison with the object. Its greatness and its value from the point of view of intellectual evolution does not depend on the object.

The history of science cannot disregard the growth of facts observed and the method of this growth, like exploration or the invention of scientific aids. Still, this history must in essence be the history of thought,—of that thought which is but one of the functions of human cognizance.

As the concept of our surroundings develops and changes, it produces ideas, some of which become the kernel of a new science, a new concept, or a new *Weltanschauung*. The feeling and knowledge of surroundings and their interrelations exist

---

[11] A földrajzi gondolat törtenete, Paul Teleki Budapest 1917, p. 14-16. Translated by Geza Teleki.

in everybody, but none [of the geographical sciences] is based fully on this idea. On the other hand none [of these sciences] monopolizes thought throughout the centuries or millenia; none of them becomes the one and only science of thought. For its broadest meaning geographical thought exists as the concept of our surroundings, within the entire complexity of our knowledge, in all its branches; but the relation between man and his suroundings also lives far beyond the limits of knowledge in our sentiments and emotions.

Our life, surrounded by thousands of phenomena on the earth's surface, has a stimulating influence upon our subconscious thoughts which are rooted in emotions; likewise, it influences mass-thinking as well as administrative, social, and poltical thinking, and it affects the evolution of scientific thought which branches in all directions. Our confinement to a certain environment is an essential characteristic of our life, while our *demographic distribution* is one of its most important factors. This also applies to all other phenomena of the earth's surface.

But situation [situs] and distribution are always dependent on conditions,— often on entire series or combinations of conditions.

Demographic distribution and situation, their motivating causes and their obstacles, are essential factors of life. Thus, all our thought complexes which deal with any phenomenon of life on earth will necessarily be a part of these factors. Into any such science [i.e., which deals with earthly phenomena] enters the thought of demographic distribution, situation, and of local, coexistent phenomena.

All these thoughts and ideas, and the opinions which in time will stem from them, cannot be separated from geography. This, then, is actually the essence of the history of geographic thought. Because, unless we are given to reasoning *a priori* (deductively), i.e., searching for the history of one certain theory or opinion, geographic science was at all times primarily what it was believed to be.

Geographers as well as an increasing number of persons outside this science begin to realize the great synthetic concept of the globe in geography.

We have come close to the unifying concept and knowledge of the global surface inasmuch as we now consider it, as a whole, as the largest region and life-unit of the earth. . . .

The smaller an area, the stronger its individuality; as the area increases its individuality lessens, but the more general aspects become the unifying factors of the entire area. The transition between the regional description of small area and the general geography of the entire earth is negligible, and we are unable to draw sharp boundaries, least of all a sharp dualism, between the two. The entire surface of the globe can just as well be the subject of a synthetic geography. . .as can the smaller regional units. This is even more so today, since the entire earth's surface is embraced not only by the major, general natural phenomena, like climate or the oceans, but also by human economy—and by human science which connect very distant points into a whole in the course of historical evolution.

The thoughts which link the great synthesis of earthly life to the synthesis of thought, often emerge in the course of history. They emerge with the Greeks, like Parmenides and Aristotle. With the Greeks these thoughts are more frequent and more characteristic, since they are attached to the undifferentiated concept of pre-scientific periods. From here on, developing from various side-branches, they appear in similiar forms in pantheistic philosophies throughout the ages. They appear with thinkers and scientists in various forms: with Leonardo da Vinci, Varenius, Gatterer, Ritter, Humboldt, Peschel, with Reclus, as well as with Taine and Montesquieu; they emerge as sentiments and inferences, as so many intuitions which have always existed since the process of human thinking began. But the empirical knowledge of and scientific certainty concerning the permanent organic evolution of all terrestrial phenomena belongs solely to the modern era.

This does not mean, however, that no geographic science existed up to now.

That era which came to the full realization of the complexity, the organic character, the evolutionary capacity and permanently changing nature of phenomena, energetically demanded a synthetic geographic science. The fact that this science now exists and that we call it modern geography does not mean that geomorphology, climatology or ecology are in themselves not geographical sciences of equal rank.

It is clear that the entire world does not consist of a chessboard of equally important, equally uniform . . .regions. . . Here I want to stress the fact that precisely the same areas can be considered part of differing regional units.

The oldest region of the United States of America, New England, for instance, belongs geologically to the Appalachian mountain system which, due to its structure, materials and age, is characterized by ruggedness and difficulty of cross country movement. Yet, the surface configurations were transformed by glacial activity, a common feature of the Laurentian glacial expansion which also covers the entire area of eastern Canada, therefore, they resemble each other in their appearance, with their thousands of lakes. The northern portion of this shield lies towards the St. Lawrence river and the traditions of French colonization reach from Canada into these parts of the United States. The geographical situation of the Great Lakes makes this land an isthmus between this "sweet-water Mediterranean" and the Atlantic ocean; thus it is linked to an organic unit with the northernmost outskirts of the Piedmont and the Coastal Plain, as well as with the northern portions of the Ohio Basin, which is the region of productive transformation and of transportation of goods originating in the central region of the continent.

Because of the barrier-like character of the Appalachians everything east of these mountains becomes part of an area which reflects the uniformity of early colonization and rich historical traditions, even by European standards, unlike the inner parts of the continent. From the point of view of the world-geographic situation, this region, together with the European lands around the English Channel and the Atlantic oceanic areas in the center (which, because of their dense shipping can be regarded as a part of the human ecumene) has the densest world traffic. And finally, to a certain extent, it also is part of the region of the continental shelf, the shallow sea of fishing banks, which influenced its nutrition and industry, especially in earlier days. However, New England in itself is a well confined, typical region with a typical human product, too, the old-style yankee.

Yet, by defining this land with all its characteristics as a region we cannot say that we are drifting away from geographic spirit if, due to certain regional factors, we consider it part of a larger regional unit. Thus, geologically it may be linked to the Appalachians, morphologically to the Laurentian Shield, climatologically to the entire northern coastal zone, economically to the area of the Great Lakes, while from the point of view of world economics it may be tied to areas beyond the ocean. Even in sciences where the above listed factors are separate objects of study there is a geographic element; and the geographic spirit is introduced by studying our objects so as to tie earthly and local phenomena to each other in relation to areal and distributional factors.

That all these sciences had to develop along such lines is due to geographic thought, and to the preservation and development of geographic thinking in other sciences. This made it possible that a synthetic geographic science, . . .a science of terrestrial life, originated and had to come into being.

This science [geography] can take its place among natural, historical and social sciences.

A characteristic aspect of geography as measured against analytic natural sciences and genetic historical sciences is that it does not observe the systematically and genetically component elements, but [rather, it studies all] interrelated earthly phenomena in relation to the extent of their influences and their relative values in terrestrial life.

Geography has always been placed between the natural and social sciences—perhaps because both historians and natural scientists pursued its study or because the principles of areal distribution and habitat. . .manifested themselves in natural and historical processes.

Modern scientific theory which classifies sciences on the basis of the psychological dualism of outer and inner experience, rather than on the basis of the usual method of natural and spiritual metaphysical dualism, accepts the fact that natural science, which always endeavors to lay down certain laws, as well as the objects of history which develop through selection of determinative values, originates from one and the same group of absolute reality. This, then, is exceedingly important to the historian of geography, because it clearly tells him that modern geographic science was made possible only through modern scientific theory.

It copies the great synthesis of nature. The synthetic, symbiotic, geographic concept also becomes principle.

But, the searching intellect builds systems and classifications. It classifies on the basis of qualities, appearance and effects. It observes all phenomena in relation to their habitats and distributions, i.e., in their relation to the earth's surface. And thus, into all sciences concerned with phenomena on the surface of our globe geographic thought enters as a method. From the point of view of geographic thought these objects and phenomena are all equal, their value being expressed in their ensemble. This is summarily expressed by the penetration of [the] principles and methods [of geography] into all the analytical sciences. Yet, as a science geographic thought will come into its own only if and when man is able to understand this ensemble, the great synthesis of life.

JOVAN CVIJIC (1865-1927)

Cvijic was the most prominent geographer of the Balkan Peninsula, at least the best known in the West. Like many geographers from this general area he received his training in Vienna under Albrecht Penck and Eugen Oberhummer, the editor of Ratzel's principle work. The influence of the French school of geography is also discernible in Cvijic's writings. He spent part of World War I at the Sorbonne in Paris and is credited with preparing some of the scientific geographic justification for the establishment of the boundaries of Yugoslavia set forth in the Versailles Treaty. In this respect he ranked fourth with Isaiah Bowman and helped to convince statesmen of the practical value of geography. But despite his striving for scientific impartiality, Cvijic was accused of national prejudice by Italian and Bulgarian geographers, such as Marinelli and Ivanov, men of acknowledged reputation.

Cvijic began as a physical geographer using the ideas of Penck and expanding them on the basis of his field work in the limestone areas of the northwestern Balkan Peninsula. As a product of this field work he became the founder of Karst morphology. Many of his terms have been adopted in German and English—though not in French—terminology.

The Balkan Peninsula, Human Geography[12]

Before the present tragic events, I intended to publish the collected results of my research on the Balkan Peninsula, starting with the problems of physical geography to which I had devoted the major part of my time and my efforts. However, the Balkan wars of 1912 and 1913 had forced my preoccupation to questions of human and political geography. The present war pushed them into the foreground, and they were in my mind when I was fortunate enough to be invited to participate in the teaching of geography at the old illustrious institution of the Sorbonne[1]. . . .

I, therefore started my teaching at the Sorbonne by discussing my studies of the human geography of the Balkan countries. . . .I had touched on these questions before in my classes at the University of Belgrad, and several of them had occupied my mind fervently for a long time; but up to now I never had contemplated them as a whole. I needed much thinking in order to present this overall picture of the human geography of the peninsula and to arrange scientifically the mass of facts pertaining to a discipline the object of which is not yet precisely established. This was the more difficult as my ideas of human geography deviate in certain respects from those of Ratzel and Mr. Jean Brunhes, which they have explained in their notable books. I always felt that they took too little cognizance of man himself, and did not devote sufficient space to problems which belong, if you will, as well to sociology as to geography, but which geography should not neglect. . . .

---

[12] *La Peninsule Balkanique, Geographie Humaine*, J. Cvijic, Librairie Armand Colin, Paris, 1918.

1) Cvijic was a war refugee in France at that time.

I do not pretend to take no notice that at the present moment it is difficult to speak of certain problems with full impartiality; I have tried to stay with the scientific truth. My conclusions depend also on numerous observations which I have made during my travels before the present events. I made them without any partisanship just in order to take account myself.

* * *

The natural regions, which we are about to delimit, are the main geographical regions of the peninsula. There exist others, much smaller, formed mostly by the *zupas* which we want to neglect for the present.

There are diverse factors which are to be considered in the process of delimiting a large natural region. Without question, the first factors are the morphological traits; they are the ones which constitute the essential features. They are derived, to a large degree, from the geomorphical evolution of the region. But there are also the climate and the biological factors, first of all the vegetation. However, climate and vegetation are themselves largely influenced by the morphology....

The notion of a geographical region is influenced, even if involuntarily, by historical and sociological elements in countries which have an historical past. A region may be as well-defined as possible from the morphological point of view, but it does not realize its unity, to speak figuratively, if human activity and historical events are not superimposed. Human societies adjust themselves to the geographical environment. They develop the seeds which nature deposited. In different natural regions a special way of life develops, accompanied frequently by different habits and by a noticeably different way of thinking and acting. Such ethnic and social differentiation is completely developed in a number of *zupas* of the Balkan Peninsula. It is more accentuated than in units of the same order in western Europe. From an ethnic and social point of view, as well as from a morphological, the *zupas* constitute perfect wholes. However, across the great natural geographic units, a common way of life could assert itself only in exceptional cases and for different reasons. These regions are mostly inhabited by different peoples. In addition, the Balkan Peninsula is distinguished by a lack of continuity in its historical development. . . .

In general, the great natural regions of the Balkan Peninsula do not correspond to historical and social units in the same degree as do those in western Europe. Rationally, they can not be determined except by morphological characteristics, strengthened only here and there by ethnography and history.

* * *

The geographical environment influences not only the general run of history, the distribution of civilization, migrations, ethnographic distribution, the type of agglomerations and habitations, but also directly or indirectly, the psychological character of the population. We consider, therefore, an important aim of geography to be the determination of the psychological character of the population in different geographical regions and to indicate the part which geographical conditions took in the formation of this character. However, human geography should not neglect the other causes, historical, ethnical and social, which contribute to the formation of the mentality of peoples and overlap with geographical causes.

This type of research presupposes an intimate knowledge of peoples and their ethnic groupings. I shall limit myself to giving a classification of the South Slavs alone. I know best of all the ethnic groups of the Balkan Peninsula. . . . Every year from 1887 to 1915 I traveled through the areas which they inhabit; I studied them; I met peasants and educated people; I have lived among them and, knowing their language and their dialects, I could understand their social life and follow the development of their mentality.

The problem presents, nevertheless, exceptional difficulties; some may even call them unsurmountable. Is not the soul of the other person for us an absolute riddle? Is not man the most impermeable secret for man? The ideas and the motives of human groups are hidden frequently from an accurate study. They are like a fluid which runs through our fingers. On the other hand, in this domain more than in any other, observers are tempted to press the facts in order to draw certain conclusions. They often put reasoning and speculating in place of minute and accurate researching. People have too great a tendency to overestimate their co-nationals, especially those from their native region. Some very guarded observers still see only certain characteristics and remain blind to others. Others, with the accuracy of a photographic film, perceive quite well the psychology of the masses, but do not know how to evaluate comparative values. Everything depends on the quality of the observer, especially on his spiritual integrity. Judgments given by people of different generations tend to be very different. Everyone is so dominated by the spirit, the passions and the prejudices of his time, that it is almost impossible to be impartial.

Many opinions uttered about the intellectual and moral character of peoples, have been shown to be wrong. True scientists display, in this matter, a well-justified scepticism. Nevertheless, despite the difficulties of the task, it is impossible to remain disinterested in these studies which can throw such a vivid light on the customs and the behavior of peoples and their ethnic groups. In addition, it is possible to diminish the chance of error and come closer to the truth by restricting the observations to the group which one knows best and by applying rigorous research methods to this study.

I have acquired most of the results discussed in this study by observation and experience. The direct observation, observation on the place itself, gives more and better results in the Balkans and among the Yugoslavs [13] than in western Europe, because the Yugoslav population is less widely travelled, less modified and almost made uniform through the influence of modern civilization. Their psychological characteristics are simpler and clearer. . . .

Besides these general methods, I used frequently two special methods for the study of psychological characteristics. The first is the method of "psychic traverses" (or ethno—psychic) which has a certain similarity to geological traverses.

---

[13]The author uses the term Yugoslav as meaning all southern Slavic peoples, including also the Bulgarians.

In each region there is one definite direction along which the psychological characteristics of different groups appear with greater clarity, as one goes along. . . .by following one of these directions, the traveller will perceive the differences between groups better the farther he advances from his point of departure. . . .To choose such a traverse it is necessary to have already quite satisfactory preliminary tentative ideas about the populations of the different regions. . . .

The other method consists first of all of noticing the differences which exist between the population of a "beehive country" and that of a colonized area the population of which comes from the same "hive". . . .By comparing the psychological characteristics and the social organization of the population which stayed in the primary territory and the emigrated population, one can grasp the influence of the geographical environment and the social environment upon the evolution of the psychological characteristics. Such displacements constitute a series of anthropogeographical experiences which can inform us exactly about the transformation of psychic characteristics.

In order to define the psychological characteristics of the Yugoslavs, I often utilized the data of ethnography, especially those which are given by customs, dialects, and even by the popular concepts about the value of human life. . . .Secondarily to direct observations one can best determine the character, the thinking, and the consciousness of the Yugoslav ethnic groups by studying their folklore. The national songs and the folk-tales of the Serbian people were collected by Vuk Karadzic at the beginning of the nineteenth century. . . .

To what degree can results of linguistic and anthropological studies provide us with better understanding of differences between the ethnical groupings of the Yugoslavs? The linguistic characteristics are, without question, very instructive, especially the dialects. We shall use them frequently in order to make the differences between the ethnic groups more understandable. However, they are only one indication of many which characterize the psychic type of a population.

The anthropological researches have, indeed, no relation to studies which want to determine psychical characteristics.

The direct influences of the geographical environment are that of the terrain, the climate, and the different atmospherical phenomena (air and light) upon human physiology and psychology. They alone influence directly without intermediate factors and without the interposition of social facts. Such are the impressions which high mountains and their crags exert upon man, the great plains and their wide horizons, the sea and its tremendous surface, either quiet or stirred by waves, views eminently inspiring feelings and thoughts; large fertile plains which delight the heart of the farmer; the karst with its grottoes, chasms, abysses, rivers which disappear and reappear and evoke in us the feeling of mystery and of the unknown. In enclosed regions, such as closed-in valleys, the feeling of isolation grips man. The impressions of a hilly landscape with gracious forms smiling and green, and gently inclined valleys, are quite different. Each of these landscapes and it particular physiognomy shapes the soul of people who look at it every day.

But the strongest influence seems to stem from the climate. It exerts an obvious physiological influence, especially upon the muscles, the heart and the lungs and through them upon the psychological disposition. Much more difficult to appraise are the direct influences of the climate upon the psychic life, activities and emotions.

Doubtless, man is strongly impressed by a clear sky or a sky spattered with light clouds and luminous reflexes, by the splendor of sunrise and sunset, by the forms and colors of clouds, by the changing hues of rivers, lakes, seas. . . .

The three types of influences of geographical factors upon men are subject to changes because the physical environment itself changes, either naturally, or through the intervention of man, but not very profoundly during a historical epoch. We notice the variations of indirect influences. There is deforestation; vegetation develops on a different terrain; the cover of unconsolidated material has undergone important changes; swamps have been drained. . . .

JOHANNES G. GRANO (1882-1956)

Granö belonged to a relatively large group of Finnish geographers who have done important research in geography.

They all had at least part of their training in German universities and are more or less under the influence of German geographical thinking. Granö is the most important and best known because he has devoted much of his thinking and writing to methodological problems. While other Finnish geographers seem to have followed, more or less faithfully, Hettner's ideas, Granö went his own way, though probably influenced by the German psychologist W. Hellpach and possibly also by A. Penck and O. Schlüter. He traveled widely in Asia and published the results of his studies in seven languages: Finnish, Swedish, English, Estonian, French, German, and Russian, in the latter language especially the results of his explorations in the Altai Mountains of Central Asia.

Pure Geography [13]

The purpose of this study is to prove that the environment, surrounding man, understood as the complex of phenomena and objects which can be perceived by the senses, constitutes the proper aim of geographical research. The justification for this concept will be given, and the theoretical and practical effects will be investigated.

Scientific description furnishes us the necessary material for the complex. Also the delimitation and definition of this entity has to be founded on a purely descriptive basis. Further, the geographical physiology [14]—especially the physiology of landforms—and the genesis of our research object, as well as its importance as part of a greater whole, can be perceived and interpreted scientifically only if we know exactly the observable features of an area. Therefore, an accurate and purposeful description is by all means necessary, from a physiological and genetic point of view, for geographical research. . . .

* * *

The importance of art for geographical description is undeniable. If we were artists, we could present many things which are characteristic for our geographical subject, things

[13] "Reine Geographie," J. Granö, *Acta Geographica*, Vol. 2, Helsinki, 1929, translated from the German.

[14] The interrelation of phenomena

which change their forms under our clumsy hands, or are shattered, or that we simply neglect. As surely as there is an environment, it is an object of science. Geography will learn sooner or later to treat it as such in a scientific manner. It is too early to say that the scientific period of geography is drawing to a close and an artistic period is approaching, before one has come to a genuine agreement about the nature of its object, and before serviceable methods have been developed, and before it has been shown to what results they will lead.

Would it not be almost inexcusable if we put exciting aesthetic emotions into the foreground in transmitting the results of our studies? Because thereby we would widely and consciously give license to arbitrariness and chance. Do not believe that under the tutelage of art it is possible to get an objective perception of the harmony of the environment in space and its rhythm in time. Would scientific labor not go astray completely if we would regard as the only important thing, how we execute our task, but not *what* we investigate, *what* we present, and *what* we explain?

The concept that we possess of the areas and regions of the earth's surface, on the basis of personal observation, is the total picture dependent on the sum total of our sensual observation and on the extent of the area which we have fused in observation, as well as on the duration and accuracy of our observation. The sensually observed unit has a definite extent both in space and in time. Our visual faculty determines the extent of space, and the duration of our life, the limits in time.

With respect to the central position which perceiving man occupies in the discussed whole—both regarding space and time—we can call it *the environment perceived by man through his senses*, or briefly, *environment*.

The environment is the object of geographical research. This object belongs to the natural sciences also if we pay attention to man and his activity, as far as it appears in that sensually observable whole which will be discussed by us. Nature is for us not only the uninhabited deserts and virgin forests, mountains and wide surfaces of the oceans, but also settlements, villages and cities. . . .

* * *

Now, if we endeavor to treat the properties of the environment, we have first to emancipate ourselves from the influence of the neighboring and auxiliary sciences of geography. Our objects are tied to space; their observable properties, however, are not so closely dependent upon the surface of the earth, the water, the climate, etc. as to force us to choose as a starting point one or several of the systems of the neighboring sciences. Rather the question arises, whether it would not be advantageous to destroy completely the barriers, by which our neighboring sciences have divided the geographical whole into several areas of research.

We formulate a concept of the environments and their phenomena, if we investigate the objects perceived by our senses from which the unitary impression is derived. We call those properties phenomena as far as they are related to the sensually perceived environment. They appear either as topological phenomena, which can be perceived in space, or as chronological phenomena, properties in time. In both cases they can indicate type, being qualitative ones, or an amount, being quantitative. Of course, it is necessary in classifying the phenomena to distinguish the different senses. Without entering more in detail into an explanation of the phenomena, we shall give here an outline of a system of phenomena, sufficient for the purpose of our research.

I. Topological phenomena (phenomena of being).
  A. Qualitative phenomena.
    1. General phenomena: distribution (groupings).
    2. Specific phenomena.
      a. Visual phenomena: light (sources of light), colors, forms
      b. Acoustical phenomena: sounds.
      C. Olfactory phenomena: odors.
      d. Tactilic phenomena: warmth, humidity, moisture, pressure resistance, inclination, bearing capacity.
  B. Quantitative phenomena.
    1. General phenomena: distance (distance in space).

2. Specific phenomena.
   a. Size (extent in space).
   b. Strength (intensity).

II. Chronological phenomena (phenomena of occurrence).
  A. Qualitative phenomena.
    1. General phenomena: rhythm (grouping in time).
    2. Specific phenomena.
      a. Motion.
      b. Change.

III. Quantitative phenomena.
  a. General phenomena: periods (distance in time).
  b. Specific phenomena.
    1. Duration (extent in time).
    2. Velocity.

* * *

Although the action of some geographical factors appears quite independent and original, nevertheless, as we noted before, it is closely connected with the spatial and temporal environment in which it occurs. It is advisable to keep in mind these different aspects when investigating their actions: on the one side the activity as it may occur characteristically at any place and at any time, on the other side the meaning of a certain position as it changes and directs an activity. We know, for example, that eminences of the earth's surface have a dispersing function independent from place and time: water runs down, snow falls. Contrariwise, everywhere on the earth the cave formation gathers water and debris in its deepest parts. However, this dispersing and gathering action functions, of course, differently at individual places, depend- on the amount of rainfall, on the direction of the wind, on weathering, etc. . . .

As soon as the researcher has become familiar with the occurrences and formations of his area, he is able to tell to what degree the observed phenomena have been caused in the present time. Everything in the environment which is a function of present day forces we call harmonic; the more such factors occur, the more harmonic is the geographical unit (or whole). Yet we may encounter phenomena in the research area which cannot be explained by the activity of present day forces. They are *disharmonic,* and, in contrast to the modern formations, they may be *ancient formations,* or, in contrast to the local formations, transported from some other place—*exotic formations,* either developed in the present or in the past.

If we. . .define *pure geography as the science of the human environment,* we have to relegate most parts of the former general geography to a preparatory introduction as a separate auxiliary science. Thereto belong climatology, oceanography, limnology, plant and animal geography, as well as economic and political geography; with all these, however, pure geography remains closely linked.

The same is true in regard to geomorphology, because, as important as the forms of the earth's surface may be in many respects, they do not constitute by themselves the subject of our science, but only insofar as they are perceived as phenomena within the respective complex and insofar as they are of essential importance geographically-physiologically in this very complex. We are not entitled to consider them forthwith as of greater importance in the geographical presentation than other phenomena. Very often it becomes evident that the forms of the water or of the vegetation, the transformed substances, are of greater importance in geographical evaluation than the landforms.

Regarding ethnography, we may assume that there exists unanimity—that we have to consider it a separate science, although its limits are not fixed for the time being. . . .The delimitation of geography according to our proposal is most incisively felt in the independent position of economic and political geography; concerning this suggestion, many geographers will have grave doubts.

* * *

Most geographers, probably, consider Schlüter's point of view too narrow—that geography has to restrict its field to what one can perceive with one's senses. They believe that the spiritual environment also. . . .has to be investigated and interpreted scientifically. Although it would be tempting to regard regions with all their phenomena, including the spiritual ones, as the object of geography, the observation of the spiritual environment in our basically natural science [15] would lead us entirely too far afield. It would also be very difficult to execute in practice, even if we were ready to keep generalizations and if we would found our regionalization only upon valuations, and not upon thorough inductive investigation.

The phenomena of the spiritual environment at any place, and especially where the settlement pattern and communication net is very dense, are dependent on space in an entirely different manner than are the phenomena of the sensually observable environment. Thus, from this point of view, it is doubtful whether those two regional breakdowns can be taken into consideration in the same way as can the phenomena which can be observed by our senses.

STEN DE GEER (1886-1933)

Sten de Geer is one of many Scandinavian geographers who are well-known outside their own countries. Some of them, like Fridtjof Nansen and Otto Nordenskiöld, first established names for themselves as explorers, but later became academic geographers of renown. Others, like Gerard de Geer, Sten de Geer's father, who first established a date for the Ice Age through the enumeration of varves; Eric Nordenskjöld, who connected ethnography to geography, the oceanographer, U. Sverdrup; and the glaciologist, H. W. Ahlmann, are primarily known as academic geographers.

Sten de Geer was primarily interested in methodology, and in that interest he reflected the influence of Hettner. However, by stressing that geography should investigate first of all the locations of phenomena, he differed from Hettner. He is probably best known through his work on population, urban, and industrial geography—part of which is based on a sojourn in the United States—and the cartographical presentation of research in these areas. His development of presentation by dot maps is important.

---

[15] Natural in the sense of pertaining to material things

On the Definition, Method, and Classification of Geography[16]

Ever since the dimmest antiquity the spirit of man has felt the need of geographical, i.e. earth-describing, knowledge. Acquaintance with one's own country has constantly stood out as necessary from a practical standpoint, and curiosity has been great with regard to foreign countries; but regarded as a science, geography was slow to raise itself above the primitive stage of collecting data. It was not until facts began to be systematically brought into relation with one another, and conclusions to be drawn therefrom, that geography became a true science. It was then, too, that there arose the question of its proper method and its limits in relation to older sciences. Now one side of geography, and now another, has primarily caught the interest of a generation; and the general conceptions of the essential character of the new science have varied accordingly.

To judge by the many different attempts which, down to the last few years, have been made to formulate the scope and function of geography, the difficulties of giving an exact definition of geography in a simple formula have obviously been great, even from a purely objective point of view. Some students in their definitions have desired to lay special stress on one of the most important and most interesting groups of problems in geography, and have thus sought to define more with regard to the center than to the circumference, with the consequence that their definitions have become too narrow. Others have striven for definitions wide enough to embrace all the groups of problems included in the subject, but in doing so have manifestly stretched the limits too far, so that various other sciences sometimes have been able to find a place within those limits. . . .

Formulated in a brief way, the present writer's definition (of 1915) runs as follows: Geography is the science of the present-day distribution phenomena on the surface of the earth. . . .

---

[16] *Geografiska Annaler*, ed. by the Svenska Sälskapet for Antropologi och Geografi, Vol. V, 1923.

The words "the present-day" imply a limitation which is desirable in the matter of method of investigation and conception, as against the time sciences, to which sequence in time is more important than position in space. Geography here touches the boundary of geology, which is the history of inorganic matters of palaeontology, which studies the history of plants and animals; and of history in the usual sense of the term, which has as its object the vicissitudes of the human race.

This limitation with regard to time would require too comprehensive qualifications in order to make it clear that it must not exclude the use of the geographical method of investigation in the study of the past state of things, although experience generally shows that the further one goes back in time, the more rapidly do the difficulties develop and the more rapidly does the utility of geographical treatment diminish. But the limitation as regards time does not exclude the idea that the past may be of geographical interest so far back as it is of any real importance for the comprehension of the present. . . .

The words of the definition, "distribution phenomena," constitute its main words and state the real object of geography, whereby the specific character of our science as the special science of space is properly determined. . . .

By absolute distribution, in that case, is meant the appearance or non-appearance of the various objects within a region. They may, however, appear in different degrees. This brings us to the quantitative question as to the intensity of distribution, i.e. relative distribution, commonly expressed by the means of a third dimension, giving height or depth, density, value, force or time. The relative distribution relations between different objects must also be included. The comparative study of the distribution of the phenomena of the earth's surface leads to the drawing of distinctions between different geographical regions and provinces within which the objects, which are more important from the viewpoint of intensity of distribution, occur together, . . . a synthesis of distributions. . . .

The treatment of individual distribution phenomena, therefore, forms a necessary part of every geographical enquiry and cannot be ascribed to any other science, provided that the object is situated on the surface of the earth. From this it follows that the concept of distribution phenomena can and must be employed in order that the definition may embrace the whole of geography's sphere of activity-distribution, relations and synthesis included.

The last words of the definition, "on the surface of the earth," form the necessary limitation in space as against non-geographical objects belonging to astronomy and the study of the interior of the earth, which is connected with astrophysics. . . .

The word geography means describing the earth according to the view just now set forth. Therefore, the name of our science would not in itself be sufficiently exact to correspond fully to the demands of our definition. . . .The question is whether "on the surface of the earth" does not come nearer the truth.

It is often assumed that the surface of the earth, itself, with its envelope of air and water, types of soil and types of rock, its plants, animals, population and human economic life forms the object of geography. The supposition that this was the case has been a contributing cause to that accumulation of a motley mass of disconnected facts from various sciences that was formerly regarded as constituting geography, and that to some extent continues to distinguish geographical text books.

According to this concept, geography as a science would clearly have to reckon among its subdivisions the natural sciences, except astronomy, and also the social and economic sciences, which would be quite unreasonable. . . .

The geographer undoubtedly requires a searching knowledge of the special objects and must in his investigation always have a certain amount of dealings with them all. But, as it evidently cannot be the special objects, themselves, with all their qualities, which form the object of geographical investigation, we are driven to the supposition that it is on some certain quality or circumstance concerning these objects that this research has specialized. The present writer believes that this quality or circumstance is to be found in the distribution phenomena of the objects. . . .As soon as we accept this way of putting it, the supposed, unreasonable trespassing of geography on the preserves of other sciences vanishes and its character as a unitary science emerges. Distribution phenomena must be regarded as abstract qualities—i.e. general qualities or circumstances in the material objects, and as it is these qualities that form the subject of geography, it also follows that *the object of Geography in its very nature is non-material and abstract.*

Among material objects, therefore, no boundary can be traced around the domain of geography, except in space between astronomy and geography. On the other hand, a boundary can be drawn around all the geographic qualities of material objects and that line ought to be drawn whether it can be regarded as "desirable" or not. . . .

Essentially, therefore, geography is not a special but a general science, like statistics, mathematics, philosophy, and even history in its broadest sense. Of them all it is true that in appearance, or from the standpoint of material objects, they concern themselves with the most heterogeneous matter; but in reality they are restricted to the study of certain abstract qualities in the objects or to purely abstract problems.

Each of these sciences has its own method of work, which is quite different from that of the object sciences. The empirical treatment of quantities by statistics, the rational treatment of quantities by mathematics, the treatment of logical thinking by philosophy, the treatment of position or distribution in space by geography, and the treatment of development and distributions in time by history—all these would seem to be applicable to all kinds of objects, and would seem to some extent to be operations that most men of science need to carry out. . . .

* * *

The methods of geography in the study of the distribution phenomena that form its object vary greatly, being dependent both on the nature of the object and the theoretical and practical aim of the investigation, and also on the investigator's own temperament and the resources at his disposal.

The chorographical way of thinking, i.e. areal philosophy, is, as a rule, the essential thing in geographical research. It presupposes the direction of interest in a certain quarter and a special power of association. Important presuppositions, as a rule, are geographical knowledge with regard to the entire surface of the earth, acquaintance by direct observation in nature with some parts or another of that surface, and acquaintance with the objects of the special sciences. . . .

As a rule, the *chorographical way of thinking and cartographical* work must go hand in hand in the course of geographical investigation. As the material under enquiry becomes voluminous and many-sided, as it becomes difficult to obtain a comprehensive view of it, and as the demands for exactitude increase, the resource of cartography becomes of greater and greater importance—not only as a means of orientation in its widest meaning, but also as an integral part of scientific research itself. Consequently, cartography can no longer be left entirely to merely technically expert cartographers, but it must be taken over by the geographical investigators themselves and transformed according to the requirements of science. . . .

* * *

If the object of geography is conceived as abstract, forming not the surface of the earth, but rather the phenomena of distribution on that surface, geography can and must be conceived as a science completely definable and independent in its limits and methods. But, in that case, the sub-divisions of geography also must be assumed to have the same kind of abstract objects. . . .

We can, when we proceed to classify geography, take as our basis of division either the distribution phenomena or the surface of the earth. We can ask ourselves: "What are the different kinds of distribution phenomena which geography has to investigate?" The answer would be a complete inventory of geography, arranged as general geography. But, we can also ask ourselves: "What are the different parts of the earth's surface that geography has to investigate?" The answer to this is an equally complete inventory of the entire contents of our science, but arranged as special or regional geography.

RUDOLF KJELLÉN (1864-1922)

A Swedish political scientist, Kjellén, was the orginator of geopolitics. Under the influence of Ratzel, he came to believe political geography to be an indispensable adjunct to political science. He went beyond Ratzel in developing the concept of the state as a biological organism. His ideas were carried further by Karl Haushofer and his students in Germany. As a matter of fact, Kjellén's influence on Haushofer is much more basic than the often quoted influence of Mackinder. Kjellén is included here because of his great influence on geographers with an interest in political geography and geopolitics who were to follow him, even though he never considered himself a geographer.

The Great Powers [17]

At present there are approximately fifty political bodies or powers on our planet. Among them eight are great powers which are acknowledged as such before the others. They constitute the aristocracy and upper class of nations, thought their boundaries are changing; and they have indefinite privileges but actual influence of the first order upon the political world.

Like every aristocracy, the great powers emerged because of internal necessity, by natural growth, and by natural selection in the struggle for life, i.e. through purely historical processes, independent from the rules of formal juridical development. This high society regenerates itself by inviting cooperation in important undertakings. Whether an addition to their ranks should be made depends completely on world public opinion. Basically no power has a claim to nobility in history except that which is inherent in its own strength and will for power. . . .

. . .In the present European political order we know six living great powers [18] and five "retired' ones. [91] This entire process occurred during the last four centuries. The non-

---

[17] Stormakterna, Stockholm, 1911-13, translated from the German translation, *Die Grossmächte der Gegenwart* (*The Great Powers of Our Time*), B. G. Teubner, Leipzig and Berlin, 1914, p. 1-4, 199-207.

[18]Austria-Hungary, France, Germany, Great Britain, Italy, Russia

[19]Holland, Portugal, Spain, Sweden, Turkey

European representation originated during our own century. It gives to the present political constellation a thoroughly novel character in all history.

As a matter of fact, the feudal-aristocratic character of the present political map corresponds to two very prominent peculiarities of the general physiognomy of our times. One is the strange concentration in large enterprises. . .the other is the spread of economic interdependence over our entire planet. It has been called "the planetary situation," the development of an economic and political world system which displays increasing solidarity and community of interests instead of isolated, local systems as in the past.

In such a period it is only natural to observe also a kind of capitalization of political power on the whole globe. And we can understand that some people assert that development is ruled by a law, according to which "the great states are becoming larger and larger, and the small ones smaller and fewer." (Lord Salisbury, 1899).

To what degree this law ought to be recognized as fixed and clear, depends on the concept of the essence of a great power, as it appears in empirical revelations. An investigation of these forms of life will also shed light on the justification of the existence of small nations.

It is obvious that such an investigation has to be strictly genetic. In such an approach states are not only geographical, statistical facts, but first of all types of life, the most imposing of all types of life on this Earth. As we saw great powers emerge and grow, so we saw them also wilt and die; therefore, they are at least partially subject to the laws of life and can, therefore, be studied by biological methods. The modern zoologist, however, is not satisfied to observe and describe the outward appearance of the animals only. Similarly, political science cannot halt after stating the type of constitution and the number of states, but it has to draw its attention to their organic unity and their intrinsic being. Only thereby is it possible to learn something about the inner life-power of the individuals and then about the greater or lesser necessity for the types.

We shall attempt here such a treatment of the comtemporary great powers. Each power is regarded as the political integration of four elements, according to whether it is viewed from a geographical, ethnic, social, or constitutional angle. Viewing from these four sides, we call such a power an empire, a nation, a society, or a state in the restricted sense. From these four angles the essence of the great power shall be viewed according to its more or less harmonious development, and it will become clear that also in connection with these features, the foreign policy of the great powers developed more or less organically, for better or worse.

At the same time we shall not overlook the subjective factors of politics, such as the opinion of nations about themselves and others, the degree and depth of emotions, the capacity of leading personalities for judging the situation and for utilizing favorable circumstances. Here science is at its limit and the art of the statesman begins. But this art cannot deviate too much from the objective conditions which limit the understanding and foolishness of nations. Science does not negate the free will of nations, but it recognizes a solid framework in the surrounding conditions on which it bases its conclusions concerning their conditions with relative certainty.

From the outset it strikes us that neither large areas (Brazil), nor large population, nor both together (India, China) confer the privileges of great power status. The entry of Japan into the selected group proves that such status does not depend either on belonging to the Aryan race or to the Christian religion. Also the legal form is immaterial. Great powers have all possible constitutional forms, from the Caesarism of Russia to English parliamentarianism, from French centralism to American federalism.

That leads us indirectly to a first and basic conclusion. Great power status is not a mathematical concept, but a dynamic one—not an ethnic or cultural, but a psychological idea. Great numbers and extent are necessary, also a high degree of civilization and a certain harmonious constitutional form, but they constitute great power status only if they are endowed with ample powers, which are mirrored in claims and influences upon the rest of the world. We add: a will to more power. Basically no great power is satisfied. Great powers are expanding states. Therefore, we see that all have appendages or spheres of interest. . . .

. . . .The great powers all originate in the temperate zone, because only there national will retains its vigor. They all belong to the northern hemisphere, because only there the copious articulation of land guarantees a hardened friction between a national will and a severe natural selection. The claim to a position favorable for communications derives from the strong will characteristic of a great power; the same is valid for a healthy climate and sufficient space.

This condition illuminates also the life process of the great powers. They develop and disappear together with the will to growth. They can suffer not only a bodily death, but also a spiritual one: the resignation, the voluntary cessation from the struggle for the highest goal, the spontaneous relinquishment of the claims to participate in the political and cultural development of humanity. Great powers, like primitive nations, die from lack of will to life in its fullness and vigor.

Concerning the means of power we distinguish two opposite types of great powers; the economic on a monetary basis, and the military on the basis of armaments. . . .Because the sea is the means of commercial income, and the land the area of military recruitment, the opposing types of character correspond to opposing types in outward form, a maritime and a continental.

In our research we could not recognize a specific nation heading for universal rule. We think we are able to recognize a limit for the spread of the great power type. The great power will still grow; but this type will not occupy the entire globe. There is room left for the small nations. The number of small states is decreasing, but they will not disappear entirely—and it will depend on the development of power and the prudence of the individual state, whether it will belong to the select group or not. That is the experience so far and there is no reason to assume that it will be changed in the future .

In our days it appears sometimes as if force moved about in the political world according to the law of the jungle—that the strong will devour the weak. This law is strong in history, indeed, but it is not all-powerful. Power has not the last word in history, but rather civilization, spiritual as well as material, moral as well as physical. Nations which have no destiny of their own are tools for history in its work of civilizing. This process is certainly best served by the cooperation of great and small powers. The specific task of our time—colonization—created a system of large estates in our political order; another period may experience a reaction in favor of political small ownership as soon as the planetary scene is completely filled. The instinct in man for differentiation is as strong as the instinct for association, and civilization would suffer by the final suppression of one or both.

Thus, in the ultimate analysis, the idea of the small national state is protected by the idea of mankind itself. Above the small national state looms the great power; but above the great power stands humanity which needs both of them for its own fulfillment.

CHAPTER 11

RUSSIAN AND SOVIET GEOGRAPHERS

Prior to the mid-19th century, Russian geography developed independently, largely free from the philosophies of geography which were then developing in Western Europe. During that time Russian geography was primarily devoted to the exploration of Siberia, Central Asia, and the Arctic, although Russian expeditions ranged as far as Bellingshausen's Antarctic explorations of 1819. Occasionally men of different nationalities, like the Dane, Vitus Bering (1680-1741), or the German, Peter Simon Pallas (1741-1811), travelled under the Russian flag and with Russian companions. The only Russian of that time who contributed significantly to geographic thought was Mikhail V. Lomonosov (1711-1765), who is better known for his contributions to Russian letters and for the founding of the University of Moscow. Lomonosov received the latter years of his formal education at Freiberg, Germany, and like his contemporaries, *The Instigators,* had the breadth of interest and knowledge to be classed a polyhistor.

Russian geographical thought in the latter half of the 19th century was much stimulated by German geography, especially by the writings and teachings of Hettner. The influence of classical German geography upon the thinking of geographers in other countries can be shown convincingly in the Russian professional literature. This influence is further emphasized today by the vehement striving of the Soviet geographers to emancipate their science from all "bourgeois" influences.

Under the Marxist influence of Soviet rule geographic thought took a very distinct path; it had to be applicable to man's conquest of nature. Therefore, economic geography flourished, as did physical geography to a somewhat lesser extent, but all other phases of human geography have been almost neglected.

A discussion of the nature of geography is proceeding in the Soviet Union with a vehemence which the academic character of the subject hardly seems to justify. However, in the U.S.S.R. it apparently is a matter of professional survival for one's method to be recognized as the "correct" one. This discussion, economic geography versus physical geography, displays current development in Soviet geographic thought and emphasizes that, despite far-reaching agreement, Soviet geographic thought is not monolithic. Of course, the common basis is Marxism-Leninism and dialectical materialism. Although recognition is usually given to dialectical materialism (see the article by Gerasimov), it is often difficult to determine the exact effects of this philosophy on the writings of Soviet scientists.

Of the writers who follow, Semenov and Berg represent the pre-Soviet era in Russian geography and will be introduced individually with their writings. However, since less is known in the West of Soviet geographers, they will be introduced together here. Similarities can be observed in their writings, even though they represent the two different Soviet approaches to geography. The first of the Soviet articles was written in 1955 by I. P. Gerasimov, the academician and recognized spokesman of Soviet geography who led the delegation to the International Geographical Congress in Stockholm in 1960. Ya. G. Feigin, a corresponding member of the Academy of Sciences of the Ukrainian Soviet Socialist Republic and an economic geographer, represents the pre-World War II philosophy of economic geography. The authors of the next two articles, M. I. Al'brut and V. A. Anuchin, are less well known outside the Soviet Union, but are included here because their articles are representative of the philosophical discussions in Soviet geography in the mid-20th century. The last of the Soviet geographers, A. A. Gregoryev, who is an academician and the director of the Institute of Geography of the Academy of Sciences of the U.S.S.R., is primarily a physical geographer. All of these men have done field work in the Soviet Union and have published extensively.

V. P. SEMENOV-TYAN-SHANSKIY (1870-1942)

Semenov was the son of the famous explorer of Central Asia, P. P. Semenov, who received the title of Tyan Shanski from the great mountain chain on the Mongolian-Siberian boundary. When the Bolshevist Revolution broke out, the younger Semenov had already won a great reputation as one of the leading Russian geographers, which helped him to retain his intellectual independence later. It would be difficult to find changes in his basic ideas attributable to the Revolution. Thus the statement which follows, though written in the post-Revolutionary period, can be accepted as a summation of Russian geographical thought of the preceding epoch.

Region and Country[1]

The Circle of Geography and Geographic Laws

Geography is a completely independent science, studying the spatial interrelationships of life on earth in the broadest sense of the word, that is, beginning with the life of rock and ending with the life of man. If the spatial relationships concern the present period of the life of the earth, then we, although not completely accurately, call the science studying it geography or, more precisely, *zemlevedeniye* or *stranovedeniye*,[2] depending on whether the study encompasses our whole planet or different parts of it. If the spatial relationships concern past geologic periods of our planet, then we are concerned with the zemlevedeniye or stranovedeniye of the ancient face of the earth, or with palaeogeography, which is generally considered a division of geology. If we study the spatial interrelationships of past periods of the historic life of mankind, then we are concerned with historical geography, which is generally considered a division of history. If we take the vital elements of the earth, then there are six, namely; 1) dry land, 2) water, and 3) air as basic envelop-

---

[1] *Rayon i Strana*, V. P. Semenov-Tyan-Shanskiy; *Gosydarstvennoye Izdotel'stvo*, Moscow, 1928, p. 38. Translator anonymous.

[2] For both words there is no accurate English equivalent. The first part of both means country, land, the second, knowledge. The German *Erdkunde* and *Landeskunde* would fit best.

ments of the earth on the one hand and 4) vegetation, 5) animals, and 6) man as derivatives of sunlight and heat on the other hand. Having arranged them (these elements) geometrically correct, we will have a hexagon. Connect the points of the hexagon by lines — spatial connections. There are fifteen. This means that there are fifteen spatial interrelationships that are necessary for the complete geographic representation of the earth and any of its parts. Describe the hexagon as a circle, and we will obtain a closed figure of the geographic science. The connections . . . are arranged in the following classification of the divisions of geography:

I. *Inorganic Geography*

<table>
<tr><td>1) Dry land and water
2) Dry land and air
3) Water and air</td><td>The geography of the basic envelopments of the earth (epeirography or orography; hydrography which comprises oceanography; potomography * and limnography **; and aerography or climatology).</td></tr>
</table>

* Hydrography of rivers.
** Hydrograpyh of lakes.

II. *Organic Geography*

<table>
<tr><td>4) Dry land and vegetation
5) Water and vegetation
6) Air and vegetation</td><td>Phytogeography</td><td rowspan="2">Biogeography</td><td rowspan="3">Geography of the derivatives of sunlight and heat</td></tr>
<tr><td>7) Dry land and animals
8) Water and animals
9) Air and animals
10) Vegetation and animals</td><td>Zoogeography</td></tr>
<tr><td>11) Dry land and man
12) Water and man
13) Air and man
14) Vegetation and man
15) Animals and man</td><td colspan="2">Anthropogeography</td></tr>
</table>

III. *The Geographic Synthesis*

16) Economic geography or the geography of productive forces, natural or artificial, exploited and unexploited by man, and the geography in general of his economic activities.

17) Political geography or the geography of territorial and spiritual dominations of human associations.

Any division consists of two elements: 1) descriptive and 2) philosophical as well as the statics and dynamics of the subject.

When studying the spatial interrelationships of the vital elements of the earth, the geographer must first of all devote attention to the arrangement of them on the earth's surface, the amount of space occupied by them, and the direction in which the manifestation of their life or activity occurs. The arrangement, size and direction are the static elements of geography and are the subject of so-called descriptive geography, which is completely necessary and without which it would be impossible to progress; but at the same time it is far from being all-absorbing. No less important in geography is another element, namely the dynamic element, that is, the study of the spatial interrelationships in which one or another of the vital phenomena on the earth has been or will be manifest. The good geographer must be able to draw a living, clear, detailed picture of all — even remote parts — of the continents and seas of the earth, even if, for some cosmic reason, the poles moved to the equator and the equator to the poles. Furthermore, he must be prepared, fully-armed with his complex geographic knowledge, for more or less precise indications of those changes in the spatial interrelations which inevitably must occur as a result of the slow processes occurring on the earth. These include such processes as the age old fluctuations of the amount of dry land and water or the fluctuations of climate, as well as all catastrophes in the form of seismic and volcanic phenomena or sharp changes in the fate of mankind during and after world-wide shocks such as world war and revolution. That is why, in such periods, there is the intensified demand for geographers that we see today. The dynamic element of geography supplies the chief food for fruitful philosophic conclusions and constructions, which may be called in a given instance "geosofskiy" (geographic adjective modifying conclusions). It was not without reason that the French geographer, Vidal de la Blache said that the idea that the earth represents something complete with harmonious parts imparts to geography the beginnings of a method, the fruitfulness of which is more and more evident with the breadth of its application. Such, in the roughest sense, are the correlations of the different aspects of geography, which one must remember in order not to diffuse ones efforts and unnoticeably digress.

Correlations in organic geography (no. 12) are as much more complex than correlations in inorganic geography (no. 3), as the combinations in organic chemistry are more complex than the combinations in inorganic chemistry. From this, the very slight elaboration of organic geography in comparison with inorganic geography is understandable.

Therefore, the second and third spatial geographic connections, that is, dry land and air, and water and air are found in a mixed situation, under the strongest influence of the vital activity of organisms, so that they, in actuality, do not strictly represent inorganic geography, but transition geography between inorganic and organic.

The basic difference of organic and transitional geography from inorganic is that the investigated phenomena in them is primarily arranged zonally, while in inorganic geography, azonal arrangement of phenomena predominates, with only a mechanical dependence on convergance and divergence of phenomena under the known corners and of their resultant forces.

Organic or sun geography has lagged behind inorganic geography in its scientific elaboration for even another reason, that it seems scarcely to change radically. The fact is that so called pre-historical and historical geology is available to us, that is, the science that makes it possible to guess the origin of the forms of the earth's surface, their petrographic and mineral composition and also, partially, the organic life, on the basis of those physio-chemical traces which have been left on the face of the earth and in the accessible parts of the earth's bowels during past geologic periods. It is true, that the degree of preservation of these traces varied depending upon age, and that whole layers of ancient formations frequently remain completely mute and mysterious like the sphinx. . . .

* * *

Geography, as was said above, studies the laws of the spatial interlationships of life. In accordance with this, geographic laws may be divided on the one hand into laws of 1) location and confines of the arrangement of some subject or phenomena on the face of the earth, 2) laws of direction, in which the arrangement occurs, 3) laws of quantitative distribution of subjects and phenomena on the earth's surface, 4) laws of combinations or association or symbiosis, 5) laws of the grouping of subjects and phenomena in some planimetric form, and 6) laws of the interaction of contiguous environments. On another plane, geographic laws are divided into 1) laws of the interrelationships of the basic envelopments of the earth — dry land, water, and air — or laws of physio-geography, 2) laws of the interrelationships of derivatives of sunlight and heat — that is, vegetation, animals, and man — or biogeographic and anthropogeographic laws, and 3) laws of the interrelationship of the very activity of man depending upon natural conditions and his adaptability to them, or economic geographic and political geographic laws.

Geographic laws, in comparison with laws of many other sciences, are to a considerable extent fragmentary, accidental and still only slightly arranged in an orderly manner. Therefore, it is generally necessary to limit oneself to an incomplete mention of them.

LEV SEMEONOVICH BERG (1875-1950)

Berg was one of the prominent pre-revolutionary Russian geographers. Starting as an ichthyologist (a student of fish life), he soon expanded his interest to the habitat of fishes: lakes, and later rivers and oceans. Progressing therefrom to geography, geomorphology, and finally to the history of geography, he became one of the most productive, original and thorough Russian researchers in geography. He was influential in familiarizing Russian geographers with the thought of many western geographers, from Richthofen to de Martonne, and from Davis to Hettner. His reputation was high enough to assure his standing under the Soviets, despite occasional criticism. He apparently never repudiated the definition of geography which he had formulated in 1915, referring explicitly to Hettner and de Martonne.

The Subject and Scope of Geography [3]

Geography is a science of horizontal and vertical distribution, of various objects and events on the surface of the earth (within its crust, in the atmosphere and in the hydrosphere) in the past as well as in the present and in the future.

As it has been explained by Hettner, geography is a chorological science, studying the placement of objects and phenomena. However, geography does not study the separate individual objects; rather, it analyzes the mutual relations of accumulated objects. Geography is not a chorography of individual objects and phenomena, but a chorography of human, animal, and vegetable communities (if that term may be used to name an assemblage of human, animal, and vegetable groups) as well as of the relief configurations on earth.

But what are the regular assemblages of organic and inorganic worlds on earth? Such regular formations make the landscapes. Geography, therefore, is a science of landscapes.

Geography does not consider the essence or the form of objects and phenomena; it is mainly concerned with their distribution in space. Geography is a chorological science, just as history is a chronological science because it considers the distribution of objects and events in time, while completely disregarding the essence of things.

The geographic distribution of any kind of phenomena is the subject of geography. This means that geographic studies cover the natural physical phenomena on earth as well as the manifestations of material and spiritual activities of the organisms which inhabit the earth (including man),

---

[3] "Predmet i zadachi geografii", Lev S. Berg, *Geograficheskoe Obshchestvo S.S.S.R. Izvestia*, v. 51, 1915, p. 463 ff.

provided the phenomena are considered from the point of view of their distribution. Geography would therefore have an equal right to cover, for instance, the distributions on earth of mountains, rivers, storms, coral reefs, conifers, and marsupials, as well as the spread of races, religions, of the production and consumption of sugar, of various customs (like cannibalism), of fables, of juridical norms, of crime, and the like.

However, since it is impossible and useless to include everything in geographic studies, the geographer has to concentrate on objects having geographical importance.

As rightly indicated by Hettner, the individual objects and phenomena are not important to a geographer, but their appearance in connection with other objects and phenomena is. The purpose of geographic research consists in discovering the connections and the laws which regulate the distribution of individual objects, in studying the influence exerted by one group of objects and events on other groups, and in determining the results of such correlations. In other words, the final scope of geography is to study and to describe the natural as well as the cultivated landscapes. The natural landscapes are those in the creation of which man did not take part, as distinguished from cultivated landscapes in whose creation man and human culture play an important role. According to this terminology, cities and villages are a part of cultivated landscapes.

The natural landscape is a region of amalgamation in which the characteristics of climate, relief, soil and vegetation blend into one harmonious ensemble, extending over a certain zone of the earth.

The study of causes which produce what may be called the landscape-organism, and the analysis of correlation of various components — such is the scope of scientific geography.

I. P. GERASIMOV

The Present Status and Aims of Soviet Geography[4]

The purpose of this report is to review briefly the present state of Soviet geography and to formulate the principal objectives confronting the science in its present stage of development. The complexity of this task is obvious; geography is one of the oldest sciences and in all its stages of development it has embraced a vast range of natural and social phenomena peculiar to given countries, regions or other parts of the earth's surface. Two major difficulties have always stayed in the way of geography; one of them lies in the limitation of its subject matter; the other in the definition of the approach to the phenomena to be studied.

These difficulties have yet to be overcome. Heated debates have been waged about this and other questions. However, for now I want to emphasize that in spite of disagreements about methodological questions, Soviet geographers are doing work of considerable practical and theoretical importance.

Those who have devoted themselves to geographic research over the years have produced a body of factual material characterizing similarities or differences in the physical environment, economy and population of the various countries. On the basis of these facts and their explanation, comparison and generalization, the theory of geography has developed. It has striven to ascertain and clarify the connection between natural phenomena in different parts of the earth's surface or between characteristics of the population and the economy in the various countries. For these reasons the geographer's work is distinguished by its generalizing and synthesizing character which is just as essential to the progress of science as the analytical work done within the narrower framework of a more specialized scientific discipline.

Detailed geographic work . . . has played a key role in the ambitious program for the transformation of nature and

---

[4] "The present Status and Aims of Soviet Geography," I. P. Gerasimov, *Soviet Geography: Review and Translation*, English translation from the Russian by Lawrence Eckert, vol. I, no. 1-2, January-February, 1960, p. 3.

the integrated utilization of natural resources of these territories. . . .

Soviet geographers have continued the development of the theory of geography using the classic heritage and the accumulation of new factual data. However, the decisive role in the formulation of a modern theory of Soviet geography has been played by the use of the principles of dialectic and historical materialism, and by the pronouncements of the classical writers of Marxism-Leninism on the geographic environment and its significance in the development of society. On the basis of these principles and pronouncements, the subject matter of physical geography has been defined as the geographic environment, i.e., the natural conditions of a given territory taken in their entirety and mutual relationships, and the principal theoretical aim of physical geography has been defined as the formulation of laws governing the formation of the natural geographic environment as a single whole on the earth's surface and in its parts. The Marxist doctrine of the laws of development of society and of the role of the geographic environment in social production has also been fundamental in formulating a theory of economic geography because only on the basis of Marxist doctrines has it become possible to work out scientifically all the theoretical questions concerning the geography of the economy of various countries and regions.

On the basis of these concepts of its subject matter and aims, geography can no longer be regarded as a single, undifferentiated science. Geography has been divided basically into two major scientific disciplines: physical and economic geography, the geography of population being included in the latter. This division ensues from the very nature of the objects studied by geography: natural phenomena, on the one hand, and social phenomena, on the other. Physical geography studies natural phenomena and thus proceeds from laws peculiar to the development of nature, i.e., natural laws. Economic geography studies social phenomena (the distribution of production) and thus proceeds from laws peculiar to the development of society, i.e., social laws.

Physical or economic geography is further divided into general and particular geographic disciplines. This is especially true in physical geography. Here alongside a general physical geography or earth science, studying the structure, development and distribution over the earth's surface of the mutually conditioned natural phenomena constituting the natural geographical environment as a whole, we find a regional physical geography concerned with the natural geographic environment within a given part of the earth's surface. In addition to these two major divisions of physical geography, independent scientific disciplines are concerned with the study of individual elements and objects of the natural environment. They include climatology, hydrology, geomorphology, soil geography, plant geography and zoogeography, on the one hand, and oceanography, glaciology, limnology, and permafrost science, on the other. The same process of differentiation is characteristic of economic geography, whose theoretical aim is to formulate the laws of social production and of the conditions and characteristics of social production in given countries and regions. In addition to general and regional economic geography, which are concerned with the distribution of social production as a whole or within countries or groups of countries, the geography of industry, agriculture and transportation is beginning to develop and assume separate status.

Geography thus represents a whole system of scientific disciplines having their own subjects and methods of study. All these disciplines, however, form the closely interconnected complex of geographic sciences based on the overall aim of geography and on the close interrelationship between all objects studied by it. By studying the various elements or phenomena of the natural environment or of society, the separate geographic disciplines make their particular contribution to the solution of the general scientific objective of geography, which is the study of the natural geographic environment and of the geography of the economy and the population of the whole world or its parts.

The results of studies of the natural environment, economy and population of countries or other parts of the earth's surface have long been set forth in the form of geographic descriptions and maps of these countries and regions. Therefore, work of a comprehensive regional character always has been and will continue to be one of the most important kinds of output in the field of geography. As our knowledge increases and the theory of the geographic sciences develops, the content of regional description is increasingly perfected through greater precision of the geographic facts communicated, as well as through deeper scientific analysis of these facts and a broad scientific generalization. As a consequence, an elaboration of the methodology of regional description and mapping has always been one of the most important tasks of geography. Its solution is essential for continued progress of the whole system of geographic knowledge.

The present report cannot of course characterize exhaustively the state of each of the above mentioned geographic disciplines in the USSR. . . .

Soviet geography, in short has undoubtedly achieved considerable advances in the development of theory and in the introduction of the results of its work into the national economy and Soviet culture.

Nevertheless, these achievements are still insufficient in the light of the great cultural demands of the Soviet people and the requirements of communist development. The work of Soviet geographers still suffers from considerable defects that must be removed if our science is to continue its forward march.

The principal defects have been aired in the protracted discussion of general theoretic questions that have taken place in the last few years in our scientific journals. . . . A recapitulation of the discussion has shown that the main reason for the serious defects in the present state of geographic theory is the fact that Soviet geographers have not yet learned how to make creative use of the philosophy of dialectical materialism in their specific discipline.

This has been evident especially in the inadequate struggle Soviet geographers have put up against the pseudo-scientific, idealistic and metaphysical views of leading bourgeois scholars and against the reactionary nature of many contemporary foreign geographic concepts of a neo-Malthusian, geopolitical or racist character. Moreover, some elements of idealistic or metaphysical concepts proposed by leading geographers, such as A. Hettner, have been uncritically accepted by some Soviet geographers, such as Academician L. S. Berg. This great Soviet geographer to some extent repeated the mistakes of many naturalists who in the 19th and at the beginning of the 20th century, in spite of the fact that they had discovered the objective laws of the development of nature in their specific research, were under the influence of incorrect methodological attitudes in their own general theoretical views.

The discussion has also brought out scholastic errors in the work of Academician A. A. Grigor'yev, which he has acknowledged and is striving to correct; as well as vulgar nihilistic pronouncements by some Soviet geographers, such as A. M. Smirnov and P. S. Makeyev, on the delimitation of natural regions and in palaeography.

Among other methodological defects of Soviet geographic work is the inadequate emphasis given to the influence of the economic activity of society upon its natural environment. This defect in a number of studies in physical geography has led to a purely naturalistic approach to the geographical characterization of a given area, the absence of a clear assessment of its natural resources and a lack of evaluation of the possibilities of economic development. It should be stressed that such physical geographic studies assume an abstract, abstruse character that does not satisfy the requirements of a socialist national economy and culture.

At the same time the discussion brought out a similar defect in economic geographic studies that content themselves with a superficial analysis of the role of the natural environment in the economic activity of society. Such an approach also results in the abstract, abstruse character of such studies, the stereotyped utilization of mere sociological plans, and an underestimation of the local geographic characteristics in the development of society.

A number of economic geographic studies conducted by Soviet geographers have also suffered from serious methodological defects in underestimating or incorrectly understanding the inseparable connection between the productive relations and the productive forces in the development of economic geographic phenomena. In some cases, self-sufficient significance has been attached to the productive forces, which have been studied and analyzed without due regard to productive relationships. In other cases the study of the distribution of social production has been made without sufficient consideration of the conditions of the geographic environment that influenced it. In both cases, the commission of theoretical errors has prevented a fruitful treatment of theoretical and practical questions of economic geography.

The discussion also showed that the vast amount of factual data being accumulated in geographic studies in the USSR is still not being subjected in due measure to theoretic elaboration and generalization. This is hampering the further development of the theory of Soviet geography and results in the appearance of theoretic views of an abstract scholastic character, insufficiently grounded and verified on the basis of specific geographic studies.

The past discussion has thus shown that while Soviet geography has attained considerable theoretic and practical accomplishments, it has been confronted by many new tasks that require further stimulation of theoretic thought. This should be directed not only toward meeting the demands of current studies, but also towards finding more efficient ways of utilizing the natural wealth of our land and the productive forces of our people for the welfare of the communist society being built in the USSR.

These tasks and these new requirements may be briefly formulated as follows:

1. A major task of Soviet geography is the promotion of geographic field work in all the regions of the country in conjunction with their further economic development, the transformation of nature and new large-scale construction projects.

2. It would be wrong to limit the present tasks of geographic field work to the study of regions of new agricultural development. Soviet geography is also confronted by the im-

portant tasks of further studying well-known and thoroughly developed territories.

3. It must be added that Soviet geographers are expected to produce not only geographic studies of the Soviet Union but also of foreign countries, both the people's democracies and the capitalist countries.

YA. G. FEIGIN

Introduction to Economic Geography of the USSR [5]

Economic geography is the science of the areal distribution of production and of the conditions of its development in different countries and regions. Production ". . . encompasses the productive forces of society as well as the producing (economic) relationships of human beings, and thus the embodiment of their unity in the process of production of material goods." [6]

In studying where something is produced, economic geography, proceeding from basic laws of political economy, must set forth the conditions of development and distribution of productive forces in particular countries and regions.

In order to obtain this information, economic geography investigates the distinguishing features of the contemporary economic development of different countries and regions, the natural-geographic conditions of their economic development, and also the economic inter-relations among countries and regions.

Economic geography not only describes the distribution of production, but by means of analysis and generalization of concrete material, studies those specific principles according to which this distribution occurs in a particular country, region or branch of the economy.

---

[5] "Introduction to Economic Geography of the USSR," Ya. G. Feigin. Ed. by S. S. Balzak, V. F. Vasyutin, and Ya. G. Feigin, 1940, translated under the Russian Translation Project of the American Council of Learned Societies by Robert M. Hankin, Olga Adler Teitelbaum and others, Macmillan, 1948.

[6] Stalin, Questions of Leninism, 11th ed., p. 551 (note in the Russian edition)—Because they only serve to prove the "correct position" of the author without contributing anything new, the numerous quotations from Lenin and Stalin have been omitted in this reprint.

The principles of the distribution of production cannot be separated from the general laws of the development of a given socio-economic system. Consequently, attempts to prove the non-historical nature of the principles of distribution, and the applicability of these very same principles of distribution to all socio-economic systems, in all countries and regions, is unscientific, and basically contradicts Marxism-Leninism. . . .

The capitalist means of production of material goods is linked indissolubly with the fundamental, extremely uneven, inefficient distribution of productive forces. The distribution of capitalistic production is founded on the capitalist's pursuit of profit, and on anarchy, competition, and the law of unequal development of capitalism, the operation of which is reinforced particularly during the epoch of imperialism.

The international division of labor in the capitalist world, and the distribution of production, are based on the oppression of some countries by others, and by the forced conversion of a majority of countries and regions into agrarian raw-material colonies for the highly developed mother-countries.

The basis of the distribution of production forces in the USSR is the program of building a communist society . . . there is being created a new economic geography for the Soviet Union, with a more uniform distribution of production throughout the country. More and more, industry is being located near both the sources of raw materials and the regions where the manufactured goods are consumed. The former backwardness of the national republics is being eliminated. The distribution of agricultural production is becoming more uniform. Regions previously exclusively consuming are becoming producing regions, and the complex development of production in the economic regions is being assured.

In studying the conditions of the development and distribution of production, economic geography gives an important position to the natural conditions of countries and regions.

However, the Marxist-Leninist understanding of the role of the natural-geographic environment has nothing in common with crude geographic theories according to which the natural-geographic environment is considered as the determining factor in the development and distribution of productive forces. The economic characteristics of countries and regions, and also the territorial division of labor are explained by bourgeois geographers and economists on the basis of natural-geographic conditions.[7] Thus, for example, the important German bourgeois geographer A. Hettner considered that the characteristics of the economy, way of life, and political structure of a particular country are all determined exclusively by its natural-geographic conditions.[8] With the aid of this premise, Hettner justified colonial oppression by imperialist countries, since colonies, according to Hettner, by virtue of their natural-geographic conditions are not capable of developing independently and need the assistance of "civilized" countries.

The American professor Huntington, author of a textbook of economic geography widely used in the United States, goes even further than Hettner. He explains the distribution of population, industry, and agriculture, and also the level of

[7] To select the utterances of one of a few people, which may be vulnerable, and to represent them as the typical opinion of all the opponents, is a well known trick of the political and especially the communist controversialist. Here, however, it is transferred into scientific discussion. It hardly need be said that environmentalism has been almost completely abandoned in all Western countries. Note of the American editor.

[8] This statement is hardly an adequate summary of the views of Hettner; it probably reflects an internal dispute in the Soviet Union over the principles of the distribution of production, a dispute in which the views of Hettner may have been quoted by a group whose views did not prevail. Hettner himself states that the consideration of natural factors can "arrive only at possibilities; the decision lies with man." (Alfred Hettner, "Die Geographie des Menschen," *Geographische Zeitschrift*, Vol. XIII, 1907, p. 413, as quoted by Richard Hartshorne, "The Nature of Geography," *Annals of the Association of American Geographers*, Vol. XXIX, 1939, p. 299.) Note by the editor of the American edition.

development of particular countries by climatic conditions alone.[9]

. . . With the growth of productive forces and the perfection of productive techniques, human society increasingly recognizes the laws of nature and increasingly subordinates them to society itself,[10] using natural resources for developing social productive forces.

Under conditions of socialist economy the utilization of natural resources is planned and systematic, whereas under capitalism it is most inefficient and ruthless.

Nor are density of population and its growth decisive factors in the development and distribution of productive forces, although without a certain minimum of population the development of productive forces is impossible. The decisive factor in the distribution of productive forces is the means of production of material goods, the means of acquiring the necessities of life required for the welfare of the people.

Each branch of the national economy, and even each branch of industry and agriculture, in addition to over-all general traits, has its own specific distributional characteristics. But these characteristics are indissolubly linked with the socio-economic and natural-geographic conditions in particular countries and regions. For this reason the distribution of production must be studied not only by countries and regions, but also by branches.

The principles of distribution of socialist production, differing basically from the principles of capitalist distribution, necessitate a study of the economic geography of the socialist

[9] It is true that Ellsworth Huntington lays great stress on the climatic factor; but the assertion that he explains "by climatic conditions alone" shows only a superficial acquaintance with his writings. His *Principles of Economic Geography* (New York: John Wiley, 1940, 715 pp.) reveals an appreciation of the complex physical, economic, political and historical factors involved in the analysis of patterns of distribution of economic activities. Furthermore, his analysis of physical factors includes location, relief, soil, vegetation, and minerals, as well as climate. Note of the American editor.

[10] That is the often quoted *transformation of nature* which the Soviets declare as desirable and possible under a communist system.

country and of the capitalist world, as two independent branches of the same scientific discipline.

In economic geography it is of utmost importance to study the details of the economic development of the different industrial sections of the country — the economic regions.

. . . An economic geography of the USSR is concerned with the distribution of the entire national economy and its particular branches throughout the territory of the USSR. It also studies the distinguishing characteristics of socialist construction in the different regions of the country, their productive forces, the dislocations which occur in them, and also the possibilities and avenues of their future development.

. . . Among economic geographers of the USSR, various bourgeois theories have had wide circulation — the teachings of Hettner, the German (p. XLIII) geographer, and the location theories of Weber,[11] von Thünen,[12] and others.

These would-be "scientific" and "objective" theorists, minimizing contradictions of distribution of capitalist production, set out to prove its "rationality", to justify colonial plunder by the "harmony" of international division of labor, etc. Among bourgeois economists and geographers "disinterested research" — to use an apt expression of Marx — "yields to the quarrels of hack writers, and impartial scientific investigations are supplanted by prejudiced, officious apology." [13]

To justify the separation of economic geography from other sciences, bourgeois scholars present the special, so-called "chorographic" (purely spatial) approach to the phenomena under study. The basis of "chorography" is the artificial separation of time and space, and examination of all economic-geographic manifestations only in terms of space, excluding the time factor. The German geographer, Hettner, developed most fully this "chorographic" point of view in economic geography with all the ensuing consequences. "The examination

---

[11] Alfred Weber's theories are available in English in *Alfred Weber's Theory of Location of Industries*, ed. by Carl Joachim Friedrich (Chicago: University of Chicago Press, 1929), 256 pp. Note of the American editor.

[12] Johann Heinrich von Thünen, *Der Isolierte Staat*, 2nd ed., 1842. Note of the American editor.

[13] Marx, *Capital*, Vol. 1, 1935, p. XIX. Note in the Russian edition.

of objects and processes of the earth's surface from the chorographic point of view," writes Hettner, "is the interpretation of them not as objects in themselves, and in their relation to the development in time, but in their association in space." [14] Hettner's concept of space and time is purely theoretical, that is, he considers them only as a form of perception and not as existing in reality independent of our consciousness.[15]

Hettner in essence defines existence, not in terms of time, but only in space. As a matter of fact "existence without time is as absurd as existence without space" (Engels). A genuine study of the distribution of production of various countries and regions is excluded by Hettner by virtue of this concept. Economic geography is concerned not only with (p. 340)) facts coinciding in space, but also, as is the case with other economic sciences, it is concerned with facts which are constantly changing in time. According to Hettner, the economic geographer must study phenomena in a static frozen aspect. Thus, at the basis of Hettner's teaching of economic geography lies antihistoricism. The antihistoricism of Hettner, as of other bourgeois scholars, is one of the means used to immortalize capitalism and to defend its existence. Hettner openly declares that geography must be geared to serve the interests of the bourgeoisie.

Together with "chorography", as has already been shown above, the basis of Hettner's teaching is crude environmentalism.

---

[14] Hettner's *Geography: Its History, Nature, and Methods*, p. 164 (note in the Russian edition). The quotation apparently is from a Russian translation of Hettner's work. The original appears in Alfred Hettner, *Die Geographie, Ihr Wesen und Ihre Methoden* (Breslau, Ferdinand Hirt, 1927), p. 217. Hettner viewed reality as having three coexisting aspects, all of which are essential to an understanding of the whole: (1) the analysis of similar objects and processes by the systematic disciplines such as chemistry, botany, economics or sociology; (2) the interpretation of objects or events in their time setting by history; (3) the interpretation of objects in their space associations by geography. Note of the American editor.

[15] That is a correct statement of the philosophical position of Kant's transcendental idealism, which had such immense influence upon philosophers and scientists throughout the 19th century and is even today very strong. Lenin wrote a philosophical treatise against Kant.

Bourgeois professors, many of whom were revealed to be enemies of the Soviet people, tried by all possible means to popularize and implant the teachings of Hettner in the USSR. Using the teachings of Hettner, they showed that the Soviet Union by virtue of its natural conditions of geographic position should remain an agrarian country, and in the international division of labor must fulfill the role of an agrarian raw-material subsidiary to the industrially developed West European countries. On this basis they demanded the abolition of the monopoly over foreign trade.

The teachings of Hettner were widely distributed throughout the economic geographic literature. Several authors showed themselves to be followers of the antiscientific, theoretical conceptions of Hettner. They were preaching attitudes of crude environmentalism and attributing to the geographic environment the decisive role in the development and distribution of productive forces, and in the development of particular countries and regions. Another, no less harmful point of view on the question of the role of the geographic environment was widespread. Several woebegone authors completely ignored the natural geographic conditions of the development of particular countries and regions. By every means they minimized the role of natural-geographic conditions in the development and distribution of productive forces. In practice this was expressed by a disdainful neglect of the study of natural resources and of natural-geographic conditions for the development of countries and regions.

M. I. AL'BRUT

Let Us Clear Up, Once and for All, Differences on Methodological Questions in Economic Geography [16]

Previous volumes of *Geografiya i Khozyaystvo* contained several articles by V. A. Anuchin on theoretical problems in economic geography.

---

16 "Let Us Clear Up, Once and for All, Differences in Methodological Questions in Economic Geography," M. I. Al'brut, *Soviet Geography: Review and Translation*, English translation from the Russian by Lawrence Eckert, vol. 2, no. 3, March 1961, p. 23.

. . . If Anuchin intends to defend his ideas, he will probably be willing to reply to certain questions that puzzle his readers. On that assumption we would like to pose the following questions to Anuchin:

1. The All-Union Conference of Geographers of 1929, in which N. N. Baranskiy[17] participated, adopted a resolution that said in part: "The geographical division of labor is the basic concept of economic geography uniting the research of individual specialized disciplines and the research on individual regions; the geographical division of labor should be the basic category in any scientific system of economic geography."

Anuchin's statement that economic geography is not concerned with the study of production relationships contradicts that resolution. Does Anuchin regard the geographical (territorial) division of labor as the basic category of economic geography?

2 (related to the first). We know that Lenin was the first to introduce an analysis of production relationships into economic regionalization. Economic regionalization happens to be intimately linked with the territorial division of labor. Would Anuchin agree that economic geography is concerned with economic regionalization? If yes, how does this jibe with his statement that economic geography does not study production relationships?

* * *

4. Anuchin once clearly stated the scientific unsoundness of the theory of the unity of geography:

"Physical geography deals without doubt with the study of nature and the laws of nature. Economic geography studies phenomena of a social character and deals with the study of phenomena governed by laws of social development. There is no question therefore that it belongs among the social sciences. It follows that there is a fundamental difference be-

---

[17] N. N. Baranskiy (1881-1963) is the "grand old man" of Soviet economic geography. By his consistent attempts to write economic geography on a Marxist basis in many textbooks for all grades of schools he has a pervading influence. In addition he seems to be highly respected personally.

tween economic geography and physical geography because physical geography studies objects governed by the laws of nature, which determine the character and essence of physical geography as a natural science.

"If geography were to be regarded as a unified science and we ignored these fundamental differences, then it would have to discover and study laws that covered both nature and society. But such special geographic laws do not exist. There are laws of nature and there are laws of social development. The laws of nature do not operate in the spheres of social relationships, and the laws of social development do not govern nature." . . .

Has Anuchin now rejected his views on the fundamental difference between physical and economic geography?

* * *

6. Anuchin wrote sarcastically about the "distribution man" Zhirmunskiy: "Denying the existence of geography as a whole, Zhirmunskiy acknowledges the existence of separate geographical sciences. There is, for example, a geography of population; it studies the distribution of population. There is a geography of plants; . . . Zhirmunskiy also acknowledges the existence of an economic geography, whose business is the study of the distribution of production. . . . It so happens that the principles of distribution of all these objects are, understandably, quite different: population and, say, white wormwood are governed by entirely different principles of distribution so that there obviously cannot be any unity among the many geographies listed by Zhirmunskiy. Not to mention the fact that in reality such 'isolated geographies,' concerned only with the distribution of elements and phenomena, do not by far add up to geography." . . .

In opposition to the "distribution school" Anuchin evidently asserts that the laws of distribution of population and, say, wormwood are the same.

We would like Anuchin to give a straight answer to the question: Are there, in his opinion, universal laws of distribution, common for both natural and social phenomena?

9. Anuchin maintains that economic geography is not an economic science. Does Anuchin reject also the thesis that economic geography bases itself as a science on the laws and conclusions of political economy?

V. A. ANUCHIN

On the Subject and Scope of Economic Geography[18]

In this connection we must first of all concede the existence of two points of view. Some economic geographers see the subject of their science in distribution (either of productive forces or of social production). In essence this point of view can be termed dualistic because inevitably it breaks the unity of the material world into two parts (natural and social) and draws a sharp, indelible boundary between the natural and the social sciences, specifically between physical and economic geography, no longer making it possible to speak of geography as an integrated science. That view rejects the possibility of general geographic research; geography as a science is "liquidated" and is replaced by the mechanical sum of physical and economic geography. In the process economic geography is torn away from the system of geographic sciences and is made part simply of the system of economic sciences (thus giving rise to a peculiar "science", no longer a geographic economic geography).

Other economic geographers, supporting the monistic view of geography, start from the recognition of the unity of the material world of nature, part of which is human society. In addition to the further development of physical and economic geography, they see the need for general geographic studies that would synthesize the achievements of both physical and economic geography.

Despite considerable differences on the question of defining the general subject of geography, all supporters of the second school view geography in the concrete form of matter develop-

---

[18] "On the Subject of Economic Geography" (Answers to M. I. Al'brut's Questions), V. A. Anuchin, *Soviet Geography: Review and Translation,* translated by Lawrence Eckert, vo. 2, no. 3, March 1961, p. 26.

ing under the influence of the interrelationships between nature and society and perceptible in the form of areal complexes.

Being a supporter of the monistic view of geography, the author of this article will try once again to formulate his concept of the general subject studied by geography as a whole, and his concept of that part which is the subject of study of economic geography.

* * *

Fundamental differences between physical and economic geography do exist. But they exist within geography and reflect only one aspect of the essence of geography. Another aspect (which Al'brut does not see) lies in the fact that the entire complex of geographic sciences has a common object of study. That object common for all geographic sciences is the landscape envelope of the earth, which, with certain qualifications can be termed the geographic environment.

The landscape envelope of the earth is made up of the earth's surface (together with the bottoms of seas and oceans) plus the hydrosphere and the atmosphere. Besides the lithosphere, air masses, waters, soil cover and biocoenoses, the landscape envelope contains a complex of elements of a social character that have arisen and developed as a result of social production under the determining influence of production relationships. That social complex within the landscape envelope has important distinctive qualities and can in no way be considered part of the biosphere, as some geographers have tried to do in the past. The landscape envelope contains not only the results of man's activity; it also contains human society itself. And regardless of the specific laws of development of that society, regardless of the social structure and social relationships, mankind will remain a component part of the earth's landscape envelope as long as it inhabits the earth.

The landscape envelope differs from the other envelopes of the earth mainly in the fact that life has arisen and developed within it. It offers conditions for the origin and development of life, including life in its highest form — human society. And these very conditions later became the environment within which social life developed. However, not the entire landscape envelope became an environment for society. We can hardly speak of the bottom of the oceans, for example, as such an environment. We must therefore distinguish the landscape envelope as a whole from that part within which society and the rest of nature are in constant direct interaction. That part we call the geographic environment.

The geographic environment, consequently, includes only one part of the earth's landscape envelope, but that part is intimately linked with and dependent on all other parts. For example, the peaks of the Himalayas are not part of the geographic environment, but as a distributor of moisture for huge areas they exert a strong influence on the geographic environment. The ice of the polar regions is not part of the geographic environment, but it determines the water level of the oceans. If the ice were to melt, many parts of the land now inhabited would be under water and the geographic environment formed in those parts would perish. In short, although we separate the geographic environment from the landscape envelope we must not forget that the entire landscape is indirectly part of the geographic environment. The difference between the two is therefore rather small, certainly qualified and, perhaps, even a little formal. Therefore, while considering the geographic environment as the general object of study for all geographic sciences (including, of course, economic geography), we must make the qualification that some geographic research inevitably will be concerned with those parts of the landscape envelope that do not constitute thus far a geographic environment.

All definitions of the geographic environment as being only a natural category . . . are one-sided and therefore incorrect. . . .

Society and nature are not completely identical. Society is not a mechanical aggregate or a simple sum of biological individua. The life of people is not a simple biological phenomenon; it possesses a specific quality distinguishing it from the rest of nature. But that specific quality does not put human society outside of nature and outside of the earth's landscape envelope; since it exists and develops within the geographic environment, mankind is part of that environment, constituting a component with special qualities. Thus there is no break between society and the rest of nature, but there are internal distinctions within the material world. The interrelationships between society and nature take place within the whole, within nature in the broad meaning of the word.

We often encounter the view that the very term "geographic environment" refers to a condition for the development of something that is not part of it. According to that view, if the geographic environment is a condition for the development of human society, human society can in no way be included within the environment. That point of view is only seemingly persuasive. It is true that from a strictly logical point of view something cannot develop within an environment and be at the same time part of the environment. Nevertheless, that is the situation, despite the fact that it contradicts strict logic and a formal, metaphysical way of thinking. . . .

Most of the social sciences are concerned with the study of society as a whole. They are concerned with the study of specific laws of social development that are the causes of that development. They are concerned with all social relationships that exist within human society, including production relationships. In such an approach all the rest of nature is quite legitimately opposed to human society and is regarded as the external natural environment. The influence of the rest of nature on society is regarded as an external influence. Such an approach is absolutely correct in all cases where human society is studied as a whole. Such an abstraction from the actually existing unity of society and nature is necessary for deeper research into the essence of human society as such.

But such an approach becomes incorrect if it is concerned with the study of human society not as a whole but as a part of a whole, namely as part of nature. Social geography differs from other social-economic sciences precisely because it is concerned with the study of society and its elements as parts of a larger material study; it does not study society as such, nor specific internal laws of development, but regards society as a component part of the conditions under which the process of social development takes place. Therein lies the fundamental difference between social geography as a subject and the social-economic sciences, and therein lies the basis for the unity of social geography and natural, physical geography which also studies nature not as a whole (that is done by other natural sciences) but as part of a whole, as part of an object of study that is the same for all geographic sciences — the geographic environment.

* * *

In short, the subject of economic (social) geography is the social elements of the geographic environment and not human society as such. The main distinguishing feature of geography is its concern with the interactions between nature and society as an internal process of development of the geographic environment, in which the complex of social elements exerts on all other elements of the environment a specific, purposeful influence, determined mainly by production relationships.

* * *

But it should not be assumed that just because the findings of one science can be used by other sciences, such sciences can merge with one another. Many sciences would be unthinkable without the wide use of the data of mathematics, but it does not follow that they thus become branches of mathematics. Physical geography would be unthinkable without the use of geological data, but that does not make it a branch of geology. Economic geography would be unthinkable without the use of data of economic sciences (especially political economy), but that does not make it an economic science.

* * *

It should be noted here that the meaning of geographical division of labor has not been adequately worked out from a theoretical point of view. The view that the geographical division of labor is synonymous with social division of labor taken as an areal expression arouses serious doubts, and in our opinion can hardly be considered correct. Of course, any division of labor is social in character. But not every social division of labor can be called geographical.

The subject of a science should determine its specific features; it should determine differences (and not similarities) between it and other sciences; it should determine the specific tasks of a given science. The subject of economic geography is the territorial complexes of productive forces, or, if we look at the subject somewhat more broadly, the social elements of the geographic environment.

That subject is studied by economic geography chorologically, i.e. through the use of the geographic method, which encompasses the study of all objects and phenomena in their development expressed in terms of areal differences. In that sense the term "chorology" can be replaced by the term "distribution" because both terms express the methodological (rather than the subject) character of geography. One of the forms of geographic method is regionalization.

* * *

Now a few words about regionalization. Regionalization does not express the material object of study but a very important form of the method of geographical perception. Regionalization is a methodological, not a subject category. By means of regionalization (geomorphic, climatological, physical-geographic, or industrial, transportation, agricultural, economic-geographic) geographers study the geographic environment both in terms of individual component elements, and in terms of complexes of such elements. There can be no geography without regionalization because geographers perceive their study objects in terms of territorial complexes, and consequently all geographic research starts with and ends with regionalization. Such a regional approach is the methodological basis of any of the individual geographic sciences and of geography as a whole. Chorology, territoriality, regionalization, distribution, differences from place to place — all these concepts used by geographers, despite particular differences, essentially express the same thing. They express the geographic method.

The idealism of Hettner's concept, as well as the idealism of present day supporters of the distribution school in economic geography, lies in the fact that they make a methodological category the subject of the discipline and thus try to deprive geography of its materialistic character. (In fact, what kind of a science do you get by depriving it of a material object of study!)

* * *

Regionalization is of considerable practical importance because it is applied not only in the process of scientific perception but also in the process of economic administration. In particular when we speak of economic-geographic regionalization it must be emphasized that the importance of identifying objectively formed economic geographic regions (or regions in process of formation) lies not only in the fact that it helps perceive territorial complexes of productive forces but also in the fact that economic-geographic regionalization furnishes the basis for governmental regionalization, which in turn is a major method in economic planning in countries with a Socialist mode of production. That is an additional reason why Soviet economic geography should have the regional approach as its methodological basis.

A. A. GREGORYEV

The Progress of Soviet Geography During the Last Thirty Years.[19]

Not long before the revolution a change occurred in the concept of the nature of geography, similar to the change which occurred somewhat earlier in Germany. This trend in the development of geography stood in close relation with the general tendency of the development of "bourgeois" science in the epoch of monopolistic capitalism. For the methodical concept of geography a classification was chosen as a basis which stood in complete contrast to the actual condition of substance, time and distribution. Therefore, geographical research was limited to problems of distribution, the investigation of the contemporaneous, spatial spread of things and phenomena which constitute the geographical landscape. The scientific methodological principles which spring from such a

[19] "Die Fortschritte der sowejtischen physichen Geographie in den letzten 30 Jahren," A. R. Gregoryev, *Petermanns geographischen Mitteilungen*, vol. 92, 1948, p. 19 ff, translated from Russian by H. Haack. The Russian original was published in *Izvestia Akademiya Nauk*, Seriya Geograficheskaya i Geofisicheskaya, vol. 1, 1947, pp. 373 ff.

concept lead to a complete refusal to investigate the processes of emergence and development of the geographical substance. They lead geographical science to a formalistic, descriptive doctrine of the landscape; put into first place the investigation of the individual differences of countries and localities, which depend on purely local, non-repeating conditions; ignore the investigation of the general properties and those following definite laws of the various territories; deny even the possibilities of the existence of such laws. Completely different from such a regional geography appears the geography which has achieved wide recognition among us. Its basic goal is descriptive of types of natural landscapes and their zonal arrangement, strictly observing all these principles.[20]

Although the former kind of scientific method was in complete contrast to the requirements and questions of Soviet economy, it dominated Soviet geography into the period of Stalin's First Five-Year Plan.[21] Even in the first years of this Five-Year Plan the true character of this "bourgeois" geographical methodology was bared thoroughly; and then was begun the elaboration of new scientific methods which were based upon the methodology of dialectical materialism.

At the very beginning of the first post-war Five-Year Plan success was finally reached in completing the basic and most important principles of a new scientific method of physical geography, in introducing them into scientific practice, and thus enabling their further penetration into scientific work. The impact of these theoretical researches is clear in the writings of the present author.

* * *

Physical geography: The most important principles of the new physical geography consist of the following:

The *research object* of physical geography is the structure of the inner (geographical) crust of the earth as the area of mutual influence, and especially of mutual interpenetration of

---

[20] Although no name is mentioned, there is little doubt that the author had Hettner in mind, and probably also Passarge. Whether the lesser vehemence of his attack than that of Feigin is a personal character trait or due to the passage of time, it is impossible to say.

[21] 1928-32.

atmosphere, lithosphere, hydrosphere, and biosphere, and of the processes which function within them in transforming some types of energy into others, making allowance for the changes brought about by the activities of human society.

The aim (of the study) of physical geography is not only the structure of the crust of the earth, but also the physical-geographical processes acting within it, their mutual influence and penetration into the natural substance.

The essence of the new scientific method is given in a deepened investigation of the physical-geographical process both as a whole and in its parts, considered as inseparable members of the whole. The basis of this research is the isolation and investigation of the active basic forces of the internal development as a physical-geographical process, as a whole and in its elements. The description and analysis of the outward appearance of a territory is finally one of the compulsory objects of this research. Relying on this scientific method, a genetic classification of the physical-geographical processes of the dry land was worked out; on this classification a system of territorial, graded order was established (from the continents as a whole, down to the most detailed physical geographical district). It is founded on the different character of the main forces of development peculiar to each territorial stage of the physical-geographical process and the scale of the geological process. Thus the fundamentals were based on a theory of the "outer" or "surface" physical geographical processes, geologically the briefest of all physical-geographical processes. This theory was proved on the home land of the Subarctic(!). Upon this theory is based the very important law of the "intensification of the physical-geographical process," finally formulated in 1946. It demonstrated the dependence of the physical-geographical process on the amount of warmth in its mutual relation to moisture. . . .

Palaeogeography: . . . Its most important theoretical object is the elucidation of the development of the earth's crusts as regulated by laws, and of its physical-geographical processes. . . . Thus palaeogeography as a geographical discipline pursues more comprehensive tasks by far than the palaeogeography of the geologist, which actually is concerned only with the distribution of dry land and sea over geological periods. The palaeogeography of the geographer aims at recognition of the character of mutually influencing changes of the physical-geographical substance, using for its purposes the material of historical geology, palaeobotany, palaeogeology, archaeology, etc.

Chemical geography: The study of the physical-geographical substance and the physical-geographical process necessitated including in the field of geographical research a number of new problems with which physical geography had not dealt before. To these belong — besides palaeogeography — the doctrine of the peculiarities of the chemical aspect of the physical-geographical process in the physical-geographical substance of the various areas of the globe. . . .

Idealistic methodology which had hindered, as we said before, the development of Soviet physical geography, exerted only small influence upon the development of the individual branches (geomorphology, climatology, hydrology, soil science, biogeography), because according to the idealistic classification of the sciences, they have nothing in common with physical geography. Each of them developed at the beginning of the Soviet epoch, at least in their theoretical aspects, completely independently. Their ideological connection with general and regional physical geography and their mutual fertilization began reviving and deepening in accordance with the new dialectic-materialistic principles in geography because, in consonance with them, all these branches constitute a uniform whole — they merge into a uniform system of geographical science.

This trend utilized the important concept of the most authoritative foreign scholars — W. Davis and W. Penck.[22] It permitted one to attack the problems of relief more thoroughly than had been possible before, while avoiding the negative approaches of those scholars (schematism, over-

---

[22] It seems that the two Pencks, the father Albrecht and son Walter, have been confused.

simplification of series of phenomena, neglect of local factors, etc.).[23] Without restricting itself to the area of the USSR, Soviet morphology turned to one of the basic problems of world geomorphology — elucidation of the regularities according to natural laws in the structure of the earth's surface as a whole.

[23] At least the last of these reproaches seems without foundation.

CHAPTER 12

UNITED STATES GEOGRAPHERS

Introduction

The term "school" always seems to imply the logical development of a rather specific, well-structured philosophy. Usually this is not at all the case. In any particular culture "field" the forces which produce special and typical aspects of thought are diverse and numerous, and at a given moment it may be extremely difficult to know which of a series of current trends will persist.

In the 19th century there was almost no American geography. Yet the German tradition was represented here, in a positive and dynamic fashion, in the person of Arnold Guyot. American science was either not ready for geography or not ready for Ritterian geography. By the end of the century the work of George P. Marsh could have been tremendously influential, yet at the time of publication it apparently was not. Only at the end of the century did geography suddenly become the preoccupation of a rather considerable number of scientists. When it did, it was uniquely American. And it owed much of its vigor and direction to the tremendous influence of a single man — William Morris Davis.

At the time when geography became acceptable in higher intellectual levels of American life, there were almost no trained geographers to guide its development. Reviewing geographic progress for the twentieth anniversary of the Association of American Geographers in 1924, Davis noted this: ". . . curiously enough a great part of this progress has been accomplisht (sic) by the labor of others than professional geographers; geographers are indeed among our latest acquisitions, and until lately they came to us largely from non-geographic sources. But altho we have often been nurtured in other nests than our own, that does not mean that our few geographical forbears have abandoned to others the duty of rearing their young, for it has been too generally the case that they had no young to rear; it is from the generous over-supply of fledglings in others' nests that many of us have come." [1]

A list of some of the famous American "geographers" exemplifies this early background in other disciplines: Powell, Gilbert, Wheeler, Abbe, Marbut, Maury, Ward, Salisbury. It was through the efforts of such men as these that the term *geography* entered the American scientific lexicon. These were the geographers who founded the Association of American Geographers, a project instigated by Wm. Morris Davis. Of the organization's early members Brigham says, "There were . . . some of the ablest representatives of climatology, also creative minds dealing with distributional phases of botany and zoology and a very considerable number of geologists and physiographers. Not a few of these have in the years, perhaps without knowing what they were doing, so yielded to the thrall of geography, that the center of their activities and reputation has swung into that field." [2] It was the association of the geographic science with the physical earth sciences that gave it its early impetus. In the majority of cases, geography entered the colleges and universities through a door clearly marked "Geology."

The failure of geography to "catch on" until the turn of the century is clearly evident in the university record. The first college professor of geography, according to Dryer, was John Daniel Gross at Columbia College (now University); Gross

---

[1] Wm. Morris Davis, "The Progress of Geography in the United States," *Annals of the Association of American Geographers,* Vol. XIV, No. 4, December, 1924, pp. 159-160.

This entire volume of the *Annals* is a most remarkable collection of documents. In addition to Davis' article, there are others by Brigham and by Dryer on the same general topic. Elsewhere in the volume are to be found Colby's famouse paper on the California raisin industry Sauer's paper on the survey method, and a paper on geography and natural selection by Huntington. If ever a volume of a journal deserved to be re-issued for general sale, this one does.

[2] Albert P. Brigham, "The Association of American Geographers—1903-1923," *Annals of the Association of American Geographers,* Vol. XIV, No. 3, September, 1924, p. 112.

was professor of both German and geography from 1784 to 1795. He was succeeded by John Kemp who was professor of geography from 1795 to 1812. Arnold Guyot held a chair (probably the first in the country) of physical geography and geology at Princeton from 1854 to 1880. Daniel C. Gilman was professor of political and physical geography at Yale from 1863 to 1872.[3] The influence of these men was remarkably limited. When Dryer made a survey of the position of geography in American and European universities in 1897 there were only three professors of geography in the entire United States. They were Davis at Harvard, Tarr at Cornell, and Libbey at Princeton. By way of contrast, Dryer's 1924 survey reported geography courses offered in 73 universities and colleges; there were 239 instructors! But there were only seven departments of geography.[4]

Of course, geography had long been firmly established in the lower schools. The first American "school geography" was published in 1784; the author, Jedidiah Morse, was a minister in Charlestown, Massachusetts.[5] Dryer lists the stages in the development of secondary school geography as the following: (1) gazetteer stage, (2) wonder book stage, (3) natural teleology stage (the Guyot influence), (4) general physiography stage (the Huxley influence), (5) specialized physiography stage (the Davis influence), (6) biogeography stage (again the Davis influence, this time his "ontography"), and (7) human stage.[6] Thirty years later he might have added an eighth stage — social studies — by which the character of geography has been strongly affected.

Representatives of the American School

Pretty clearly one need not look much beyond 1897 to trace the development of geographic thought in America. Yet one

---

[3] Charles Redway Dryer, "A Century of Geographic Education in the United States," *Annals of the Association of American Geographers*, Vol. XIV, No. 3, September, 1924, p. 143.

[4] *Ibid.*, pp. 142-147.

[5] Clifton Johnson, "The First American Geography," *Journal of Geography*, Vol. III, No. 7, September, 1904, p. 311.

[6] Op. cit., pp. 130-134.

needs to "sample" the geography of the 19th century, at any rate. There were at least two unusually fine publications: Guyot's *Earth and Man,* and Marsh's *The Earth as Modified by Human Action.* There was the work done by The American Geographical and Statistical Society. There were the geographical explorations that preceded the expansion of this country. (Of particular interest is the "Report Upon United States Geographical Surveys West of the One Hundredth Meridian in Charge of Capt. George M. Wheeler." Published in 1889, it reported in seven volumes the field surveys of some 359,000 square miles carried out in the decade 1869-1879.)

"Geography" meant rather loosely anything to do with the nature of the land, and there were few "geographers" to worry about a more precise definition. The fate of American geography in the 19th century typifies the futility of an idea without a home. Many outstanding concepts have been effectively "lost" because they were produced in an unfavorable environment. The tremendous importance of geography in 19th century Germany simply had no parallel in the United States.

One conspicuous event in the last decade of the 19th century appears to have promoted the study of geography. The National Education Association appointed a "Committee of Ten" in 1892, headed by President Eliot of Harvard, to study the twin problems of uniformity in pre-college school programs and of college entrance requirements. This committee in turn organized nine "conferences" of ten selected members each to consider each of nine specific fields of study. The Conference on Geography met several times in Chicago, and a report of their recommendations appeared in the *Bulletin of the American Geographical Society* in 1895.[7] As one might expect, there was not unanimous agreement; there were both a Majority Report and a Minority Report. The former did not define geography, although the Conference was "confronted with the question." Instead, it emphasized the following areas of the discipline:

---

[7] Israel C. Russell, "Reports of a Conference on Geography," *Bulletin of the American Geographical Society,* Vol. 27, No. 1, 1895, pp. 30-41.

1. *Elementary Geography,* a broad treatment of the earth and its inhabitants and institutions, to be pursued in the primary, intermediate, and lower grammar grades.

2. *Physical Geography,* a more special but still broad treatment of the physical features of the earth, atmosphere and ocean, and of the forms of life and their physical relations, to be pursued in later grammar grades.

3. *Physiography,* a more advanced treatment of our physical environment in which the agencies and processes involved, the orgin, development, and decadence of the forms presented, and the significance of the features of the earth's face, are the leading themes, to be pursued in the later high-school or early college years.

4. *Meteorology,* a specialized study of atmospheric phenomena, to be offered by schools that are prepared to do so properly, as an elective in the later high-school years.

5. *Geology,* a study of the earth's structure and its past history, to be offered by schools prepared to do so properly, as an elective in the last year of the high-school course.[8]

This "organization" of the science, and the failure otherwise to define, hardly merits some of the statements made by Russell, one of the committee members. In the full report of the Conference, outlines of methods of instruction were drawn up; Russell says that comparing these with the tables of contents in "the classic works on Geography by Ritter, Humboldt and Guyot, it will be seen that a new element has been introduced into the science by the modern school. Rational geography has supplanted mere description.[9] In concluding his report, Russell says, "Those who have taken an active part in modernizing and vivifying geographical science, are of the opinion that in the educational revolution now in progress, it should be placed in the first rank in all grades of study from the primary to the post-graduate. Its claim for such a conspicuous place is, as expressed in the report before us, because it *develops the powers of observation, the powers of scientific imagination and the powers of reasoning."* [10]

---

[8] Ibid., pp. 31-32.

[9] Ibid., p. 40.

[10] Ibid., p. 41. The italics are Russell's.

Of the ten members of the Conference, the only ones whose names appear in the geographic literature of the period, or later, are Davis and Chamberlin. One is tempted to believe that it was this Conference which interested Davis in the "new" science. Certainly the Committee of Ten, by naming geography as one of the disciplines to be considered, had much to do with the creation of a growing interest in the field.

By 1900 the intellectual environment proved to be extremely favorable to the geographic science. Whether Davis actually helped create this environment or not it is difficult to say, but in any case he definitely took advantage of it. One cannot read the geographic literature of the period without recognizing his pre-eminence. He wrote prolifically; he defined and redefined geography; he marked its limits and stated its associations; he proposed its proper objectives; he outlined its methodology. He so symbolized American geography for the period chosen here that one could almost characterize the thought of the time by selections from Davis' writings alone.

In the first two decades of the 20th century geography developed very rapidly. People were trained as "geographers," and as such they concerned themselves with the proper scope and definition of the discipline. European geography — particularly German geography — began to have an influence it had never achieved through Guyot. More societies were formed and more journals launched. Papers revealing the attitudes of geographers toward geography began to appear in the journals. The American preoccupation with the nature of the geographic discipline had started.

It continues to this day. Early highlights in the development of an American philosophy of geography were Barrows' "Geography as Human Ecology," in 1923, and Sauer's "Morphology of Landscape," in 1924. Sauer himself considers Barrows' paper a turning point of sorts. Writing in 1941, he said, "Perhaps in future years the period from Barrows' 'Geography as Human Ecology' to Hartshorne's late résumé will be remembered as that of the Great Retreat." [11]

---

[11] Carl O. Sauer, "Forward to Historical Geography," in Annals of the Association of American Geographers, Vol. XXI, **March**, 1941, p. 2.

There is no question that the emphasis in geographic thinking in the early decades of the 20th century underwent one rather consistent and uni-directional change: there was a gradual transition from emphasis upon the *physical* aspects of landscape to emphasis upon the *human* aspects. First the organic-inorganic relationships were stressed, specifically in Davis' definition of geography as *ontography,* a definition followed to its logical conclusions by Tower. Then the human-physical relationships were stressed, culminating in Barrows' widely adopted term, *human ecology.* But while geography was being *defined* in this fashion, a significant part of geographic research was actually concerned with the physical landscape. Tarr and Davis and Martin and Fenneman were advancing the frontiers of physiography, while Semple and Huntington and Smith and Jefferson were emphasizing human geography.

The other philosophical developments were not quite so sharply defined. *Relationships* were emphasized, but so was *distribution.* And the overwhelming significance of *region* was alluded to from time to time. Just exactly how these concepts fitted together in one culminating pattern was the problem. Again and again it was stated that geographers could not decide what geography was. And on the other hand individual geographers affirmed in scholarly papers that geographers could indeed decide what geography was, and it was "as follows." Unfortunately, there was a good deal of variety in what "followed," depending on the interpretations of the author.[12]

The record is there, however, and an attempt has been made in the following pages to represent it in a fair and unbiased fashion: from earth to man, from region to relationship, from

[12] G. B. Roorbach sent out a questionnaire, in 1913, to geographers in both the United States and Great Britain. On the basis of 29 replies — 25 American and 4 British — he put together a statement entitled, *The Trend of Modern Geography;* this appeared in the Bulletin of the American Geographical Society, Vol. XLVI, No. 11, November 1914. It is an excellent summation of the then current thought, and it does not appear in the following pages only because there is no place here for an opinion poll of this sort.

philosophical considerations to the practical problems of teaching, from high school to university.

ARNOLD HENRI GUYOT (1807-1884)

The outstanding American geographer of the 19th century was not a native American: he was born in Switzerland. Guyot was sent to the University of Berlin to train for the ministry, and while there he attended lectures by such men as Ritter, Steffens, and Hegel. He soon became engrossed in the natural sciences. It is not difficult to see the personal forces which influenced the development of this interest: his mentor was Ritter, his patron was von Humboldt, and his closest friend was Louis Agassiz, the famous 19th century American naturalist. Guyot managed to blend the natural and moral philosophy of the time into a teleological definition of geography that exceeded even that of Ritter.

He began his teaching career as Professor of History and Geography at the College of Neuchatel. When political difficulties forced the closing of the College of Neuchatel, Guyot accepted the invitation of Agassiz, who had already settled in Cambridge, Massachusetts, to join him at Harvard. Through Agassiz, Guyot met various people who were to help him establish himself professionally in this country.

The Massachusetts Board of Education appointed him to lecture on methods of instruction in the state normal schools. He began a long and mutually profitable association with the Smithsonian Institution (where he aided in founding the Smithsonian Meteorological Bureau — later to become the United States Weather Bureau). He was appointed to the Chair of Physical Geography and Geology at Princeton in 1854. During his long Princeton career he lectured at the State Normal School at Trenton, the Princeton Theological Seminary, the Union Theological Seminary, Columbia College in New York, and at the Smithsonian.

Earth and Man, from which the statements that follow were taken, was first given as a series of weekly lectures at the Lowell Institute in Boston. Given in French, the lectures were then translated and appeared serially in the *Boston*

Daily Traveler. Later they were published in book form. Unquestionably, Guyot established his reputation in the United States by these lectures.

The Earth and Man: Lectures on Comparative Physical Geography, In Its Relation to the History of Mankind [13]

The subject to which I propose to call your attention, is Comparative Physical Geography, considered in its relations to the history and the destinies of mankind. But the term geography has been applied to such different things, the use, the misuse rather to which it has been subjected, has rendered it so elastic and ill-defined, that, in order to prevent misconception, I must first of all explain to you what I understand by *geography.*

If, preserving the etymological sense of the word geography, we should, with many authors, undertake to limit this study to a simple description of the surface of the globe and of the beings which are found there, we must at once renounce the idea of calling it by the name of science, in the lofty sense of this word. To describe, without rising to the causes, or descending to the consequences, is no more science, than merely and simply to relate a fact of which one has been a witness. The geographer, who thus understands his study, seems to make as little of geography as the chronicler of history. It would be easy to show that even the power of describing well ought to be denied him; for if he renounces the study of the laws which have presided over the creation, over the disposition of the terrestrial individuals in their different orders: if he will take no account of those which have given birth to the phenomena that he wishes to describe, soon, overwhelmed beneath the mass of details, of whose relative value he is ignorant, without a guide and without a rule to make a judicious choice in the midst of this infinite variety of partial observations, he remains incapable of mastering them, of grouping them in such a manner as to bring prominently forward those which must give character to the whole, and thus

[13] *The Earth and Man,* Arnold Henri Guyot, Gould and Lincoln, Boston, 1856.

dooms himself to a barren confusion at least; happy, if in place of a faithful picture of nature, he does not finally profess to give us, as such, the strangest caricature.

No! Geography — and I regret here that usage forbids me to employ the most suitable word, *Geology,* to designate the general science of which I speak — Geography ought to be something different from a mere description. It should not only describe, it should compare, it should interpret, it should rise to the *how* and the *wherefore* of the phenomena which it describes. It is not enough for it coldly to *anatomize* the globe, by merely taking cognizance of the arrangement of the various parts which constitute it. It must endeavor to seize those incessant mutual actions of the different portions of physical nature upon each other, of inorganic nature upon organized beings, upon man in particular, and upon the successive development of human societies, in a word, studying the reciprocal action of all these forces, the perpetual play of which constitutes what might be called the life of the globe, it should, if I may venture to say so, inquire into its physiology. To understand it in any other way, is to deprive geography of its vital principle; is to make it a collection of partial, unmeaning facts; is to fasten upon it forever that character of dryness, for which it has so often and so justly been reproached. For what is dryness in a science, except the absence of those principles, of those ideas, of those general results, by which well-constituted minds are nurtured?

Physical geography, therefore, ought to be, not only the description of our earth, but the physical science of the globe, or the science of the general phenomena *of the present life of the globe, in reference to their connection and their mutual dependence.*

This is the geography of Humboldt and of Ritter.

But I speak of *the life of the globe,* of the *physiology* of the great terrestrial forms! These terms may perhaps seem here to be misapplied.

I ask your permission to justify them, for I cannot find better, to express what appears to me to be the truth.

Far from me the idea of attempting to assimilate this general life of the inorganic nature of the globe to the individual life of the plant or the animal, as some unwise philosophers have done. I know well the wide distance which separates inorganic from organic nature. I will even go further than is ordinarily done, and I will say that there is an impassable chasm between the mineral and the plant, between the plant and the animal, an impassable chasm between the animal and the man. But this nature, represented as *dead*, and contrasted in common language with *living* nature, because it has not the same life with the animal or the plant, is it then bereft of all life? If it has not life, we must acknowledge that it has at least the appearances of life. Has it not motion in the water which streams and gushes over the surface of the continents, or which tosses in the bosom of the seas? — in the winds which course with terrible rapidity and sweep the soil that we tread under our feet, covering it with ruins? Has it not its sympathies and antipathies in those mysterious elective affinities of the different molecules of matter which chemistry investigates? Has it not the powerful attractions of bodies to each other, which govern the motions of the stars scattered in the immensity of space, and keep them in an admirable harmony? Do we not see, and always with a secret astonishment, the magnetic needle agitated at the approach of a particle of iron and leaping under the fire of the Northern light? Place any material body whatsoever by the side of another, do they not immediately enter into relations of interchange, of molecular attraction, of electricity, or magnetism? The disturbance of the equilibrium at one point induces another elsewhere, and the movement is propagated to infinity. And what will it be, if we rise to the contemplation of all the phenomena of this order together, exhibited by a vast country, by an entire continent?

Thus, in inorganic nature likewise, all is acting, all is changing, all is undergoing transformation. Doubtless this is not the life of the organized being, the life of the animal; but is not this assemblage of phenomena also a life? If, taking life in its most simple aspect, we define it as a *mutual exchange of relations*, we cannot refuse this name to those lively actions and reactions, to that perpetual play of the forces of matter, of which we are every day the witnesses. Yes, gentlemen, it is indeed life, but undoubtedly in a very inferior order of things. It is life; the thousand voices of nature which make themselves heard around us, and which in so many ways betray that incessant and prodigious activity, proclaim it so loudly that we cannot shut our ears to their language.

This general life, this physical and chemical life, belongs to all matter. It is the basis of the existence of all superior beings, not as the source, but as the condition. It is in the plant, it is in the animal; only here it is subservient to a principle of higher life of a spiritual nature, of a principle of unity, the mysterious force of which, referring all to a centre, modifies it, controls it, and organizes it, for the benefit of an individual.

Now it is precisely this *internal* principle of unity belonging to organized nature, which is wanting in individuals of inorganic nature; and that is the difference.

In inorganic nature, the bodies are only simple aggregations of parts, homogeneous or heterogeneous, and differing among themselves, the combination of which seems to be accidental. Nevertheless, to say nothing of the law that assigns to each species of mineral a particular form of crystallization, we see that every aggregation, fortuitous in appearance, may constitute a whole, with limits, and a determinate form, which, without having anything of absolute necessity, gives to it, however, the first lineaments of individuality. Such are the various geographical regions, the islands, the peninsulas, the continents; the Antilles, for example, England, Italy, Asia, Europe, North America. Each of these terrestrial masses, considered as a whole, as an individual, has a particular disposition of its parts, of the forms which belong only to it, a situation relatively to the rays of the sun, and with respect to the seas or the neighboring masses, not found identically repeated in any other.

All these various causes excite and combine, in a manner infinitely varied, the play of the physical forces inherent in the matter composing them, and secure to each a climate, a vegetation, and animal life; in a word, an assemblage of physical characters and functions peculiar to it, and really giving it something of individuality.

It is in this sense that we shall speak of the great geographical individuals, that we shall be able to define them, to indicate their characters, to mark their differences; in a word, to apply to them that comparative study, without which there is no true science. But let us not forget that these individuals have the cause of their existence, not *within,* like organized beings, but *without,* in the very circumstances of their aggregation. Hence, gentlemen, the great importance of external form; the importance of the geographical forms of contour, of relief of the terrestrial surface; of the relations of size, of extent, of relative position.

We shall see all the great phenomena of the physical and individual life of the continents, and their functions in the great whole, flowing from the *forms* and the *relative situation* of the great terrestrial masses, placed under the influence of the general forces of nature.

But, gentlemen, it is not enough to have seized, in this point of view, entirely physical as yet, the functions of the great masses of the continents. They have others, still more important, which if rightly understood, ought to be considered as the final end for which they have received their existence. To understand and appreciate them at their full value, to study them in their true point of view, we must rise to a higher position. We must elevate ourselves to the moral world to understand the physical world; the physical world has no meaning except by and for the moral world.

It is, in fact, the universal law of all that exists in finite nature, not to have, in itself, either the reason or the entire aim of its own existence. Every being exists, not only for itself, but forms necessarily a portion of a great whole, of which the plan and the idea go infinitely beyond it, and in which it is destined to play a part. Thus inorganic nature exists, not only for itself, but to serve as a basis for the life of the plant and the animal; and in their service it performs functions of a kind greatly superior to those assigned to it by the laws which are purely physical and chemical. In the same manner, all nature, our globe, admirable as is its arrangement, is not the final end of creation; but it is the condition of the existence of man. It answers as an instrument by which his education is accomplished, and performs, in his service, functions more exalted and more noble than its own nature, and for which it was made. The superior being then solicits, so to speak, the creation of the inferior being, and associates it to his own functions; and it is correct to say that inorganic nature is made for organized nature, and the whole globe for man, as both are made for God, the origin and end of all things.

Science thus comprehends the whole of created things, as a vast harmony, all the parts of which are closely connected together, and presuppose each other.

Considered in this point of view, the earth, and all it contains, the continents in particular, with the whole of their organized nature, all the forms they present, acquire a new meaning and a new aspect.

It is as the abode of man, and the theatre for the action of human societies; it is as the means of the education of entire humanity, that we shall have to consider them, to appreciate the value of each of the physical characters which distinguish them.

Such, gentlemen, are the great problems our study lays before us. We shall endeavor to solve them by studying, first, the characteristic forms of the continents, the influence of these forms on the physical life of the globe; then, the historical development of humanity. We shall have succeeded, if we may have shown to you—

1. That the forms, the arrangement, and the distribution, of the terrestrial masses on the surface of the globe, accidental in appearance, yet reveal a plan which we are enabled to understand by the evolutions of history.

2. That the continents are made for human societies, as the body is made for the soul.

3. That each of the northern or historical continents is peculiarly adapted, by its nature, to perform a special part corresponding to the wants of humanity in one of the great phases of its history.

Thus, nature and history, the earth and man, stand in the closest relations to each other, and form only one grand harmony.

Gentlemen, I may treat this beautiful subject inadequately; but I have a deep conviction that it is worthy to occupy your leisure, as it will occupy for a long time to come, if I am not mistaken, the most exalted minds and those most ripened for elevated researches. For him who can embrace with a glance the great harmonies of nature and of history, there is here the most admirable plan to study; there are the past and future destinies of the nations to decipher, traced in ineffaceable characters by the finger of Him who governs the world. Admirable order of the Supreme Intelligence and Goodness, which has arranged all for the great purpose of the education of man, and the realization of the plans of Mercy for his sake!

GEORGE PERKINS MARSH (1801-1882)

Marsh did not identify himself as a geographer. He was a politician and a diplomat. He was a member of the United States diplomatic corps in Italy for twenty-one years, and it was here that he revised his original book, *Man and Nature,* and republished it with the title, *The Earth, as Modified by Human Action.* The second edition was used for two reasons: its title was more indicative of Marsh's theme, and the preface was of considerable interest. But the passages which follow are almost identical in both books.

The Earth, As Modified by Human Action [14]

The object of the present volume is: to indicate the character and, approximately, the extent of the changes produced by human action in the physical conditions of the globe we inhabit; to point out the dangers of imprudence and the necessity of caution in all operations which, on a large scale, interfere with the spontaneous arrangements of the organic or the inorganic world; to suggest the possibility and the importance of the restoration of disturbed harmonies and the material improvement of waste and exhausted regions; and, incidentally, to illustrate the doctrine that man is, in both

[14] The Earth, As Modified by Human Action, George P. Marsh. Scribner Armstrong & Co., New York, 1877. Preface to the First Edition, pp. v-viii; Preface to Second Edition, pp. ix-x, 56-63, 111, 152, 396-397, 437, 643.

kind and degree, a power of a higher order than any of the other forms of animated life, which, like him, are nourished at the table of bounteous nature.

In the rudest stages of life, man depends upon spontaneous animal and vegetable growth for food and clothing, and his consumption of such products consequently diminishes the numerical abundance of the species which serve his uses. At more advanced periods, he protects and propagates certain esculent vegetables and certain fowls and quadrupeds, and at the same time, wars upon rival organisms which prey upon these objects of his care or obstruct the increase of their numbers. Hence the action of man upon the organic world tends to degrade its original balances, and while it reduces the numbers of some species, or even extirpates them altogether, it multiplies other forms of animal and vegetable life.

The extension of agricultural and pastoral industry involves an enlargement of the sphere of man's domain, by encroachment upon the forests which once covered the greater part of the earth's surface otherwise adapted to his occupation. The felling of the woods has been attended with momentous consequences to the drainage of the soil, to the external configuration of its surface, and probably, also, to local climate; and the importance of human life as a transforming power is, perhaps, more clearly demonstrable in the influence man has thus exerted upon superficial geography than in any other result of his material effort.

Lands won from the woods must be both drained and irrigated; riverbanks and maritime coasts must be secured by means of artificial bulwarks against inundation by inland and by ocean floods; and the needs of commerce require the improvement of natural and the construction of artificial channels of navigation. Thus man is compelled to extend over the unstable waters the empire he has already founded upon the solid land.

The upheaval of the bed of seas and the movements of water and of wind expose vast deposits of sand, which occupy space required for the convenience of man, and often, by the drifting of the particles, overwhelm the fields of human industry with invasions as disastrous as the incursions of the ocean. On the other hand, on many coasts, sand-hills both protect the shores from erosion by the waves and currents, and shelter valuable grounds from blasting sea-winds. Man, therefore, must sometimes resist, sometimes promote, the formation and growth of dunes, and subject the barren and flying sands to the same obedience to his will to which he has reduced other forms of terrestrial surface.

Besides these old and comparatively familiar methods of material improvement, modern ambition aspires to yet grander achievements in the conquest of physical nature, and projects are meditated which quite eclipse the boldest enterprises hitherto undertaken for the modification of geographical surface.

The natural character of the various fields where human industry has effected revolutions so important, and where the multiplying population and the impoverished resources of the globe demand new triumphs of mind over matter, suggests a corresponding division of the general subject, and I have conformed the distribution of the several topics to the chronological succession in which man must be supposed to have extended his sway over the different provinces of his material kingdom. I have, then, in the introductory chapter, stated, in a comprehensive way, the general effects and the prospective consequences of human action upon the earth's surface and the life which peoples it. This chapter is followed by four others in which I have traced the history of man's industry as exerted upon Animal and Vegetable Life, upon the Woods, upon the Waters, and upon the Sands; and to these I have added a concluding chapter upon great Physical changes proposed to be accomplished by the art of Man.

It is perhaps superfluous to add, what indeed sufficiently appears upon every page of the volume, that I address myself not to professed physicists, but to the general intelligence of observing and thinking men; and that my purpose is rather to make practical suggestions than to indulge in theoretical speculations more properly suited to a different class from that for which I write.

In preparing for the press an Italian translation of this work, published at Florence in 1870, I made numerous corrections in the statement of both facts and opinions; I incorporated into the text and introduced in notes a large amount of new data and other illustrative matter; I attempted to improve the method by differently arranging many of the minor subdivisions of the chapters; and I suppressed a few passages which seemed to me superfluous.

In the present edition, which is based on the Italian translation, I have made many further corrections and changes of arrangement of the original matter; I have rewritten a considerable portion of the work, and have made, in the text and in notes, numerous and important additions, founded partly on observations of my own, partly on those of other students of Physical Geography, and though my general conclusions remain substantially the same as those I first announced, yet I think I may claim to have given greater completeness and a more consequent and logical form to the whole argument.

Since the publication of the original edition, Mr. Elisée Reclus, in the second volume of his admirable work, *La Terre* (Paris, 1868), lately made accessible to English-reading students, has treated, in a general way, the subject I have undertaken to discuss. He has, however, occupied himself with the conservative and restorative, rather than with the destructive, effects of human industry, and he has drawn an attractive and encouraging picture of the ameliorating influences of the action of man, and of the compensations by which he, consciously or unconsciously, makes amend for the deterioration which he has produced in the medium he inhabits. The labors of Mr. Reclus, therefore, though aiming at a much higher and wider scope than I have had in view, are, in this particular point, a complement to my own. I earnestly recommend the work of this able writer to the attention of my readers.

* * *

It was a narrow view of geography which confined that science to delineation of terrestrial surface and outline, and to description of the relative position and magnitude of land and water. In its improved form it embraces not only the globe itself and the atmosphere which bathes it, but the living things which vegetate or move upon it, the varied influences they exert upon each other, the reciprocal action and reaction between them and the earth they inhabit. Even if the end of geographical studies were only to obtain a knowledge of the external forms of the mineral and fluid masses which constitute the globe, it would still be necessary to take into account the element of life; for every plant, every animal, is a geographical agency, man a destructive, vegetables, and in some cases even wild beasts, restorative powers.

The rushing waters sweep down earth from the uplands; in the first moment of repose, vegetation seeks to re-establish itself on the bared surface, and, by the slow deposit of its decaying products, to raise again the soil which the torrent had lowered. So important an element of reconstruction is this, that it has been seriously questioned whether, upon the whole, vegetation does not contribute as much to elevate, as the waters to depress, the level of the surface.

When man has transported a plant from its native habitat to a new soil, he has introduced a new geographical force to act upon it, and this generally at the expense of some indigenous growth which the foreign vegetable has supplanted. The new and the old plants are rarely the equivalents of each other, and the substitution of an exotic for a native tree, shrub, or grass, increases or diminishes the relative importance of the vegetable element in the geography of the country to which it is removed. Further, man sows that he may reap. The products of agricultural industry are not suffered to rot upon the ground, and thus raise it by an annual stratum of new mould. They are gathered, transported to greater or less distances, and after they have served their uses in human economy, they enter, on the final decomposition of their elements, into new combinations, and are only in small proportion returned to the soil on which they grew. The roots of the grasses, and of many other cultivated plants, however, usually remain and decay in the earth, and contribute to raise its surface, though certainly not in the same degree as the forest.

The smaller vegetables which have taken the place of trees unquestionably perform many of the same functions. They radiate heat, they absorb gases, and exhale uncombined gases and watery vapor, and consequently act upon the chemical constitution and hygrometrical condition of the air, their roots penetrate the earth to greater depths than is commonly supposed, and form an inextricable labyrinth of filaments which bind the soil together and prevent its erosion by water. The broad-leaved annuals and perennials, too, shade the ground and prevent the evaporation of moisture from its surface by wind and sun. At a certain stage of growth, grass land is probably a more energetic evaporator and refrigerator than even the forest, but this powerful action is exerted, in its full intensity, for a comparatively short time only, while trees continue such functions, with unabated vigor, for many months in succession. Upon the whole, it seems quite certain, that no cultivated ground is as efficient in tempering climatic extremes, or in conservation of geographical surface and outline, as is the soil which nature herself has planted.

Transfer of Vegetable Life

It belongs to vegetable and animal geography, which are almost sciences of themselves, to point out in detail what man has done to change the distribution of plants and of animated life and to revolutionize the aspect of organic nature; but some of the more important facts bearing on the first branch of this subject may pertinently be introduced here. Most of the cereal grains, the pulse, the edible roots, the tree fruits, and other important forms of esculent vegetation grown in Europe and the United States are believed, and — if the testimony of Pliny and other ancient naturalists is to be depended upon — many of them are historically known, to have originated in the temperate climates of Asia. The agriculture of even so old a country as Egypt has been almost completely revolutionized by the introduction of foreign plants, within the historical period. "With the exception of wheat," says Hahn, "the Nile valley now yields only new products, cotton, rice, sugar, indigo, sorghum, dates," being all unknown to its most ancient rural husbandry. The wine grape has been thought to be truly indigenous only in the regions bordering on the eastern end of the Black Sea, where it now, particularly on the banks of the Rion, the ancient Phasis, propagates itself spontaneously, and grows with unexplained luxuriance. But some species of the vine seem native to Europe, and many varieties of grape have been too long known as common to every part of the United States to admit of the supposition that they were introduced by European colonists.

Geographical Importance of Birds

Wild birds form of themselves a very conspicuous and interesting feature in the *staffage,* as painters call it, of the natural landscape, and they are important elements in the view we are taking of geography, whether we consider their immediate or their incidental influence. Birds affect vegetation directly by sowing seeds and by consuming them; they affect it indirectly by destroying insects injurious, or, in some cases, beneficial to vegetable life. Hence, when we kill a seed-sowing bird, we check the dissemination of a plant; when we kill a bird which digests the seed it swallows, we promote the increase of a vegetable. Nature protects the seeds of wild, much more effectually than those of domesticated plants. The cereal grains are completely digested when consumed by birds, but the germ of the smaller stone fruits and of very many other wild vegetables is uninjured, perhaps even stimulated to more vigorous growth, by the natural chemistry of the bird's stomach. The power of light and the restless habits of the bird enable it to transport heavy seeds to far greater distances than they could be carried by the wind.

General Meteorological Influence of the Forest

The physico-geographical influence of forests may be divided into two great classes, each having an important influence on vegetable and on animal life in all their manifestations, as well as on every branch of rural economy and productive industry, and therefore, on all the material interests of man. The first respects the meteorology of the countries exposed to the action of these influences; the second, their superficial geography, or, in other words, the configuration, consistence, and clothing of their surface.

For reasons assigned in the first chapter, and for others that will appear hereafter, the meteorological or climatic branch of the subject is the most obscure, and the conclusions of physicists respecting it are, in a great degree, inferential only, not founded on experiment or direct observation. They are, as might be expected, somewhat discordant, though one general result is almost universally accepted, and seems indeed too well supported to admit of serious question, and it may be considered as established that forests tend to mitigate, at least within their own precincts, extremes of temperature, humidity, and drought. By what precise agencies the meteorological effects of the forest are produced we cannot say, because elements of totally unknown value enter into its action, and because the relative intensity of better understood causes cannot be measured or compared. I shall not occupy much space in discussing questions which at present admit of no solution, but I propose to notice all the known forces whose concurrent or conflicting energies contribute to the general result, and to point out, in some detail, the value of those influences whose mode of action has been ascertained.

Instability of American Life

All human institutions, associate arrangements, modes of life, have their characteristic imperfections. The natural, perhaps the necessary defect of ours, is their instability, their want of fixedness, not in form only, but even in spirit. The face of physical nature in the United States shares this incessant fluctuation, and the landscape is as variable as the habits of the population. It is time for some abatement in the restless love of change which characterizes us, and makes us almost a nomad rather than a sedentary people. We have now felled forest enough everywhere, in many districts far too much. Let us restore this one element of material life to its normal proportions, and devise means of maintaining the permanence of its relations to the fields, the meadows, and the pastures, to the rain and the dews of heaven, to the springs and rivulets with which it waters the earth The establishment of an approximately fixed ratio between the two most broadly characterized distinctions of rural surface — woodland and ploughland — would involve a certain persistence of character in all the branches of industry, all the occupations of habits of life, which depend upon or are immediately connected with either, without implying a rigidity that should exclude flexibility of accommodation to the many changes of external circumstance which human wisdom can neither prevent nor foresee, and would thus help us to become, more emphatically, a well-ordered and stable commonwealth, and, not less conspicuously, a people of progress.

Agricultural Draining

I have commenced this chapter with a description of the dikes and other hydraulic works of the Netherland engineers, because both the immediate and the remote results of such operations are more obvious and more easily measured, though certainly not more important, than those of much older and more widely diffused modes of resisting or directing the flow of waters, which have been practised from remote antiquity in the interior of all civilized countries. Draining and irrigation are habitually regarded as purely agricultural processes, having little or no relation to technical geography; but we shall find that they exert a powerful influence on soil, climate, and animal and vegetable life, and may, therefore, justly claim to be regarded as geographical elements.

Nothing Small in Nature

It is a legal maxim that "the law concerneth not itself with trifles," *de minimis non curat lex;* but in the vocabulary of nature, little and great are terms of comparison only; she knows no trifles, and her laws are as inflexible in dealing with an atom as with a continent or a planet.The human operations mentioned in the last few paragraphs, therefore, do act in the ways ascribed to them, though our limited faculties are at present, perhaps forever, incapable of weighing their immediate, still more their ultimate consequences. But our inability to assign definite values to these causes of the disturbance of natural arrangements is not a reason for ignoring the existence of such causes in any general view of the relations between man and nature, and we are never justified in assuming a force to be insignificant because its measure is unknown, or even because no physical effect can now be traced to it as its origin. The collection of phenomena must precede the analysis of them, and every new fact, illustrative of the action and reaction between humanity and the material world around it, is another step toward the determination of the great question, whether man is of material nature or above her.

WILLIAM MORRIS DAVIS (1850-1934)

So much has been written *by* William Morris Davis and *about* William Morris Davis that the business of writing anything more seems somewhat redundant. He was the author or co-author of more than 500 books and articles; he founded the Association of American Geographers and was three times its president; he lectured at the University of Berlin and the Sorbonne; and there is hardly an academic honor worth mentioning that Davis did not receive. Whether one, in retrospect, agrees with Davis' concepts of either geography or geomorphology, there can be no question that he dominated both these fields during his long career. Dynamic and convincing, Davis forcefully impressed his fellow scientists with the rationale of his thinking.

To the definition of geography Davis contributed the concept of "ontography," the study of the relationships between organic and inorganic life. This had no real currency beyond the first two decades of the century, and there were very few ontographic studies carried out — even by Davis. The idea could not compete with that of the relationship between man and his environment: except for limited periods, geography has been essentially anthropocentric. But Davis represented — admittedly in an exceptionally dynamic fashion — the trend toward the objective and measurable, and the physical aspects of place were more susceptible of this kind of treatment than were either "man" or "relationships."

"The Rational Element in Geography" [15]

Abundant conference and correspondence with teachers of all grades in recent years make it evident that the introduction of the "causal notion in geography," as McMurray has phrased it, is warmly welcomed wherever it its well under-

[15] "The Rational Element in Geography," William Morris Davis, *The National Geographic Magazine*, Vol. X, January, 1899, pp. 466-467.

stood. The traditional lists of capes are doubtless still memorized and recited in some schools, to the exclusion of examples involving explanation and correlation as elements of geographical study; but such schools do not rouse the pride of progressive superintendents. Enterprising teachers are constantly striving toward a more rational treatment of geography, and with every advance in their own understanding of its problems empirical statements are replaced by reasonable explanations in their teaching, much to the advantage of the scholars.

The two chief causes of the change now in rapid progress from an empirical to a rational geography originated outside of the limits of geography proper. One of the causes is the understanding of the evolution of land forms that has been contributed by geology; the other is the belief in the evolution of organic forms contributed by biology. To these must be added the better knowledge of meteorology through the application of physics to the study of the atmosphere, as well as the results of strictly geographical exploration of lands and seas; but all this is of secondary importance alongside of the revolution that has been worked by the acceptance of inorganic and organic evolution. The study of the earth in relation to man, as now illuminated, has become wonderfully more interesting at this end of the century than it was in Ritter's time in the beginning, and we may well believe that the explorations of the twentieth century will profit greatly by the more sympathetic appreciation of nature that geographers will then carry into the field.

"An Inductive Study of the Content of Geography" [16]

The Need of Comparing Opinions.—One of the objects to which this Association may well direct its attention is the nature of the whole subject of Geography, under whose broad shelter our individual studies are carried on. If we work only in view of our chosen field within the whole area of geogra-

[16] "An Inductive Study of the Content of Geography," W. M. Davis, *Bulletin of the American Geographical Society*, Vol. XXXVIII, No. 2, February, 1906, pp. 67-84.

phy, we lose something of breadth, although we may gain much in depth. Our work will become more serviceable to others if it is presented in such a manner that its relations to the whole subject are made clear. Not only so; we may often benefit ourselves by systematically setting forth the place of our individual studies in geography as a whole, for we may be thereby led to discover that the systematic sequence of parts is interrupted here and there by gaps, which can be filled by well-directed effort. We should, I think, all profit if in the presentation of papers at these meetings some attention were given to an exposition of the speaker's ideas concerning the part that his topic occupies in the whole subject; we should thus better appreciate our relations to each other; and this I hold to be important, for one of the manifest difficulties ahead of us is the possible lack of natural association and coherence between such topics as magnetic surveys of the ocean, the distribution of certain kinds of toads, and the deserts of eastern Persia. . . .

I am disposed to say that any statement is of geographical quality if it contains a reasonable relation between some inorganic element of the earth on which we live, acting as a control, and some fact concerning the existence or growth or behaviour or distribution of the earth's organic inhabitants, serving as a response; more briefly, some relation between an element of inorganic control and of organic response. The geographical quality of such a relation is all the more marked if the statement is presented in an explanatory form. There is, indeed, in this idea of a causal or explanatory relationship the most definite, if not the only, unifying principle that I can find in geography. All the more reason, then, that the principle should be recognized and acted upon by those who have the fuller development of geographical science at heart.

Geography as the Study of Location or of Distribution.—There still exists in some quarters a tendency to limit geography by definition to the study of location, leaving the study of all the things that are located to other subjects. There is so little support for this narrow view of the subject to be found in modern geographical books that it need not be further considered. Another and more widely-accepted definition treats geography as the science of distribution. This is particularly a British view of the subject, and at least one British geographer urges that the distributed things should not be regarded as belonging to geography at all; but his writings are broader than his definition. While location and distribution must always be important elements of geography, all geographical books give much attention to the nature of the things that are distributed, and all recent books give much weight to the relations in which the distributed things occur: hence relationship seems to me the primary principle of the two, and distribution takes a secondary rank. The thing must be known before its distribution can be serviceably studied. The division of the peoples of Europe into groups or nations in consequence of the division of Europe by gulfs and mountain ranges is a geographical relation, in which the unlikeness of the things distributed takes precedence over their distribution.

Indeed, if geography is only the science of distribution — that is, the regional aspect of other subjects — it would be hardly worth while to maintain the study of geography apart from that of the subjects whose regional aspect it considers. Moreover, if geography is defined simply as the science of distribution, then the distribution of anything at all is a fit subject for geographical study. Under such a definition the distribution of hypersthene andesite or of books of poetry would be part of our responsibility; but there is nowhere any indication that geographers feel responsible for the distribution of such things. Again, if distribution is given first rank, the regional or special occurrence of all sorts of things is thereby given so great an importance that an insufficient place would be left for the systematic consideration of geographical things; yet most books first present things of a kind together — that is, they present the subject systematically — before they take up the distributional or regional treatment of different kinds of things.

As a matter of fact, nearly every example that is presented in this essay as an example of a geographical relation might, if desired, be presented as an example of distribution; and nearly all statements of distribution may be turned around so that they shall enter into or constitute relations; hence the total content of geography would be much the same under either principle. The relations that could not be presented under the lead of distribution are those which are the same everywhere; but it seems to me rather arbitrary to include relations that vary from place to place, and to exclude relations that are world-wide in their uniform occurrence. For example, the composition of the atmosphere or of the ocean, always accepted as an appropriate matter for mention in elementary texts, deserves no place in geography, treated as the science of distribution, until the minute variations of composition from place to place are considered.

In any case, location and distribution are fundamental elements of geography, and maps of the lands and charts of the oceans are essential in its every chapter. In view of the importance of these elements, some are disposed to attach an undue value to surveying as a part of geography. But surveying properly belongs in geography about where writing belongs in literature; and if it is given higher rank the student may, by misfortune, turn his chief attention to the art of mapping instead of to a study of the things that are mapped.

Physiography and Ontography.—If the principle of explanatory relationship be adopted as a general guide to the content of geography, it follows that neither the inorganic nor the organic elements which enter into geographical relations are by themselves of a completely geographical quality; they gain that quality only when two or more of them are coupled in a relation of cause and effect, at least one element in the chain of causation being inorganic and one organic. When they are considered separately, but as if in preparation for an understanding of the causal relations in which they will be later presented in the study of geography proper, they may be considered sub-geographic; and then the inorganic elements may be called physicogeographic or physiographic; and the organic elements may be called ontographic. Common usage recognizes the first of these divisions, but not the second, as we shall see later. It is well to emphasize the clause, "as if in preparation for an understanding of the causal relations in which they will later be presented in the study of geography proper"; for many items which, under this proviso, are of physiographic or of ontographic quality, may under another proviso belong in other departments of knowledge.

Physiographic Matters.—This may be made plainer by citing particular cases in which a number of different topics, familiar from their occurrence in books on geography, will be seen to fall under other subjects when they enter into non-geographical relations. For example, the size and rotation of the earth and the general movements of the tides are undoubtedly physiographic elements, yet both may be treated appropriately under astronomy when they are considered in their relations to other planets. Sea-water, when regarded as a liquid compound which holds various salts in solution, may be studied properly by the chemist with regard to its composition; nevertheless sea-water, as the medium in which organic forms live, is an indispensable subject for physiographic inquiry. The horizontal strata of plateaus are a fit topic for geological investigation, as regards their origin and history; but they are no less a subject for physiographic investigation as affecting present form. It, therefore, seems impossible to determine, merely by a consideration of the thing studied, whether it belongs to physiography or not.

A given object may belong under several different sciences, and may be treated in text-books on different subjects; it is the relation into which the object enters that determines its place.

There are, however, certain inorganic topics, commonly found in geographical books, which seldom, if ever, enter into relations with organic topics, and which would, therefore, under the strict application of the principle of relationships, be ruled out of physiography, and thus out of geography also. Such are cirrus clouds and haloes, the crevasses and blue veins of glaciers, and the polar flattening of the earth. Nevertheless, most or all of these topics will probably hold their places in books on physiography, because they serve to complete the picture of the whole earth as the home of life. In any case, little is gained by a very strict or over-logical application of a useful principle of classification in a problem such as we are considering.

Ontographic Matters.—The determination of the science under which a thing belongs by means of the relations into which the thing enters is an even more important guide in ontography than is physiography. For example, one may read in a certain text-book of geography that all forms of life consume food. In so far as the assimilation of food and the organs by which it is accomplished are concerned, the consumption of food belongs under physiology; but the consumption of food is an ontographic matter in so far as it brings an organism into contact with the rest of the world and thus causes it to enter into geographical relations. Commercial geography is largely concerned with relations that grow out of this element of ontography. Water is essential in organic processes of many kinds. This is, again, a physiological matter, if it is examined with reference to the processes of circulation; but it is ontographic when it is found to lead to a relation with the sources of water supply; villages gathered around deep wells on the chalk uplands of northwestern France are examples of the geographic relation thus brought about.

Plants and animals tend to diffuse themselves or to be diffused over the earth. This is a fundamental fact, usually associated with the study of biology; but the limits of diffusion and in many cases the means of diffusion are determined by physiographic controls, hence the tendency to diffusion is an ontographic matter.

The need experienced by all forms of life to secure food, already instanced, leads to many other relations than those of commercial geography. The need of food is satisfied without going in search of it if the food is contained in a moving medium that surrounds the organism; hence those organisms that live chiefly upon food contained in one or the other of the two great mobile envelopes of the earth, the atmosphere or the hydrosphere, are often rooted or fixed: the air or water currents carry the needed food to the waiting plant or animal — and this is surely too important a geographical relation to be omitted from a broad consideration of our subject. Other organisms take advantage of the currents of air or water to be passively carried about by them, taking their food when they happen to come upon it. If they are land-dwellers, they are so small that they can easily be wafted about by the winds; if they are dwellers in water, they may gain greater size by assuming about the same specific gravity as that denser medium, so as to float easily in its perpetual currents. Still a third class of organisms move of their own volition; and in connection with these there are all manner of geographic relations. Some of them involve the development of wings, whereby motion can be effected in the comparatively unsustaining air, as in the case of many insects and birds, of a few mammals, and formerly of some reptiles; some involve the development of fins to produce motion in the sustaining water. These examples are as good illustrations of organic responses to inorganic controls as are the canoes and the steamships of uncivilized and of civilized man.

It follows from the preceding paragraph that the more closely our standard geographical material is examined, the more clearly it appears that its ontographic as well as its physiographic elements may fall into other sciences when they are treated in other relations; and that they become most distinctly geographic when they enter into the causal relations of the kind set forth above. The rise and fall of the tides is a physiographic matter when it is seen to determine the distribution of certain forms of life, such as barnacles, or to influence the availability of harbours for the entrance of shipping; the occurrence of coal is a physiographic matter when it is found to influence the industry of a district and the commerce between nations; the small sizes of spores, pollen, and germs is an ontographic matter when it is seen to be related to their transportation by the thin air; the sensitiveness of organisms to temperature changes is an ontographic matter when it is shown to affect the distribution of plants and animals over the earth. Yet all these matters may be treated with entire justice under other sciences than geography. It is, therefore, to my reading, of capital importance in determining whether a statement is of geographical or subgeographical nature to know how far it constitutes or enters into causal relations of the kinds that have been here considerd.

Is Ontography a Part of Geography?—It is perfectly true that many of the illustrations just given are not commonly regarded as belonging under geography; but it seems to me that their exclusion is illogical and arbitrary. They are practically all to be found in certain standard geographical works, and many more might be taken from such books as Ratzel's *Anthropogeographie* and Beddard's *Zoogeography*. The general principle by which one should be guided in determining the relevancy of such matters is as follows: If a certain relation between an inorganic control and a responding organism is a geographic relation, then all similar relations are also geographic. For example, a well-known text-book makes the statement that water-plants are supported by the relatively dense medium in which they grow, and hence do not need strong woody stalks such as many land-plants have. This is an excellent example of a geographical fact: it involves a relation between an organic growth and an inorganic medium. But the flight of birds, the small size of germs, the essential agreement between the specific gravity of fish and of water, the universal habit of breathing oxygen, all involve similar relations. The first example seems to me undeniably geographic; the others are no less so. To exclude the latter from geography while including the former would be to set very arbitrary limits to our subject.

It may, perhaps, be objected that flight and breathing are processes of too ancient origin to be considered as geographical; but inasmuch as they are maintained into the present time, by inheritance through persistent conditions of environment, they have the same right to a place under geography as is enjoyed by such examples as the prevalence of the fishing industry on the Dalmatian coast, or the custom of the French farmers on the chalk uplands of living in compact villages; for these habits, also, are not independently originated by each man who follows them, but are continued by inheritance through persistent conditions of environment.

There are certain matters, frequently encountered in textbooks of physical geography, which belong better, as it seems to me, under ontographic relations. Such are the distribution of plants and animals, and the races of man. The association of such topics with physical geography is probably the result of conceiving all the rest of the subject as contained under political geography. The contrast of physical and political conditions may serve well enough in elementary books, where the distribution and behaviour of man are the chief subjects in political geography, and where plants and animals are therefore thrown in with physical geography; but in the more advanced and general treatment of the subject such an arrangement is not satisfactory. It does, however, seem legitimate to introduce as often as desired ontographic responses in a physiographic text, in order to show at once the kind of response that certain controls call forth, and thus to impress the fact that the physiographic items are really related to ontographic items: a similar introduction of physiographic items is appropriate in chapters on ontography. This practice is followed by certain writers.

There are three definite positions and many indefinite positions that might be taken with respect to the attention that should be given by geographers to organic considerations. The narrowest position limits geography almost entirely to the inorganic features of the earth — that is, to physical geography or physiography. This is the view of geography held by some historians, who take unto themselves practically all the human element that is so commonly encountered in political geography. An intermediate position would include physiography and the more manifest relations into which it enters with various forms of life, and particularly with man, but would not accept responsibility as to the less manifest responses of various living things. This seems to be the position taken by many geographers, more or less consciously. The third position would treat ontography as thoroughly as physiography, and would search for all the geographic relations of physiographic controls and ontographic responses. This is certainly the broadest of the three positions, being, as many would feel, too broad, and involving too much overlapping upon other subjects. For my own part, there seems to be so manifest a necessity of gaining a responsible knowledge of ontography, at least of elementary ontography, before geography proper can be successfully treated, that ontography should come to be regarded as a part of it. The analytical and inductive methods of this paper, therefore, lead me to adopt the third position; and I believe that this position is essentially consistent with the opinion of writers who, like Ratzel and Reclus, have cultivated the most advanced or matured stage of geographical science.

The Subdivisions of Geography.—It is but natural that the different phases of human geography should have been more fully developed than the other branches of our science. Political geography, frequently overrunning civics, economics and history, has long been familiar as an elementary subject; but with us it has seldom been carried into the higher reaches of education. Commercial geography is rapidly gaining an important place in our schools, and is meeting the danger of becoming almost as empirical as the old-time lists of products of the several States. Biogeography has several parts. Anthropogeography, as expanded by Ratzel, seems destined to become an important subject in the universities, because of the greater insight that one gains through it into history. Zoogeography and phytogeography are, in my opinion, as a rule, too strictly limited to facts of distribution alone; these divisions of the subject would be expanded so as to include for animals and plants a consideration of what would correspond to the political and commercial geography of man. Palaeogeography is occasionally treated, but it must always be a fragmentary subject, because it is based on fragmentary records; it will, however, be better treated by geologists in proportion as they have had geographical training.

The growth of explanatory treatment, which makes so characteristic a difference between the content of geography in books of a hundred years ago and of today, is chiefly due to the different amounts of general knowledge in stock then and now, and consequently to the different philosophies then and now prevailing. The subject has thus gained greatly in strength, in disciplinary value and in living interest. At the same time, geography has come to cultivate more and more — some would say, to trespass more and more — upon the fields that are also cultivated by other subjects. If the trade-winds are not simply described as to region of occurrence, direction of blowing, weather conditions therein prevailing, and so on, but are also explained as parts of an extensive convectional circulation between equator and poles, modified by the deflective effect of the earth's rotation, all this explanatory matter has a strong flavor of physics. If the occurrence of plants of a certain kind in a given region is not merely asserted, but is shown to be the result of climatic conditions to which the plant responds owning to its sensitiveness to temperature and moisture, this closely resembles certain chapters of botany, and the same may be said regarding the relation of animal distribution to zoology. If the boundary of a state, the location of a city, or the industry of a district is rationally explained instead of empirically stated, the explanation is of a kind likely to be found in books on history and economics. Shall we, then, in view of this, relinquish explanatory treatment to other subjects and content ourselves with empirical statements? No. Duplication is unavoidable; and, moreover, it is reciprocal. The historian, as well as the botanist and the zoologist, must borrow from the geographer all manner of facts regarding location, extent, distribution, climate, form, movements, products, populations, and so on; the geologist can hardly make a step into the realm of the past without having made preparatory study of the present. Overlapping and duplication are unavoidable. We must each of us try as far as possible to concentrate upon his own subject; but we must at the same time borrow and quote with the utmost freedom from any other subject that will give us aid in the consideration of our own.

The Practical Value of Defining the Content of a Subject.— In occasional conferences with some of our members on such questions as have been treated in this address, I have gained the impression that they attached relatively little value to abstract considerations, and that it sufficed them to go on with their work without inquiring particularly into the general content of the subject under which it belonged, without attempting to develop what may perhaps be called the more philosophical view of the subject as a whole. There was a time when I shared this indifference to abstract inquiry — a time when I was, as it were, overwhelmed with the great quantity and variety of material with which I had to make myself more or less familiar, and when there seemed to be no more need than there was occasion of bringing it all under an orderly and systematic scheme. But that time is now a good many years ago, and since then I have passed out of the stage of life in which, we are assured, our original work is to be completed, and have entered well upon the later stage in which the contemplation and arrangement of work previously done is, we were told, more attractive than the accomplishment of new work. It is, perhaps, for some such reason that this opportunity for addressing the Association has been devoted to the reading of an essay on the content of geography as a whole, rather than to a report on more concrete matters, such as certain recent observations in South Africa. Nevertheless, I am persuaded that there is a practical value in abstract considerations such as I have presented, even for younger men, and that if a general scheme of work in accordance with some broad and philosophical view of one's chosen science is formulated by a younger geographer early in his career, he will profit greatly from it; for he will thus be led more surely and directly to detect all the facts that are pertinent to any inquiry he may enter upon. Such a scheme is always open to modification as experience increases. If the geographer undertakes field study, as I hope he may, either at home, where there is still plenty of field work to do, or abroad, where there is still more to be done, it will serve him well to know as definitely as possible the essential quality of the work before him. If he wishes to become an all-round geographer and to give a thorough geographical account of the region of his field work, he will be greatly aided in keeping his eyes open to the facts before him by bearing in mind the systematic content of the science as a whole, a part of which he proposes to study in the region he has selected.

The cultural landscape is fashioned out of a natural landscape by a culture group. Culture is the agent, the natural area is the medium, the cultural landscape the result. Under the influence of a given culture, itself changing through time, the landscape undergoes development, passing through phases, and probably reaching ultimately the end of its cycle of development. With the introduction of a different, that is, alien culture, a rejuvenation of the cultural landscape sets in, or a new landscape is superimposed on remnants of an older one. The natural landscape is of course of fundamental importance, for it supplies the materials out of which the cultural landscape is formed. The shaping force, however, lies in the culture itself. Within the wide limits of the physical equipment of area lie many possible choices for man, as Vidal never grew weary of pointing out. This is the meaning of adaptation, through which, aided by those suggestions which man has derived from nature, perhaps by an imitative process, largely subconscious, we get the feeling of harmony between the human habitation and the landscape into which it so fittingly blends. But these, too, are derived from the mind of man, not imposed by nature, and hence are cultural expressions.

The morphologic discipline enables the organization of the fields of geography as positive science. A good deal of the meaning of area lies beyond scientific regimentation. The best geography has never disregarded the aesthetic qualities of landscape, to which we know no approach other than the subjective. Humboldt's "physiognomy," Banse's "soul," Volz' "rhythm," Gradmann's "harmony" of landscape, all lie beyond science. They seem to have discovered a symphonic quality in the contemplation of the areal scene, proceeding from a full novitiate in scientific studies and yet apart therefrom. To some, whatever is mystical is an abomination. Yet it is significant that there are others, and among them some of the best, who believe, that having observed widely and charted diligently, there yet remains a quality of understanding at a higher plane which may not be reduced to formal process.

J. RUSSELL SMITH (1874-1966)

Smith had an enviable reputation in the world of geography. He was admired as a scholar and loved for the spirited and always fascinating style he brought to his writing. No other American geographer of the period contributed so much to the development of economic geography. The article which is included here reflects Smith's philosophy of geography, but more than that it reflects his philosophy of science, of education, and, in fact, of life. For J. Russell Smith put his heart into his writings. Perhaps this is why he never wrote a dull or sterile sentence.

Economic Geography and Its Relation to Economic Theory and Higher Education [17]

Five years ago Stanley Hall, adopting a figure from European politics, called Geography the sick man of the curriculum. The charge is well founded, for it certainly has lagged behind other important subjects in being rationalized and receiving due recognition of its importance. In this latter respect it has not yet come into its inheritance. It has but lately emerged from the period in which its study consisted in the deadly exercises of memorizing in a blind way lists of cities, rivers, capes, and boundaries, and the acquisition of unexplained facts concerning the distribution of various classes of things.

The theory of evolution has paved the way for modern geography, which has had to await the development, spread, and general acceptance of the revolutionizing truths commonly associated with the name of Darwin. Organisms have been found to be capable of influence by their surroundings. Life is progressive because the organism responds to its environment and the environment changes. Here is a vast field for study. This environment, and its component elements, the resulting organic responses, constitute the field in which geography has worked. The field has by no means been covered, but in some directions the publications of geographers indicate that they have reached or passed boundaries.

Anthropogeography — the geography of man — is a wide field, and if taken up systematically it might be necessary to give, theoretically at least, as large a part of the field to the

---

[17] 'Economic Geography and Its Relation to Economic Theory and Higher Education," J. Russell Smith, *Bulletin of the American Geographical Society*, Vol. XXXIX, No. 8, August, 1907.

savage as to the civilized man. Indeed, we possibly find a greater variety of conditions of life among the savage than among the civilized peoples. But Economic Geography partakes of the definition of Economics, and it comprises those geographic influences that affect the economic status of man. This shifts the emphasis from the savage to the civilized, because the latter has, in the greater complexities of his economic status, the results of the same geographic influences as the savage, and also ten or twenty times more geographic influences than has his primitive brother. The emphasis is still further placed upon civilized rather than savage man, because we, the students, are continually thinking of the lands of the savage in the terms of the civilization which will probably soon come to them. We have small interest in the savage or his mode of life except to make him a matter of record and then civilize or replace him. Economic geography, therefore, neglects the savage, and devotes itself to the study of the physical environment of civilization.

We have received from nineteenth-century biology the sweeping truth that organisms are what their environment has made them. We believe this to be true in the case of monkeys, fish, and forest trees, but just how much it means for man, for races, and for civilization we have only begun to realize. If it be true that details of our physical make-up, our personal qualities, racial qualities, our industries, and, through them, our social and political conditions and institutions, are all profoundly shaped by our physical environment, it would appear to be one of the plainest of things that all processes of education should give great attention to the study of the economic environment in all its phases. We are not yet doing so, but there is rapid progress in that direction.

Economic geography is the description and interpretation of lands in terms of their usefulness to humanity. Its net result is the understanding of the relationship between the people of a district and their physical environment, just as the manager of a great steel company understands the relation of a blast furnace to the rest of his organization, or, as a physician understands the relation of the lungs or stomach to the general health of the human body. This involves a large amount of concrete economic information. Anything affecting the economic status through the environment, or the environment through the people, has a place. The field is wider than that taken by the writers of commercial geographies. The personal equipment for the economic geographer is the ability to detect and understand factors that produce an economic effect and to discern an approximate measure of that effect. When we consider the dependence of social sciences, of industry, and of human welfare upon the proper understanding of the land in which we live, it seems surprising that this study has not already reached greater prominence in our educational systems. This surprise is all the greater because of the pedagogical advantages offered by a study of economic geography. Students are put to study foreign languages and geometry for the resulting mental discipline. Yet economic geography dips continuously into the natural sciences, and is an unending series of causes and effects whose comprehension involves the best kind of mental discipline and horizon-broadening along with the acquisition of knowledge of prime usefulness.

A satisfactory understanding of the economic conditions of any region involves a wide understanding of human activity of an industrial character and the ability to recognize resources. Industry is a result of geographic conditions — a kind of geographic index. Resources and industry go hand in hand; yet it is necessary to be able to appreciate them separately. A resource is something which may under possible conditions be made into a utility. The first thing the economic geographer desires to know about any region, even an uninhabited isle, is, what are its resources? Second, what are the means under which the resources can be converted into utilities? Third, what is the likelihood of the changes coming to pass?

We can only recognize resources by knowing how and under what conditions industry may use them. The progress of invention is constantly giving new processes, which produce new industrial possibilities and make resources where before there was, in an economic sense, but a desert waste. The application of the basic process to American steel-making enabled us to use the phosphatic ores of Michigan and converted the barren shores of Lake Superior into the world's greatest ore region. The discovery of some similar process for reducing titanic ores may shift the industry to the province of Ontario, if reports of titanic ore deposits there are well founded. The application of American agricultural methods to rice-growing may make this country the greatest rice exporter. The economic results coming from the use of a successful cotton-picking machine are difficult to anticipate. The cotton gin is apparently the economic key to the political history of the United States from 1820-1870.

In this connection the bearing of technical possibility is often much overstated, and lands are spoken of as having possibilities which could only be realized by the introduction of devices and practices which mature thought will show us must be foreign to the people of the land in question for decades to come.

Another phase of any estimate of resources and the industries that may arise from them is the influence of industries elsewhere. Alaska has — so it is claimed — agricultural possibilities quite as good as Finland, an agricultural country with several million inhabitants; but Alaska will not be utilized to any large extent while the American people have cheap, unused land in the United States. We have on our Atlantic and Gulf shores much more swamp and marsh land than Holland has reclaimed; and it will be more productive because of our warmer climate. But this resource, like Alaska, will remain idle so long as good land in Virginia and the South continues to have its present almost nominal value.

A knowledge of resource and of industry must be reinforced by some knowledge of the industrial qualities and equipment of peoples. They vary greatly. How do they vary and how has it come about? Why is it that the eloquent, intelligent, and lordly Indian could not be made to work either by Spanish master or English conqueror, and has as a consequence retreated before the white man's advance like the wild animals of the forest, while the less lordly and, probably, less intelligent Negro labours, bears burdens, and survives in our midst? I shall not discuss here the probable origin of the work quality in races, but it is probable that this trait of the white and yellow man comes as slowly as civilization itself; and being essential to any economic advance, it is practically the basis of and coincident with civilization. Yet, entirely overlooking this quality, millions of Americans enthusiastically voted for a policy of extending to another race, the Filipinos, the blessings of American liberty and civilization, and they expected these blessings to be fitted on in a few years, like styles in clothing upon the person, or sewers, trolleys, and telephones upon their towns. The American voter is beginning to realize that the Filipino changes slowly and the economist and economic geographer must consider well the qualities of peoples as well as the qualities of land and climate and the possibilities from technical improvements. This human factor was rather harshly recognized by an eminent American engineer, who, in reference to a comparison of the number of the population in one of our Western States with that of one of the independent nations of the world, said, "But how many of those people does it take to make an American?"

In gauging the usefulness of lands there is always a very considerable amount of knowledge that can be quickly inferred by one possessed of a knowledge of some of the factors in economic geography. Geographic and climatic types are often world-wide in their application. If we recognize the type we instantly know a number of resulting conditions. There is a certain amount of uniformity about flood-plains and deltas, plateaux, and mountains. Certain soils bar certain products. Rainfall, by the mere statement of its amount, may half describe a country. Below a slightly varying minimum there can be no general tilling of the soil and no forest, only pasture. Beyond sixty inches per year the successful growing of Temperate-Zone grain is difficult, because of too much rain; but both grass and forest grow with great profusion. The seasonal distribution of rainfall is, by its mere mention, as descriptive as its amount. A region with a winter maximum and a dry summer like southern California and Italy differs profoundly in its economic activities from a region of abundant summer rain like Louisiana and South China. A single statement may sometimes be as descriptive as a chapter. A student was recently reporting on the resources of a certain district and in the same paragraph mentioned good agricultural lands and salt as furnished by a lake. A salt lake implies an inland drainage basin, which implies excess of evaporation over rainfall, and a resulting aridity which rarely, if ever, permits agriculture without irrigation. A proper appreciation of the significance of the salt lake would have shown the student that his statement about agriculture could not be founded in fact if his salt statement were correct.

A knowledge of the concepts and facts involved in economic geography is essential to a satisfactory grasp of many questions in Political and Social Science. The progress of law is in part but a record of attempts at solving problems growing out of geographic and industrial situations. A good example of this is the recent discovery of our lack of any suitable irrigation law, and the many perplexing situations that have resulted from the rapid attempts to adapt agriculture and then law to geographical conditions strange to our race. The political scientist — and we need one — who will enlighten us upon irrigation law must be as familiar with agricultural processes in our trans-Missouri region as is the orange-grower of California or the alfalfa-grower of Colorado, and he needs a much wider knowledge of the economic geography of the region.

Political economy, or economics, deals much with psychology and abstract thought, but also with the material world, and therein it also depends largely upon a background of economic geography. A recent successful text-book on Economics says it is a "study of men earning a living" or "the study of the material world," etc. "The science of wealth" is a brief definition that was much used in my college days. A very successful recent book states that economics "considers all of the circumstances which affect the production and distribution," etc., of wealth, and the book then unfolds a two and one-half page description of the United States of America, and nineteen paragraphs are devoted to a sketch of the development of our industries. All of the above-mentioned difficulties involve the idea that the student should begin the study of economics with a knowledge of the world in which we live and make our living — that he should have some mastery of the contents of economic geography as indicated in this paper. The present science of economics may give students an appreciation of the economic aspects of many human devices, practices, and institutions, but it largely takes for granted, and leaves untaught, the ability to appreciate the remaining part of the field — namely, the economic aspects of the environment in which we live and think. As yet this important preparation is, with the exception of grammar-school geography, commonly left to the chance information picked up by a student whose powers of observation in this field have rarely been trained. Without the preparation of economic geography, the courses in economics are, to a considerable extent, shafts without pedestals, and much of the good result may be missed because the student lacks the concrete economic facts with which to clothe the skeletons of theory. I submit, therefore, to the economists that they would do well to see that their students are equipped with the concrete information coming from economic geography before taking up the more abstract social sciences.

ELLEN CHURCHILL SEMPLE (1863-1932)

Miss Semple was without question the outstanding woman geographer of her time — and perhaps of all time. Her interpretation of Ratzel's geographic concepts had a tremendous impact on American geographic thought. Perhaps one should not use the past tense, because Miss Semple is still associated, in American minds, with the concept of environmental determinism — an idea which is anathema to most contemporary geographers. Perhaps the inclusion of a sample of her work in this book will tend to dispel the pre-judgment which might turn new students away from her writings. As Miss Semple pointed out, she "speaks of geographic factors and influences, shuns the word geographic determinant, and speaks with extreme caution of geographic control." She wrote with a fluid and classic style unmatched by present-day geographers; she was obviously profoundly learned; and many of her ideas are by no means outmoded. American geography owes much of its character to her influence.

Influences of Geographic Environment [18]

The present book, as originally planned over seven years ago, was to be a simplified paraphrase or restatement of the principles embodied in Friedrich Ratzel's *Anthropo-Geographie*. . . . However, the writer's own investigation revealed the fact that Ratzel's principles of anthropo-geography did not constitute a complete, well-proportioned system. Some aspects of the subject had been developed exhaustively, these of course the most important; but others had been treated inadequately, others were merely a hint or an inference, and yet others were represented by an hiatus. It became necessary, therefore, to work up certain important themes with a thoroughness commensurate with their significance, to reduce the scale of others, and to fill up certain gaps with original contributions to the scene. Always it was necessary to clarify the original statement, where that was adhered to, and to throw it into the concrete form of expression demanded by the Anglo-Saxon mind.

One point more. The organic theory of society and state permeates the *Anthropo-Geographie,* because Ratzel formulated his principles at a time when Herbert Spencer exercised a wide influence upon European thought. This theory, now generally abandoned by sociologists, had to be eliminated from any restatement of Ratzel's system. Though it was applied in the original often in great detail, it stood there nevertheless rather as a scaffolding around the finished edifice; and the stability of the structure after this scaffolding is removed shows how extraneous to the whole it was. The theory performed, however, a great service in impressing Ratzel's mind with the life-giving connection between land and people.

The writer's own method of research has been to compare typical peoples of all races and all stages of cultural development, living under similar geographic conditions. If these

---

[18] *Influence of Geographic Environment,* E. C. Semple, pp. 1-14, 24-31. Henry Holt & Co., New York, 1911.

peoples of different ethnic stocks but similar environments manifested similar or related social, economic or historical development, it was reasonable to infer that such similarities were due to environment and not to race. Thus, by extensive comparison, the race factor in these problems of two unknown quantities was eliminated for certain large classes of social and historical phenomena.

The writer, moreover, has purposely avoided definitions, formulas, and the enunciation of hard-and-fast rules; and has refrained from any effort to delimit the field or define the relation of this new science of anthropo-geography to the older sciences. It is unwise to put tight clothes on a growing child. The eventual form and scope of the science, the definition and organization of its material must evolve gradually, after long years and many efforts of many workers in the field. The eternal flux of Nature runs through anthropogeography, and warns against precipitate or rigid conclusions. But its laws are none the less well founded because they do not lend themselves to mathematical finality of statement. For this reason the writer speaks of geographic factors and influences, shuns the word geographic determinant, and speaks with extreme caution of geographic control.

Man is a product of the earth's surface. This means not merely that he is a child of the earth, dust of her dust; but that the earth has mothered him, fed him, set him tasks, directed his thoughts, confronted him with difficulties that have strengthened his body and sharpened his wits, given him his problems of navigation or irrigation, and at the same time whispered hints for their solution. She has entered into his bone and tissue, into his mind and soul. On the mountain she has given him leg muscles of iron to climb the slope; along the coast she has left these weak and flabby, but given him instead vigorous development of chest and arm to handle his paddle or oar. In the river valley she attaches him to the fertile soil, circumscribes his ideas and ambitions by a dull round of calm, exacting duties, narrows his outlook to the cramped horizon of his farm. Up on the wind-swept plateaus, in the boundless stretch of the grasslands and the waterless tracts of the desert, where he roams with his flocks from pasture to pasture and oasis to oasis, where life knows much hardship but escapes the grind of drudgery, where the watching of grazing herd gives him leisure for contemplation, and the wide-ranging life a big horizon, his ideas take on a certain simplicity; religion becomes monotheism, God becomes one, unrivalled like the sand of the desert and the grass of the steppe, stretching on and on without break or change. Chewing over and over the cud of his simple belief as the one food of his unfed mind, his faith becomes fanaticism; his big spatial ideas, born of that ceaseless regular wandering, outgrow the land that bred them and bear their legitimate fruit in wide imperial conquests.

Man can no more be scientifically studied apart from the ground which he tills, or the land over which he travels, or the seas over which he trades, than polar bear or desert cactus can be understood apart from its habitat. Man's relations to his environment are infinitely more numerous and complex than those of the most highly organized plant or animal. So complex are they that they constitute a legitimate and necessary object of special study. The investigation which they receive in anthropology, ethnology, sociology and history is piecemeal and partial, limited as to the race, cultural development, epoch, country or variety of geographic conditions taken into account. Hence all these sciences, together with history so far as history undertakes to explain the causes of events, fail to reach a satisfactory solution of their problems largely because the geographic factor which enters into them all has not been thoroughly analyzed. Man has been so noisy about the way he has "conquered Nature," and Nature has been so silent in her persistent influence over man, that the geographic factor in the equation of human development has been overlooked.

In every problem of history there are two main factors, variously stated as heredity and environment, man and his geographic conditions, the internal forces of race and the external forces of habitat. Now the geographic element in the long history of human development has been operating strongly and operating persistently. Herein lies its importance. It is a stable force. It never sleeps. This natural environment, this physical basis of history, is for all intents and purposes immutable in comparison with the other factor in the problem — shifting, plastic, progressive, retrogressive man.

Geographical environment, through the persistence of its influence, acquires peculiar significance. Its effect is not restricted to a given historical event or epoch, but, except when temporarily met by some strong counteracting force, tends to make itself felt under varying guise in all succeeding history. It is the permanent element in the shifting fate of races. Islands show certain fundamental points of agreement which can be distinguished in the economic, ethnic and historical development of England, Japan, Melanesian Fiji, Polynesian New Zealand, and pre-historic Crete. The great belt of deserts and steppes extending across the Old World gives us a vast territory of rare historical uniformity. From time immemorial they have borne and bred tribes of wandering herdsmen; they have sent out the invading hordes who, in successive waves of conquest, have overwhelmed the neighboring river lowlands of Eurasia and Africa. They have given birth in turn to Scythians, Indo-Aryans, Avars, Huns, Saracens, Tartars and Turks, as to the Tuareg tribes of the Sahara, the Sudanese and Bantu folk of the African grasslands. But whether these various peoples have been Negroes, Hamites, Semites, Indo-Europeans or Mongolians, they have always been pastoral nomads. . . .

Climatic influences are persistent, often obdurate in their control. Arid regions permit agriculture and sedentary life only through irrigation. The economic prosperity of Egypt today depends as completely upon the distribution of the Nile waters as in the days of the Pharaohs. The mantle of the ancient Egyptian priest has fallen upon the modern British engineer. Arctic explorers have succeeded only by imitating the life of the Eskimos, adopting their clothes, food, fuel, dwellings, mode of travel. . . .

The more the comparative method is applied to the study of history — and this includes a comparison not only of different countries, but also of successive epochs in the same country — the more apparent becomes the influence of the soil in which humanity is rooted, the more permanent and necessary is that influence seen to be. Geography's claim to make scientific investigation of the physical conditions of historical events is then vindicated. "Which was the first, geography or history?" asks Kant. And then comes his answer: "Geography lies at the basis of history." The two are inseparable. History takes for its field of investigation human events in various periods of time; anthropo-geography studies existence in various regions of terrestrial space. But all historical development takes place on the earth's surface, and therefore is more or less molded by its geographic setting. Geography, to reach accurate conclusions, must compare the operation of its factors in different historical periods and at different stages of cultural development. It therefore regards history in no small part as a succession of geographical factors embodied in events. . . .

The study of physical environment as a factor in history was unfortunately brought into disrepute by extravagant and ill-founded generalization, before it became the object of investigation according to modern scientific methods. And even today principles advanced in the name of anthropo-geography are often superficial, inaccurate, based upon a body of data too limited as to space and time, or couched in terms of unqualified statement which exposes them to criticism or refutation. Investigators in this field, moreover, are prone to get a squint in their eye that makes them see one geographic factor to the exclusion of the rest; whereas it belongs to the very nature of physical environment to combine a whole group of influences, working all at the same time under the law of the resolution of forces. In this plexus of influences, some operate in one direction and some in another; now one loses its beneficent effect like a medicine long used or a garment outgrown; another waxes in power, reinforced by a new geographic factor which has been released from dormancy by the expansion of the known world, or the progress of invention and of human development.

These complex geographic influences cannot be analyzed and their strength estimated except from the standpoint of evolution. That is one reason these half-baked geographic principles rest heavy on our mental digestion. They have been formulated without reference to the all-important fact that the geographic relations of man, like his social and political organization, are subject to the law of development. Just as the embryo state found in the primitive Saxon tribes has passed through many phases in attaining the political character of the present British Empire, so every stage in this maturing growth has been accompanied or even preceded by a steady evolution of the geographic relations of the English people. . . .

Skepticism as to the effect of geographic conditions upon human development is apparently justifiable, owing to the multiplicity of the underlying causes and the difficulty of distinguishing between stronger and weaker factors on the one hand, as between permanent and temporary effects on the other. We see the result, but find it difficult to state the equation producing the result. But the important thing is to avoid seizing upon one or two conspicuous geographic elements in the problem and ignoring the rest. The physical environment of a people consists of all the natural conditions to which they have been subjected, not merely a part. Geography admits no single blanket theory.

The root of geographic influence often runs far underground before coming to the surface, to sprout into some flowering growth; and to trace this back to its parent stem is the necessary but not easy task of the geographer.

The complexity of this problem does not end here. The modification of human development by environment is a natural process; like all other natural processes, it involves the cumulative effects of causes operating imperceptibly but persistently through vast periods of time. Slowly and deliberately does geography engrave the sub-titles to a people's history. Neglect of this time element in the consideration of geographic influences accounts equally for many an exaggerated assertion and denial of their power. A critic undertakes to disprove modification through physical environment by showing that it has not produced tangible results in the last fifty or five hundred years. This attitude recalls the early geologists, whose imaginations could not conceive the vast ages necessary in a scientific explanation of geologic phenomena. . . .

The history and culture of a people embody the effects of previous habitats and of their final environment; but this environment means something more than local geographic conditions. It involves influences emanating from far beyond the borders. No country, no continent, no sea, mountain or river is restricted to itself in the influence which it either exercises or receives. The history of Austria cannot be understood merely from Austrian ground. Austrian territory is part of the Mediterranean hinterland, and therefore has been linked historically with Rome, Italy, and the Adriatic. It is a part of the upper Danube Valley and therefore shares much of its history with Bavaria and Germany, while the lower Danube has linked it with the Black Sea, Greece, the Russian steppes, and Asia. The Asiatic Hungarians have pushed forward their ethnic boundary nearly to Vienna. The Austrian capital has seen the warring Turks beneath its walls, and shapes its foreign policy with a view to the relative strength of the Sultan and the Czar.

The earth is an inseparable whole. Each country or sea is physically and historically intelligible only as a portion of that whole. Currents and wind-systems of the oceans modify the climate of the nearby continents, and direct the first daring navigations of their peoples. The alternating monsoons of the Indian Ocean guided Arab merchantmen from ancient times back and forth between the Red Sea and the Malabar coast of India. The Equatorial Current and the northeast trade-wind carried the timid ships of Columbus across the Atlantic to America. The Gulf Stream and the prevailing westerlies later gave English vessels the advantage on the return voyage. Europe is a part of the Atlantic Coast. This is a fact so significant that the North Atlantic has become a European sea. The United States also is a part of the Atlantic coast: this is the dominant fact of American history. China forms a section of the Pacific rim. This is the fact back of the geographic distribution of Chinese emigration to Annam, Tonkin, Siam, Malacca, the Philippines, East Indies, Borneo, Australia, Hawaiian Islands, the Pacific Coast States, British Columbia, the Alaskan coasts southward from Bristol Bay in Bering Sea, Ecuador and Peru.

As the earth is one, so is humanity. Its unity of species points to some degree of communication through a long prehistoric past. Universal history is not entitled to the name unless it embraces all parts of the earth and all peoples, whether savage or civilized. To fill the gaps in the written record it must turn to ethnology and geography, which by tracing the distribution and movements of primitive peoples can often reconstruct the most important features of their history.

Anthropo-geographic problems are never simple. They must all be viewed in the long perspective of evolution and the historical past. They require allowance for the dominance of different geographic factors at different periods, and for a possible range of geographic influences wide as the earth itself. In the investigator they call for pains-taking analysis and, above all, an open mind.

ELLSWORTH HUNTINGTON (1876-1947)

During his professional lifetime, Huntington was undoubted one of the most widely known of all American geographers. He wrote a fantastic number of highly readable books, from *The Pulse of Asia* (1907) to *Mainsprings of Civilization* (1945), in addition to literally hundreds of articles, published in scholarly journals, popular magazines, Sunday supplements — in fact, almost anywhere that provided an audience for his ideas. Huntington was a clear, incisive thinker and a brilliant writer. He limited himself to the study of two broad ideas — climatic influence and natural selection. His position as Research Associate at Yale freed him completely from the classroom and made research and writing his full time occupation. In a sense the portions of the article that follow do not represent the kinds of ideas that one usually associates with Huntington. And in large part, it is true, Huntington did not concern himself with the nature of geography. One might say, then, that the ideas that follow are more typical of 1913 than they are of Ellsworth Huntington.

The New Science of Geography[19]

Geography, although perhaps the oldest of the sciences, has changed so completely in recent years that its true nature is not commonly understood, especially in America. Like every other science, it includes three phases or stages, each of which is characterized by a special mental process. The first, or empirical stage, is concerned merely with the gathering of a great body of unrelated facts. In the second, or systematic stage, these facts are classified and arranged in definite categories; while the third, or explanatory stage, is devoted to the explanation of the facts and to the determination of the laws which govern them. To these may be added the predictive stage, in which the laws of the explanatory stage are used to predict future occurrence; but with this we are not now concerned.

No one of the latter stages can exist without all its predecessors, and in a mature science the processes of gathering, systematizing, and explaining go on side by side. For example, students of botany fall into three categories: plant-gatherers, whose chief joy is to find a new fern or alga; systematists, who laboriously describe and classify what others find; and true botanists, who use the work of their co-laborers as the basis for the discovery of new laws or of new applications of old laws.

The degree of interest possessed by these various stages varies greatly in different sciences. In most branches of knowledge, bare facts and their systematic classification are of no particular interest except to the specialist. The world at large is concerned chiefly with general laws or practical applications.

In the science of geography, the laws are no less interesting than in . . . any other branch of science, but this is rarely recognized. Attention is commonly concentrated on mere facts instead of on the laws which govern them. One reason for this is that the laws, dealing as they do with life as well as

---

19 "The New Science of Geography," Ellsworth Huntington, *The Bulletin of the American Geographical Society*, Vol. XLV, No. 9, September, 1913.

matter, are in the highest degree complex and difficult to frame. Another reason is that the facts themselves are of great interest, even apart from the laws. . . .

Because the facts in themselves are entertaining, there has been a failure to realize the necessity of coordinating them and finding out their laws. Geographers themselves have fostered this idea. The majority of them have failed to apprehend that the mere collection of facts is not science. Moreover, because of the vast number of highly interesting geographical phenomena scattered all over the world, every traveler has felt impelled to gather his own little sheaf. Having published his observations, he has considered himself a geographer, although with no more claim to the title than has the gatherer of a bunch of wild flowers to be called a botanist. Genuine geographers have rebelled against this invasion of their province by men of no adequate training. Yet instead of directing their own energies to the patient sifting of facts, in order to discover laws, they have zealously devoted themselves to mapping new portions of the earth's surface. Their work has been done scientifically and is of great value, but it belongs to the first, or empirical, state of the science. In their zeal for this work, they have often forgotten the other phases of the subject. Thus, although thousands of men, both travelers and map-makers, have been called geographers, only a handful have given their lives to the work of systematic classication, and still fewer to the final explanatory stage of the science. This, more than anything else, explains the common but fallacious idea that geography is purely descriptive and lacks the qualities of real science.

. . . Geography is primarily the science of the distribution of phenomena on the earth's surface; maps are its foundation, just as systematic floras are the foundations of botany. The geographer deals with everything whose distribution can be shown upon a map, whether it be incised meanders, chinook winds, yellow skins, or cowardice. . . .

. . . Geography stands, as it were, between the science of geology, which deals with the past and with the interior of the earth, and the great group of sciences, such as biology, ethnology, economics, and history, which deal with life as it now exists. The field of geography as the science of the distribution of phenomena upon the earth's surface is distinct and well defined; its laws, although intricate and as yet only beginning to be known, are precise and clear; and its sustained and intricate modes of reasoning are in the highest degree disciplinary.

ALBERT PERRY BRIGHAM (1855-1932)

Brigham had a great deal to do with shaping the development of geographic thought in America. As a teacher of geography at Colgate University for thirty years, as an early, energetic member of both the National Council of Geography Teachers and the Association of American Geographers, as an appealing, capable lecturer, and as a forceful, dynamic writer, he was a tireless advocate of the "new" geography. At the turn of the century he was perhaps second only to William Morris Davis in professional stature. Brigham believed fervently in the kind of geography that was being developed in the United States; he was convinced of its importance; and he brought to its support almost a missionary zeal.

Problems of Geographic Influence[20]

Importance of Geographic Influence.—We deal here with the heart of geography. The ties, infinite in number, which bind life to the earth lead surely up to man. No other phase of the subject is so insistent and so appealing as the earth's influence upon our kind. The plant and animal world joins itself to our physical habitat to enrich our environment and multiply our problems. The first members of this Association came into it from the field of geology, and these men, from meeting to meeting and from year to year, have marched steadily up toward the human goal of our science. In Mr. Roorbach's recent symposium on "The Trend of Modern Geography," by far the larger number directed their call for research toward the field of geographic influence. Whether we speak of influence, or response, or adjustment, matters little. Terminology will grow unbidden if we are exact in our thinking.

---

[20] "Problems of Geographic Influence," A. P. Brigham, *Annals of the Association of American Geographers*, Vol. V, 1915.

Here lies the weight of our theme. We all have a duty to perform in view of the ill-founded and doubtful conclusions too often set forth, and in view of the vast extent of the unknown in this field. The factors of influence are not carefully isolated. What these factors really do and how they do it are not shown. Ripley holds it certain "that the immediate future of this science will depend upon the definiteness with which its conclusions are stated and illustrated." The rich and sometimes noble and rousing periods of Ratzel leave us often in the jungle of thought. But he made a trail in the jungle, and we who follow the trail may not blame him for unexplored corners of the forest. What Ratzel thinks about definite knowledge appears in his criticism of the so-called "climatic philosophers." Here, too, Brunhes adds his call for precision: "How does the climate influence us? . . . It is just as necessary here, as elsewhere, perhaps more necessary, to rejuvenate current assumptions by analysing them, for they are far too slipshod and superficial." This call for definiteness presses on every student of geographic influence, be the phase climatic or other. It is not that we can draw mathematical conclusions in any science of man, but sharp eyes and good logic will at least lift us from chaos to order.

We are thus under bond to work this field for the perfection of essential geography. But we owe a further debt, or rather, there is a mutual exchange of help in which we must not fail of our part. Geography offers help and co-operation to all sciences that deal with man — anthropology, ethnology, history, sociology, economics, psychology, and comparative religion — and from each of these geography will gather data for its own perfecting.

The historian, for example, needs from the geographer a fuller knowledge of environmental working, and the geographer receives in turn much from the historian. The old geography knew little of the causal and historical, and some of the old history might just as well have been staged on a flat platform projected into the interplanetary ether.

If history is to strike deep roots into the earth, if it is to set forth with full discernment the molding, moods, motives, and movements of men, the historian will need help from the geographer; and the historian, skeptical of generalizations that are too easy and scorning overstatement, will respond with open hand to every real offering of the geographer.

When geography was poorer than today, Parkman wrote the human story out of its environment. James Bryce has always and without stint placed geography in the running with historical movements. And if the generalizations of Bryce, like those of Ratzel, are sometimes tinged with vagueness, let us blame, not the historian of broad outlook, but the geographer whose work is yet in arrears.

If we turn to sociology we meet insistence on the importance of environment. Let us take Giddings' definition, that "sociology is an attempt to account for the origin, growth, structure, and activities of society by the operation of physical, vital, and psychical causes, working together in the process of evolution." Or we may cite the utterance of Small, that "this force is incessant, . . . it is powerful, . . . it is a factor which may never be ignored." Yet Dr. Small in an extended chapter on environment mentions geography but once, and then not as a science which might contribute to sociology. Professor Ridgeway thinks that failure fully to recognize man as controlled by the laws of the animal kingdom leads to maladministration of alien races and blunders in social legislation. He says further, "As physical characteristics are in the main the result of environment, social institutions and religious ideas are not less the product of environment." And again, any attempt to eradicate political and legal institutions of an equatorial race "will be but vain, for these institutions are as much part of the land as are its climate, its soil, its fauna, and its flora." Ripley, in reviewing the second volume of Ratzel's *Anthropogeography,* criticises the author for neglecting acclimatization, considering its importance in social theory, and in view of the fact that theories of race dispersion turn upon our judgment in this matter. Perhaps the real state of the case is seen in the appearance not long ago of a serious and careful volume on the development of western civilization, which nevertheless exhibits an utter dearth of geographic data and principles.

We are safe then in saying that most authorities in these

sciences of man recognize environment as fundamental, but the greater part, in a sort of absolution of conscience, name the subject and take leave of it.

We need not therefore expect the historians or the sociologists to develop in any full way the principles of environmental action. They admit the need of these principles, but have not the time, perhaps not the will, to develop them. It remains for us to put content into the word environment, so that it cannot be overlooked or slighted, and so that its meaning may become available in plain terms to all.

In his *Racial Geography of Europe*, Ripley asserts that, "Today geography stands ready to serve as an introduction as well as a corrective to the scientific study of human society." This was written about twenty years ago, and yet it is today not so valid or truthful a statement as we could desire it to be. Our convictions are in the right place and much has been done, but we still suffer from a dearth of limited, local, special, and proven data, and a surplus of generalizations announced with the enthusiasm of fresh discovery, or rediscovery, unsupported by adequate evidence. We are subject to Marett's criticism of certain generalizations of Ratzel and La Play — "too pretty to be true." We are awaking to the importance of our field and this is well, but it is equally important to make haste slowly and to give human geography a content satisfying to ourselves and convincing to our fellow-workers in adjoining fields.

Difficulties of the Subject.—The pursuit of our theme is as difficult as it is important. Professor Cramb in a recent book comments on the causal idea so common in our modern thought about history. His word is equally good for us. "In man's history," he says, "nothing is more difficult than to attain to something like a just conception of a true cause." Universality and necessity are the criteria which he proposes. A stiff application of these principles would be a tonic for some geographical theorizing.

Here is an individual X. What is he? He is first a bundle of anatomical characters. How did he get them? Why is he different in these matters from some other man? A single example will show how little we know. Professor Boas will say that "haphazard applications of unproved though possible theories cannot serve as proof of the effectiveness of selection or environment in modifying types." He calls for comparison of parents of one environment with their children reared in another. He has made such investigation upon children of immigrants in New York City and concludes that distinct changes, as of head form, took place. He has done well, no doubt, all that one piece of investigation permitted. But he does not analyze the factors of change nor show what any factor does. Alongside of these apparent changes in one generation we may put an opinion of Professor Myers, who, referring to a common belief that Alpine man originated in the Alpine region in response to environment, states his conviction that the time since the glacial period would not suffice for so great a change of head form. Lester F. Ward is equally confident that "there has been no important organic change in man during historic time."

Our individual also embodies physiological and psychical activities which are affected by environment. Here the problem is immensely involved, for, as Brinton says, psychical development depends less on natural surroundings than on a plexus of relations of each man with many others.

Natural environment includes first the physical — soil, water, minerals, land form, temperature, moisture in the air, light, electricity, and all operative on an earth in interplanetary relation to the sun. Then is added the animal and plant environment, whose daily pressure on the individual and the group has held in no small way the destinies of civilization. Interwrought with all these natural forces are the human-social factors, ever more powerful since the dawn of history. Thus there is a total of infinitely variable factors producing infinitely diverse results upon the body and mind.

The environment of this day and hour is perplexing enough, but environments change; and man exchanges one environment for another. The steady drive of our enviromnent in its daily flux is replaced by the shock of a new environment entered in a day or a night or gained by long voyages across the sea. The sum of a man's heredity goes out into his new sphere with him. But how much of this is primal and persistent and how much can be shifted like a garment? The heredity doctors have not answered this question and geographers should have a care. It is a wholesome corrective to remember the number of our possible ancestors. According to Boas, an Eskimo could not have so many as you or I. Royal families share this limitation with the polar man, and one European monarch, it is said, has in the past twelve generations only the meager outfit of 533 ancestors out of a theoretical 4,096. We, however, belonging to a large population of unstable habits, might have in twenty generations more than a million each. We are too complex to come to an easy reckoning about ourselves.

By our social memory we carry the old environment into the new and thus we "compound" environments, and this ends in making environment co-extensive with the world. The universality of modern environment for any civilized man appears in our commercial interchange and speaks to us in a war whose center is in Europe, whose circle takes in the world.

* * *

Fields of Investigation.—We come now to the last phase of our discussion, the most important and difficult of all lines of investigation. What is our present status? It would be a good work if someone would review historically the progress of the idea of environmental influence. Here the barest sketch must be the preliminary to our inquiry.

We may pass by the fragmental notices of ancient and mediaeval writers. Modern seed thoughts are not uncommon, and some harvest could be gathered from the philosophers and literary writers, Hobbes, Montesquieu, Kant, Herder, Hegel, Comte, Taine, and others. Humboldt, Ritter, and Guyot laid the foundations of our modern human geography, and then came Darwin, pointing the road to fruitful study for all the sciences of organic nature and of man. Ratzel, in the spirit of Darwin, kept the unfolding of geography abreast of the progress of anthropology, history, and other human sciences in the last half-century, and now Miss Semple has placed all geographers in her debt in the expansion and precision which she has added to the work of Ratzel.

General works of lesser scope, some of them regional, have appeared in this country and in Europe. Mackinder, Herbertson, Lyde, Chisholm, and others in Great Britain, and Vidal la Blache, Brunhes, Partsch, Penck, and many others on the Continent, have made important contributions. Already we have a large and rapidly growing list of small monographs dealing with limited phases or regions in this country. In America this work is largely the achievement, direct and indirect, of the members of this Association, and the present program is sharp evidence of the force of an impulse that has gathered power among us during the ten years of our co-operative endeavor.

My first hint is in the direction of climatology in its relation to man. Here is a new science, with a growing body of observation, generalization, and record, made available in description and in maps. Climatology is beginning to be appreciated in relation to other fields of physical geography. We begin to value and to express in textbooks the relation of the atmosphere to the origin of land surfaces, glaciers, aridity, and the waves and currents of the sea. We see its functions also in relation to the mineral contents of the earth, and in relation to the origin and use of soil. Even more pronounced is the growth of ideas in relating atmosphere to fauna and flora, to plant and animal types and societies, to bacteria, and to forests, steppes, and deserts. Involved in all this relation to the inorganic and organic world is an immense indirect influence on man.

Let us look at the field of biogeography in relation to man. The distribution of plants and animals as forming large elements in environment cannot fail to involve man and to uncover many interesting relationships. This study is now in a hopeful state of vitality and progress. Our own association has a good number of workers in this field.

A wealth of pertinent facts awaits discovery and co-ordination as regards the coincident distribution of man with plants and animals.

. . . Let us turn to certain groups of phenomena in the realm of effects or results. The most important and surely the most baffling problems here are in the psychic field. Here the geographer will be peculiarly dependent on workers in sister sciences and the gap may be hard to bridge. Geographers are not as a rule specialists in psychology, and there is no reason to believe that many students in psychic fields are especially versed in geography. If we can offer a stimulus which shall lead these kinds of scholars to struggle up the stream of causality, it may be safer than for us to drift down through rapids and among rocks. But the work ought to be done, and the geographer can at least show its worth and encourage the doing of it.

In this research we are not to think that the earth was all powerful with early man, but is helpless today. Color or other race features may have then been fixed, but this is not all. If there is something in man that is found in every man, wherever he is, he is not thereby released from the pressure of environment. Psychic reaction on nature does not destroy nature's efficiency, but in a degree directs, refines, and uses it. When Professor Lester F. Ward says that "the environment transforms the animal, while man transforms the environment," he utters but a partial truth. Perhaps he was attracted by rhetorical form, for in a later passage he recovers himself, recognizing the psychic effects of environment, for, "courage, love of liberty, industry and thrift, ingenuity and intelligence, are all developed by contact with restraining influences adapted to stimulating them and not so severe as to check their growth." . . .

Another field of effects, much more accessible to the pure geographer, is the distribution of population studied in the causal way. Enough practice in statistical method for this inquiry can be readily acquired, and the results should be most fruitful. Jefferson's recent papers have been suggestive in this field of research, which involves in intimate combinations, physical, economic, racial, and social conditions. Akin to this study is the classification of towns and cities, developing the principles of origin, growth, and differentiation, as in a recent valuable paper of Chisholm. The city as a geographic organism may be freely taken as an inexhaustible theme.

Another great sphere lies in regional studies, such as states, physiographic units ,and countries. The available number of such studies of American regions, maturely developed, may perhaps be counted on the fingers of one's hands. The aim should not be alone directed upon the more obvious matters of route and industry, but also upon deep and underlying principles. What rich and alluring subjects for the intensive student would the state of Pennsylvania offer; of Kentucky, Minnesota, or California! Who will develop for us our Coastal Plain or Piedmont, treating town-sites, roads, soils, crops, industries, racial composition, and social status? Who will do a like work for the great Appalachian Valley, that magnificent and little understood unit of our East — its trails and roads, its agriculture, towns, migrations, and historical significance in colonial and current life?

* * *

Our goal is broad generalization. But the formulation of general laws is difficult, and the results insecure until we have a body of concrete and detailed observations. Quoting Brunhes, "We must then make up our minds to put aside generalities and vague analogies between nature and man. We must make it our business to search for facts of interaction." From Boas also, "It goes without saying that haphazard application of unproven though possible theories will not serve as proof of the effectiveness of selection or environment in modifying types."

Detailed investigation of single problems, in small and seemingly unimportant fields, must for a long time prepare the way for the formulation of richer and more fundamental conclusions and general principles than we have yet been able to achieve. We should not wait for someone to state or demonstrate these laws. This is yet, even for a genius, impossible. We must contribute in a partial, microscopic, sometimes unconscious way to the emergence of such laws.

NEVIN M. FENNEMAN (1865-1945)

Fenneman was a noted geologist and physiographer. Yet there was something so logical and convincing about his remarks in "The Circumference of Geography" (it was required reading for any potential geographer in the 1920's and 1930's), that one can almost imagine that geography was

Fenneman's basic interest. The fact is that Fenneman was a thoughtful, widely-read man, who had some important things to say about a number of subjects that would appear to have been of peripheral interest to an earth scientist.

"The Circumference of Geography" [21]

Regional Geography the Core of the Science.—Since geography *is to be,* it is quite right that physiography and climatology and the study of natural resources and even ecology should be of its family and bear its name, but the point here urged is that these are not the things which make geography *necessary* and *inevitable.* They may be necessary to it, but it is not necessary to them. All these might live with geography dead. All these and others belong to the regions of overlap, or ground common both to geography and to some other science, and, having two parents, would not be totally orphaned if one died; but the study of areas as before described belongs solely to geography and is, moreover, an only child. If these figures are somewhat mixed, it may be well to add in plain English that the one thing that is first, last, and always geography and nothing else, is the study of areas in their compositeness or complexity, that is *regional geography.*

It is not to be implied for one brief moment that physiography and the other branches named are not geography. They all become so when directed toward a geographic purpose. But without the touchstone of areal studies, there is nothing to make physiography other than geology, ecology other than botany, the study of natural resources other than economics.

There is, then, in geography this central core which is pure geography and nothing else, but there is much beyond this core which is none the less geography, though it belongs also to overlapping sciences. Here belong physiography and climatology, mathematical and commercial geography. Still, *the seeds are in the core, and the core is regional geography,* and this is why the subject propagates itself and maintains a sepa-

[21] "The Circumference of Geography," Nevin M. Fenneman, *Annals of the Association of American Geographers,* Vol. IX, 1919, pp. 7-8.

rate existence. Without regional geography there is no reason why geography should be treated as a separate branch.

This emphasis on areal relations instead of on the "elements" which enter into such relations is, of course, not new. It comes to much the same thing in practice as Ritter's "home of man" or Davis' "physical element and human element" or this and that man's "responses" or Keltie's "science of distributions" or Hettner's *"dingliche Erfüllung der Erdraume"* (material filling of the earth's surface). Nor is it necessary, for the purpose here in hand, to point out that every element (topography, vegetation, climate, etc.) can be treated with reference to its distribution as well as with reference to its types. Such a treatment belongs to regional geography. It should, however, be noted that the study of the distribution of any one element by itself falls somewhat short of that *distinctive* geographic flavor which comes only when the various elements are studied in their inter-relations.

Cultivation of the Central Theme of Geography as a Safeguard Against Absorption by Other Sciences.—Let us now go back to the fear above alluded to, that our subject is going to be swallowed by something else. Why this constant dread? The situation at once suggests that we live too much on our borders and not enough in the center. If we dwell mainly in systematic physiography, why should not geology claim us as a vassal? If we live largely in commercial geography, we are in similar danger from economics; and why should it not be so? We can go round the circle with the same logic. A narrowly political geography of boundaries and capitals never had any reason for a separate existence apart from history.

If we are concerned for our independent existence no amount of fortifying our border will take the place of developing our domain. What we need is more and better studies of regions in their entirety, their compositeness, their complexity, their inter-relations of physical, economic, racial, historic and other factors. No other science can swallow that and live.

HARLAN HARLAND BARROWS (1877-1960)

Barrows will perhaps be better remembered for the presidential address he made in 1922 than for any of his other publications or activities. Barrows was on the staff of the University of Chicago from 1907 until 1942, and for the earlier part of that period Chicago was a tremendously important training center for geographers. But the impact of his ideas can hardly be explained by the fact that he was in an excellent position to influence the thinking of many future professional geographers. Unquestionably Barrows' answer to the perennial geographic problem seemed to be a useful answer. For many people, it put together the complex purposes and methods of geography in a neat and logical bundle. For others, it was a retreat from the historically established patterns of the sciences. In any case, it is an important landmark in the development of American geographic thought.

"Geography as Human Ecology"[22]

. . . The center of gravity within the geographic field has shifted steadily from the extreme physical side toward the human side, until geographers in increasing numbers define their subject as dealing solely with the mutual relations between man and his natural environment. By "natural environment" they of course mean the combined physical and biological environments.

Thus defined, geography is the science of *human ecology.* The implications of the term "human ecology" make evident at once what I believe will be in future the objective of geographic inquiry. Geography will aim to make clear the relationships existing between natural environments and the distribution and activities of man. Geographers will, I think, be wise to view this problem in general from the standpoint of man's adjustment to environment, rather than from that of environmental influence. The former approach is more likely to result in the recognition and proper valuation of all the

[22] "Geography As Human Ecology," Harlan H. Barrows, *Annals of the Association of American Geographers,* Vol. XIII, 1923, pp. 3-8.

factors involved, and especially to minimize the danger of assigning to the environmental factors a determinative influence which they do not exert.

It has been said by some that though the foregoing definitional statements indicate a field for human ecology, they cannot do so for geography because the latter term has a fixed connotation. Quite the contrary. If the history of geography teaches one lesson more clearly than another, it is that the etymology of the word has not delimited the field to which it applies. In the future, just as in the past, the scope of geography will be determined largely by that of the constructive work of its followers and by the labors of men in kindred fields. . . .

Geography finds in human ecology, then, a field cultivated but little by any or all of the other natural and social sciences. Thus limited in scope it has a unity otherwise lacking, and a point of view unique among the sciences which deal with humanity. Through a comparative study of human adjustment to specific natural environments, certain reliable generalizations or principles have been worked out, while many others have been suggested tentatively. These are the requisites of any science: a distinctive field, and a controlling point of view by means of which its data may be organized with reference to the discovery of general truths or principles.

The Divisions of Systematic Geography.—If geography be regarded as human ecology, three major systematic divisions of the subject are at once to be recognized, namely economic geography, political geography, and social geography, corresponding to the three great types of human activity that are related to the earth.

According to this scheme, economic geography would seek to account for those adjustments of man to his environment which are associated with the getting of a living. Among its subdivisions would be agricultural geography, pastoral geography, the geography of extractive industries (mining, logging, fishing, etc.), commercial geography, and the geography of manufacturing. Economic geography is the best developed division of the subject, doubtless because most of the activities with which the economic geographer is concerned involve the direct utilization of earth resources and result in various readily discernible surface features which help to make up the cultural landscape. Economic geography also is the most fundamental division of the subject.

If geography as a whole be regarded as human ecology, the viewpoint of political geography follows as a matter of course. It aims to account for such relationships as may exist between man's political attitudes, activities, and institutions, on the one hand, and the natural environment on the other. Such connections must be established in most cases through the facts of geography, and not directly. Failure to recognize this, and to proceed accordingly, invites untenable generalizations and helps to make much so-called political geography really political history, with at best a geographic slant.

Theoretically at least there is a definite field for social geography, which would study the connections that may exist between the social life of peoples and their natural environments. But the facts of "living" are intangible and for the most part find any connections which they may have with the natural environment through the facts involved in "getting a living." As already suggested in connection with sociology, this body of relationships appears to form a potential field for geography rather than an assured field.

Regional Geography.—We come now to regional geography, properly recognized as the culminating branch of the science because it involves facts and principles from all the divisions and subdivisions of systematic geography. As you would expect from the statements already made, I believe that regional geography, even in its widest sense, properly is concerned only with the mutual relations between men and the natural environments of the regions or areas in which they live. I realize fully that here again I depart widely from the viewpoint of most geographers. It has been pointed out that any environmental elements (topography, soil, climate, vegetation, etc.) can be studied with reference to the facts and causes of its distribution and it has been urged that such a treatment is the function of regional geography. Does the world of science look to geography for this service? Does not geology, for example, explain the distribution of volcanoes, and zoology that of fishes? Could *any* one science hope really to explain the distribution of all the phenomena of the earth's surface with which science in general is concerned? Are not the technical methods of inquiry too diverse and the field too vast? How much would the other sciences know about the causation of the distributions with which they deal if they had waited upon geography for the information? How *can* certain geographers seriously "claim for geography to the exclusion of any other science, all study of spatial distribution on the earth's surface?" Again it is urged that in any event regional geography comes into its own when the synthetic element is introduced, and the different items are studied in the light of their interactions upon one another. Proponents of this view hold, moreover, that such a study of interrelationships in an uninhabited area would still be of the essence of geography. It does not seem to me, however, that geography has any function to perform in connection with such studies of non-human relationships.

CARL O. SAUER (1889-)

Sauer has long been a brilliant figure in American geography. At a time when American geographers were turning to a study of relationships, when environmental determinism was not the scapegoat it is now, and when, through the influence of Miss Semple, the concepts of Ratzel were more widely accepted in America than were those of Richthofen, Carl Sauer emphasized the "chorologic interest" of geographers. His methodological writings have been clear, precise, and fundamental. The paper from which the following excerpts have been taken is only one of several important and definitive statements from the pen of Carl Sauer.

"The Morphology of Landscape" [23]

Diverse opinions regarding the nature of geography are still common. The label, geography, as is the case with history, is no trustworthy indication as to the matter contained.

[23] "The Morphology of Landscape," Carl O. Sauer, *University of California Publications in Geography*, Vol. II, 1919-1929, pp. 19-48.

As long as geographers disagree as to their subject it will be necessary, through repeated definition, to seek common ground upon which a general position may be established. In this country a fairly coherent series of viewpoints has been advanced, especially through presidential addresses before the Association of American Geographers, which may be accepted as mirror and mould of geographic opinion in America. They are sufficiently clear and well known that they need not be restated. In European geography a somewhat different orientation appears to be developing. In various quarters significant activity is being displayed, probably in some measure influenced by anti-intellectualist currents. At any rate a shaking up of some vigor is under way. It may therefore be appropriate to reexamine the field of geography, keeping current views abroad especially in mind, in order to attempt a working hypothesis that may serve to illuminate in some degree both the nature of the objective and the problem of systematic method.

All science may be regarded as phenomenology, the term science being used in the sense of organized process of acquiring knowledge, rather than in the common restricted meaning of a unified body of physical law. Every field of knowledge is characterized by its declared preoccupation with a certain group of phenomena, which it undertakes to identify and order according to their relations. These facts are assembled with increasing knowledge of their connection; the attention to their connection denotes scientific approach. "A fact is first determined when it is recognized as to limits and qualities, and it is understood when it is viewed in its relations. Out of this follows the necessity of predetermined modes of inquiry and of the creation of a system that makes the relations of the phenomena. . . . Every individual science is naive as a special discipline, in so far as it accepts the section of reality which is its field *tel quel* and does not question its position in the general scene of nature; within these limits, however, it proceeds critically, since it undertakes to determine the connection of the phenomena and their order." According to such definition of the grounds of knowledge, the first concern is with the phenomena that constitute the "section of reality" which is occupied by geography, the next with the method of determining their connection.

Disagreement as to the content of geography is so great that three distinct fields of inquiry are usually designated as geography: (1) The study of the earth as the medium of physical processes, or the geophysical part of cosmologic science; (2) the study of life-forms as subject to their physical environment, or a part of biophysics, dealing with tropisms; and (3) the study of the areal or habitat differentiation of the earth, or chorology. In these three fields there is partial accordance of phenomena, but little of relation. One may choose between the three; they may hardly be consolidated into one discipline.

The great fields of knowledge exist because they are universally recognized as being concerned with a great category of phenomena. The experience of mankind, not the inquiry of the specialist, has made the primary subdivisions of knowledge. Botany is the study of plants, and geology that of rocks, because these categories of fact are evident to all intelligence that has concerned itself with the observation of nature. In the same sense, area or landscape is the field of geography, because it is a naively given, important section of reality, not a sophisticated thesis. Geography assumes the responsibility for the study of areas because there exists a common curiosity about that subject. The fact that every school child knows that geography provides information about different countries is enough to establish the validity of such a definition.

* * *

Probably not even the adherents of other, recent schools of geography would deny place for such a view of the subject, but they deem this naively given body of facts inadequate to establish a science or at the most would consider it an auxiliary discipline which compiles fragmentary evidence, to find its place ultimately in a general geophysical or biophysical system. The argument then is shifted from the phenomenal content to the nature of the connection of the phenomena. We assert the place for a science that finds its entire field in the landscape on the basis of the significant reality of chorologic relation. The phenomena that make up an area are not simply assorted but are associated, or interdependent. To discover this areal "connection of the phenomena and their order" is a scientific task, according to our position the only one to which geography should devote its energies. The position falls only if the non-reality of area be shown. The competence to arrive at orderly conclusions is not affected in this case by the question of coherence or incoherence of the data, for their characteristic association, as we find them in the area, is an expression of coherence. The element of time is admittedly present in the association of geographic facts, which are thereby in large part non-recurrent. This, however, places them beyond the reach of scientific inquiry only in a narrow sense, for time as a factor has a well-recognized place in many scientific fields, where time is not simply a term for some identifiable causal relation.

* * *

The task of geography is conceived as the establishment of a critical system which embraces the phenomenology of landscape, in order to grasp in all of its meaning and color the varied terrestrial scene. Indirectly Vidal de la Blache has stated this position by cautioning against considering "the earth as 'the scene on which the activity of man unfolds itself,' without reflecting that this scene is itself living." It includes the works of man as an integral expression of the scene. This position is derived from Herodotus rather than from Thales. Modern geography is the modern expression of the most ancient geography.

The objects which exist together in the landscape exist in interrelation. We assert that they constitute a reality as a whole which is not expressed by a consideration of the constituent parts separately, that area has form, structure, and function, and hence position in a system, and that it is subject to development, change, and completion. Without this view of areal reality and relation, there exist only special disciplines, not geography as generally understood. The situation is analogous to history, which may be divided among economics, government, sociology, and so on; but when this is done the result is not history.

The term "landscape" is proposed to denote the unit concept of geography, to characterize the peculiarly geographic association of facts. Equivalent terms in a sense are "area" and "region." Area is of course a general term, not distinctively geographic. Region has come to imply, to some geographers at least, an order of magnitude. Landscape as the English equivalent of the term German geographers are using largely and strictly has the same meaning, a land shape, in which the process of shaping is by no means thought of as simply physical. It may be defined, therefore, as an area made up of a distinct association of forms, both physical and cultural.

The facts of geography are place facts; their association gives rise to the concept of landscape. Similarly, the facts of history are time facts; their association gives rise to the concept of period. By definition the landscape has identity that is based on recognizable constitution, limits, and generic relation to other landscapes, which constitute a general system. Its structure and function are determined by integrant, dependent forms. The landscape is considered, therefore, in a sense as having an organic quality. We may follow Bluntschli in saying that one has not fully understood the nature of an area until one "has learned to see it as an organic unit, to comprehend land and life in terms of each other." It has seemed desirable to introduce this point prior to its elaboration because it is very different from the unit concept of physical process of the physiographer or of environmental influence of the anthropogeographer of the school of Ratzel. The mechanics of glacial erosion, the climatic correlation of energy, and the form content of an areal habitat are three different things.

In the sense here used, landscape is not simply an actual scene viewed by an observer. The geographic landscape is a generalization derived from the observation of individual scenes. Croce's remark that "the geographer who is describing a landscape has the same task as a landscape painter" has therefore only limited validity. The geographer may describe the individual landscape as a type or possibly as a variant from type, but always he has in mind the generic, and proceeds by comparison.

An ordered presentation of the landscapes of the earth is a formidable undertaking. Beginning with infinite diversity, salient and related features are selected in order to establish the character of the landscape and to place it in a system. Yet generic quality is non-existent in the sense of the biologic world. Every landscape has individuality as well as relation to other landscapes, and the same is true of the forms that make it up. No valley is quite like any other valley; no city the exact replica of some other city. In so far as these qualities remain completely unrelated they are beyond the reach of systematic treatment, beyond that organized knowledge that we call science. "No science can rest at the level of mere perception. . . . The so-called descriptive natural sciences, zoology and botany, do not remain content to regard the singular, they raise themselves to concepts of species, genus, family, order, class, type." "There is no idiographic science, that is, one that describes the individual merely as such. Geography formerly was idiographic; long since it has attempted to become nomothetic, and no geographer would hold it at its previous level." Whatever opinion one may hold about natural law, or nomothetic, genetic, or casual relation, a definition of landscape as singular, unorganized, or unrelated has no scientific value.

It is true that in the selection of the generic characteristics of landscape the geographer is guided only by his own judgment that they are characteristic, that is, repeating; that they are arranged into a pattern, or have structural quality, and that the landscape accurately belongs to a specific group in the general series of landscapes. Croce objects to a science of history on the ground that history is without logical criteria: "The criterion is the choice itself, conditioned, like every economic art, by knowledge of the actual situation. This selection is certainly conducted with intelligence, but not with the application of a philosophic criterion, and is justified only in and by itself. For this reason we speak of the fine tact, or scent, or instinct of the learned man." A similar objection is sometimes urged against the scientific competence of geography, because it is unable to establish complete, rigid logical control and perforce relies upon the option of the student.

The geographer is in fact continually exercising freedom of choice as to the materials which he includes in his observations, but he is also continually drawing inferences as to their relation. His method, imperfect as it may be, is based on induction; he deals with sequences, though he may not regard these as a simple causal relation.

If we consider a given type of landscape, for example a North European heath, we may put down notes such as the following:

"The sky is dull, ordinarily partly overcast, the horizon is indistinct and rarely more than a half-dozen miles distant, though seen from a height. The upland is gently and irregularly rolling and descends to broad, flat basins. There are no long slopes and no symmetrical patterns of surface form. Watercourses are short, with clear brownish water, and perennial. The brooks end in irregular swamps, with indistinct borders. Coarse grasses and rushes form marginal strips along the water bodies. The upland is covered with heather, furze, and bracken. Clumps of juniper abound, especially on the steeper, drier slopes. Cart traces lie along the longer ridges, exposing loose sand in the wheel tracks, and here and there a rusty, cemented base shows beneath the sand. Small flocks of sheep are scattered widely over the land. The almost complete absence of the works of man is notable. There are no fields or other enclosed tracts. The only buildings are sheep sheds, situated usually at a distance of several miles from one another, at convenient intersections of cart traces."

The account is not that of an individual scene, but a summation of general characteristics. References to other types of landscape are introduced by implication. Relations of form elements within the landscape are also noted. The items selected are based upon "knowledge of the actual situation" and there is an attempt at a synthesis of the form elements. Their significance is a matter of personal judgment. Objective standards may be substituted for them only in part, as by quantitative representation in the form of a map. Even thus the personal element is brought only under limited control, since it still operates in choosing the qualities to be represented. All that can be expected is the reduction of the personal element by agreeing on a "predetermined mode of inquiry," which shall be logical.

The content of landscape is something less than the whole of its visible constituents. The identity of the landscape is determined first of all by conspicuousness of form, as implied in the following statements: "A correct representation of the surface form, of soil, and of surficially conspicuous masses of rock, of plant cover and water bodies, of the coasts and the sea, of areally conspicuous animal life and of the expression of human culture is the goal of geographic inquiry." The items specified are chosen because the experience of the author has shown their significance as to mass and relation. The chorologic position necessarily recognizes the importance of areal extensiveness of phenomena, this quality being inherent in the position. Herein lies an important contrast between geography and physiography. The character of the heath landscape described above is determined primarily by the dominance of sand, swamp, and heather. The most important geographic fact about Norway, aside from its location, probably is that four fifths of its surface is barren highland, supporting neither forest nor flocks, a condition significant directly because of its extensiveness.

Personal judgment of the content of landscape is determined further by interest. Geography is distinctly anthropocentric, in the sense of value or use of the earth to man. We are interested in that part of the areal scene which concerns us as human beings because we are part of it, live with it, are limited by it, and modify it. Thus we select those qualities of landscape in particular that are or may be of use to us. We relinquish those features of area that may be significant to the geologist in earth history but are of no concern in the relation of man to his area. The physical qualities of landscape then are those that have habitat value, present or potential.

Human geography does not oppose itself to a geography from which the human element is excluded; such a one has not existed except in the minds of a few exclusive specialists. It is a forcible abstraction, by every good geographic tradition a *tour de force,* to consider a landscape as though it were devoid of life. Because we are interested primarily in "cultures which grow with original vigor out of the lap of a maternal natural landscape, to which each is bound in the whole course of its existence," geography is based on the reality of the union of physical and cultural elements of the landscape. The content of landscape is found therefore in the physical qualities of area that are significant to man and in the forms of his use of the area, in facts of physical background and facts of human culture.

For the first half of the content of landscape we may use the designation "site," which has become well established in plant ecology. A forest site is not simply the place where a forest stands; in its full connotation, the name is a qualitative expression of place in terms of forest growth, usually for the particular forest association that is in occupation of the site. In this sense the physical area is the sum of all natural resources that man has at his disposal in that area. It is beyond his power to add to them; he may "develop" them, ignore them in part, or subtract from them by exploitation.

The second half of landscape viewed as a bilateral unit is its cultural expression. There is a strictly geographic way of thinking of culture; namely, as the impress of the works of man upon the area. We may think of people as associated within and with an area, as we may think of them as groups associated in descent or tradition. In the first case we are thinking of culture as a geographic expression, composed of forms which are part of geographic phenomenology. In this view there is no place for a dualism of landscape. . . .

The systematic organization of the content of landscape proceeds with the repression of *a priori* theories concerning it. The massing and ordering of phenomena as forms that are integrated into structures and the comparative study of the data as thus organized constitute the morphologic method of synthesis, a special empirical method. Morphology rests upon the following postulates: (1) that there is a unit of organic or quasi-organic quality, that is, a structure to which certain components are necessary, these component elements being called "forms" in this paper; (2) that similarity of form in different structures is recognized because of functional equivalence, the forms then being "homologous"; and (3) that the structural units may be placed in series, especially into developmental sequence, ranging from incipient to final or completed stage. . . .

If . . . the morphologic method appears unpretentious to the student who is eager to come to large conclusions, it may be pointed out that it rests upon deliberate restraint in the affirmation of knowledge. It is a purely evidential system, without prepossession regarding the meaning of its evidence, and presupposes a minimum of assumption; namely, only the reality of structural organization. Being objective and value-free, or nearly so, it is competent to arrive at increasingly significant results. . . .

Historically "geography commenced by describing and registering, that is as a systematic study. It proceeded thereupon to . . . genetic relation, morphology." The geographic study is still thus begun. The description of observed facts is by some predetermined order that represents a preliminary grouping of the material. Such systematic description is for the purpose of morphologic relation and is really the beginning of morphologic synthesis. It is therefore distinguishable from morphology not at all in principle but in that it lies at a lower critical level. The relation is not dissimilar to that between taxonomy and biologic morphology. . . .

We canot form an idea of landscape except in terms of its time relations as well as of its space relations. It is in continuous process of development or of dissolution and replacement. It is in this sense a true appreciation of historical values that has caused the geomorphologists to tie the present physical landscape back into its geologic origins, and to derive it therefrom step by step. In the chorologic sense, however, the modification of the area by man and its appropriation to his uses are of dominant importance. The area prior to the introduction of man's activity is represented by one body of morphologic facts. The forms that man has introduced are another set. We may call the former, with reference to man, the original, natural landscape. In its entirety it no longer exists in many parts of the world, but its reconstruction and understanding are the first part of formal morphology. Is it perhaps too broad a generalization to say that geography dissociates itself from geology at the point of the introduction of man into the areal scene? Under this view the prior events belong strictly in the field of geology and their historical treatment in geography is only a descriptive device employed where necessary to make clear the relationship of physical forms that are significant in the habitat.

The works of man express themselves in the cultural landscape. There may be a succession of these landscapes with a succession of cultures. They are derived in each case from the natural landscape, man expressing his place in nature as a distinct agent of modification. Of especial significance is that climax of culture which we call civilization. The cultural landscape then is subject to change either by the development of a culture or by a replacement of cultures. The datum line from which change is measured is the natural condition of the landscape. The division of forms into natural and cultural is the necessary basis for determining the areal importance and character of man's activity. In the universal, but not necessarily cosmologic sense, geography then becomes that part of the latest or human chapter in earth history which is concerned with the differentiation of the areal scene by man.

The physical area is fundamental to any geographic study because it furnishes the materials out of which man builds his culture. The identity of the physical area rests fundamentally on a distinctive association of physical forms. In the physical world, generic character of area and its genesis are coupled so closely that the one becomes an aid to the recognition of the other. In particular, climate, itself an areal form, largely obscure as to origin, so largely controls the expression of the other physical forms that in many areas it may be considered the determinant of form association. An express disclaimer may be entered, however, against the notion of the necessity of a genetic bond in order to organize the phenomenology of the natural landscape. The existence of such bonds has been determined empirically. By regarding the relationship of forms we have discovered an important light on "the obscurity of their descent," but as geographers we are not enjoined to trace out the nature of this descent. This remains the problem of geomorphology, which indeed now appears more complicated than ever, the validity of climatic control and of great secular changes of climate being accepted.

Thus far the way is pretty well marked. We know the "inorganic" composition of landscape fairly well, and, except for a somewhat excessive aloofness existing between plant and general geography, the place of vegetation in the landscape is properly cared for.

The natural landscape is being subjected to transformation at the hands of man, the last and for us the most important morphologic factor. By his cultures he makes use of the natural forms, in many cases alters them, in some destroys them.

The study of the cultural landscape is, as yet, largely an untilled field. Recent results in the field of plant ecology will probaby supply many useful leads for the human geographer, for cultural morphology might be called human ecology. In contrast to the position of Barrows in this matter, the present thesis would eliminate physiologic ecology of autecology and seek for parallels in synecology. It is better not to force into geography too much biological nomenclature. The name ecology is not needed: it is both morphology and physiology of the biotic association. Since we waive the claim for the measurement of environmental influences, we may use, in preference to ecology, the term morphology to apply to cultural study, since it describes perfectly the method that is involved.

RICHARD HARTSHORNE (1899-)

The best-known American authority on the philosophy and methodology of geography is Richard Hartshorne. His "Nature of Geography" has long been a landmark in American geographic literature, and it is safe to say that there is not a professional geographer in the United States who is not acquainted with it. As a result, Hartshorne's influence in the profession has been unusually pervasive. Probably no one, with the possible exception of William Morris Davis, has given direction to American geographic thinking to the extent that Hartshorne has.

The excerpt included here is taken from "Perspective on the Nature of Geography," in which the author has brought up to date and expressed in a more affirmative manner his concepts of the geographic science. Very probably this volume is now on the bookshelves of most American geographers. The inclusion of this excerpt is obviously not intended to widen the circle of Professor Hartshorne's audience, but to give recognition to the impact his writings have had. In fact, this book of readings might well have been sub-titled, "From Herodotus to Hartshorne."

What Is Meant by Geography as the Study of Areal Differentiation [23]

Very early in human development man discovered that his world varied greatly from place to place. It was to satisfy man's curiosity concerning such differences that geography developed as a subject of popular interest. From earliest times travelers returning from "foreign" parts were expected to tell the stay-at-homes what things and people were like in the places they had seen, whether in adjoining, but relatively inaccessible, districts or in more remote parts.

This universal curiosity of man about the world beyond his immediate horizon, a world known to differ in varying degrees from the home area, is the foundation of all geography. Among the innumerable geographers of diverse countries who have stated this principle explicitly we may mention Strabo, Vidal de la Blache, Voltz, Sauer and Darby.

The fact that all the areas of the earth differ from each other leads also to a special interest in any cases in which separate areas appear to be alike. Closer examination reveals that they are never exactly alike, certainly not remotely as much alike as "two peas in a pod," nor even as two individuals of completely European ancestry may be alike in physical characteristics though born and raised on opposite

[23] *Perspective on the Nature of Geography,* Richard Hartshorne, Rand McNally & Company, Chicago, 1959, pp. 15-21.

sides of the Atlantic Ocean. Nevertheless, the ways in which separate areas are alike is no less significant than the ways in which they differ. Comparative study of such areas permits geography to approach the methods of laboratory sciences, in which certain facts are controlled as constants, while others vary.

This purpose may appear to be excluded from a geography defined as "the study of areal differentiation" if one omits the phrase "the study of" and thus reads "differentiation" in the active sense — that is, "to differentiate." The purpose of close examination of areas which are somewhat alike is not to demonstrate that they differ, which we know must be the case without need of examination, but rather to determine how small or large the specific differences are. If such examination shows that in respect to certain individual features or groups of closely related features — for example, atmospheric conditions determining rainfall, temperature, cloudiness, etc., which we group together as climate — the differences among several areas are very slight, we say that such areas are "similar" in climate. We may then consider these areas, and all other areas of the world in which climate conditions are "similar" in contrast to "dissimilar" conditions of other areas — that is, areas differing in minor degree in contrast to those differing in major degree — as specimen areas of the same type.

By this means we can construct a generic concept — for example, "Mediterranean type of climate" — which may be used to describe the climatic aspect of the character of any area (region) of that type. Or, in place of group concepts such as "Mediterranean" or "humid continental," in which all climatic conditions are considered together, we may establish generic concepts of the major constituents — rainfall, seasonal temperatures, etc. — and describe the total climate of any area of the world by combinations of these generic concepts, as in such symbolic forms as BSh (Koeppen) or DA'W (Thornthwaite).

Of course, in thus treating several areas as though quite alike in climate we have introduced a certain degree of error in our analysis of the character of areas. We may correct this, in larger scale analysis, by the use of more detailed generic concepts, expressed, for example, as BShwg. But no matter how far we continue this process there remain differences of some importance between any two parts of an area. This, of course, is the method by which we construct the well known systems of classification of areas of the world into various kinds of regions, sometimes called "generic regions," because they are based on generic concepts, whether of climate, landforms, soils, or agricultural systems.

"Similarity," therefore, is not the opposite of "difference," but merely a generalization under which differences deemed minor are ignored, those deemed major are emphasized. Some writers seek to avoid misunderstanding by speaking always of "differences and similarities," without recognizing that the phrase is redundant. It may well be also that the repeated use of the term "differences" gives undue emphasis to the search for "contrasts." It therefore seems advisable to use the more neutral word, "variations."

If the variations in diverse categories of phenomena which explorers and travelers reported from the many areas of the world — variations in such features as numbers, customs, occupations, and movements of people, in soils, landforms, and climate — showed no relation to each other beyond that of common location, geography would be little more than an organized catalogue or encyclopedia of facts about countries. Such an organized body of knowledge might satisfy the shallow curiosity of unsophisticated minds, and would be useful for business and statecraft, but it could not satisfy the desire for philosophical understanding. This intellectual interest has been present in mankind from the earliest recorded times. When travelers reported an unassorted and unrelated conglomeration of differences in diverse features in foreign areas, thoughtful scholars were concerned to organize these and explain them in terms of interrelations.

If these early writers depended more on imagination than on evidence, they were at least on the right track. There *are* significant interrelations among the variations in the diverse features of areas, and geographers at all times have been concerned to trace and demonstrate the connections that exist.

To emphasize the essential importance of such interrelationships in geography, Hettner, and other writers following him, included such phrases as "causally related," "causal connections," or "differences . . . interrelated with each other," in stating or expounding the concept of geography under discussion. Nevertheless, numerous critics have inferred from the phrase "areal differentiation" that geography is *limited* "to the distinguishing of areas," or "to establishing differences from one area to another," or to "mere description."

A historical explanation for his misconception is suggested by certain comments in Spate's discussion. Whereas definitions of geography previously current in British and America always included the concept of relationships between man and nature, the definition in terms of "areal differentiation" is "austere" in that it "avoids reference to this time-honored concept." But surely in any science the study of its phenomena involves the study of relationships that may be found among them. Students of astronomy, economics, geology, or zoology define their fields without mention of "relationships," or of "laws," evidently assuming that that goes without saying. The unique feature of the traditional definition of geography in English-speaking countries, (is the) . . . concentrating on one particular class of relationsips, those between man and nature. . . .

The connections or causal relationships among the phenomena of geography, as Hettner noted in 1905, are of two kinds: the mutual relationships among different phenomena at one place, and relationships or connections between phenomena at different places. The latter necessarily involve movements across areas. Water and air, even pieces of solid materials, and, of course, animals, move from place to place producing interconnections of places.

With the introduction of man to the scene, this dynamic aspect in the character of areas becomes far more important; for it is one of the particular attributes of man that he not only moves from place to place himself, but sets other things in motion as well. It is especially in their human aspects, therefore, that areas differ not merely in their morphology, but also in what Ritter called their physiology, but which, to avoid the analogy with living organisms, we had better call their functional relations, involving movement among them.

Ullman has suggested that "areal differentiation" should be considered as a subconcept of geography as "spatial interaction." The suggestion seems to me to result from a misconception of the former term, if not also of the latter. Spatial interaction can only mean relations between phenomena in different places, and these phenomena, whether in place or in movement through space, form a part of the character of each area concerned. Hence the reverse is the case: variations in stationary characteristics, or forms, and variations in characteristics of movement, or functions, whether within an area or between it and another, are both included under the concept of areal variation, or differences in areas.

That both aspects are essential is not a new thought. It was clearly expressed by Ritter and was included in Hettner's exposition of his concept of geography in 1905. Hettner indeed has warned against the exaggeration, for which he finds Ratzel in part responsible, of regarding space relations as the essential part of geography, to the neglect of differences in the content of areas. Several critics are concerned that Hettner's concept does not establish geography as a separate and distinct science, since other "field sciences" also study differences in areas. Hettner had explained that no such clear and sharp distinction should be expected, since all science is a unit which human limitations force us to divide more or less arbitrarily. The over-all point of view of geography, in its concern to analyze the character of places, differs in kind from that of a systematic science with its emphasis on analyzing a particular category of phenomena. The two points of view may be combined in particular studies, just as an economist may use the historical viewpoint and method. Whether such studies are to be considered as part of geography or as part of the systematic science, or both, is a minor question of classification, depending on the relative degree of emphasis of the respective viewpoints in the purpose of the particular study. The difference is well illustrated in Hugh Raup's discussion, in historic dependence on Humboldt, of the distinction between "geographic botany" and "plant geography." The unique purpose of geography is to seek comprehension of the variable character of areas in terms of all the interrelated features which together form that variable character.

Conclusion

The objections that have been raised to the concept under discussion are directed for the most part against the particular term with which it has become identified and do not apply to the concept itself. Whether the objections to the term are warranted or not, the evidence seems convincing that by itself the term is inadequate. At the same time it says more than is necessary. For if we examine definitions of other sciences, we may conclude by analogy that it is superfluous to assert that geography studies "differences." Every science is a study of differences — otherwise little study would be needed.

We may therefore avoid numerous points of misunderstanding if we state simply that *geography is concerned to provide accurate, orderly, and rational description and interpretation of the variable character of the earth surface.* In its simplest form, as the "dean of French geographers," Cholley, states: "L'object de la Géographie est la connaissance de la Terre"; his subsequent discussion justifies, I believe, the additional words I have used.

INDEX

Figures followed by italic *ff* indicate extended excerpts.
An n. after a figure refers to a footnote.